The Collected Writings of Walt Whitman

The Play = Ground.

When painfully athwart my brain
    Dark thoughts come crowding on,
And, sick of worldly hollowness,
    My heart feels sad and lone —
Then out upon the green I walk,
    Just ere the close of day,
And swift I ween the sight I view
    clears all my gloom away.—
For there ~~the~~ the village children come —
    The cheeriest things on earth,
I see them play — I hear their tones
    Of loud and reckless mirth.—
And many a clear and flute = like laugh
    ~~Comes~~ Flies ringing through the air;
And many a roguish flashing eye,
    And rich red cheek are there.—
O, lovely, happy children!
    I am with you in my soul:
I shout — I strike the ball with you —
    With you I race and roll.—
Methinks, white = winged angels,
    Floating unseen the while,
Hover around this village green,
    And pleasantly they smile.
O, angels! guard these children!
    Keep grief and guilt away:
From worldly harm — from evil thoughts —
    O shield them night and day!

WALT WHITMAN

Collected writings

The Early Poems
and the Fiction

Edited by Thomas L. Brasher

 NEW YORK UNIVERSITY PRESS 1963

The Collected Writings of Walt Whitman

GRATEFUL ACKNOWLEDGMENT IS MADE TO

Mr. Charles E. Feinberg,

WHOSE ASSISTANCE MADE POSSIBLE THE ILLUSTRATIONS
IN THIS VOLUME AND WHO ALSO MADE
AVAILABLE TO THE PUBLISHER THE RESOURCES OF
THE FEINBERG COLLECTION.

Preface

At least twenty-four pieces of fiction and nineteen poems by Walter Whitman appeared in print before Walter Whitman became Walt Whitman and published *Leaves of Grass* in 1855. Except for a single poem which became part of the *Leaves*, none of this fiction and early verse was reprinted by Walt Whitman until the publication in 1882 of *Specimen Days and Collect*, which included an appendix with the title (and characteristically inaccurate dates) of "Pieces in Early Youth. 1832–'42." The nine short stories and four poems of "Pieces in Early Youth" reappeared in 1892 in the *Complete Prose Works* (volume two of the *Complete Works*, volume one being the so-called "Death-Bed Edition" of *Leaves of Grass*) and have remained, until the present, the sole "authorized" representatives of Whitman's pre-*Leaves* creative efforts.

Horace Traubel and some of the other Camden disciples knew of *Franklin Evans* several years before Whitman's death and quite understandably had no wish at a later date to resuscitate an inept pot-boiler which could scarcely be a credit to anyone and especially to a cosmic bard. Some early biographers, such as Bliss Perry, referred in passing to tales not included in "Pieces in Early Youth." But it was not until Cleveland Rodgers and John Black issued in 1920 *The Gathering of the Forces* (a miscellaneous collection of Whitman's journalistic writings in the *Brooklyn Daily Eagle*) that the first of the "unauthorized" tales and verses were at last exhumed and reprinted: two short stories and a Fourth of July ode.

Of considerably more importance was the publication in 1921 of Emory Holloway's *The Uncollected Poetry and Prose of Walt Whitman*, which reprinted for the first time, in addition to the two tales which already had appeared in *The Gathering of the Forces*, nine short stories (three of which, along with two others not in Holloway, form a single title, "Some Fact-Romances," in my volume), *Franklin Evans*, and twenty poems (one, as Holloway noted, probably spurious; one other which I believe spurious; and two revisions of other poems in the group). In 1927 appeared *The Half-Breed and Other Stories by Walt Whitman*, edited by Thomas Ollive Mabbott. This volume reprinted for the first time five pieces of Whitman's fiction, one of which supplied the two sketches which completed "Some

Fact-Romances." Finally, in 1950, Joseph Jay Rubin and Charles H. Brown in *Walt Whitman of the New York "Aurora"* reprinted two more pre-*Leaves* poems, one the revision of a poem which had been reprinted by Holloway.

Whitman's early poems and fiction for years have been scattered inconveniently among various volumes, many of which are out of print. This situation is the natural result of the slow and laborious task of searching out and identifying pieces which Walter Whitman wrote but which Walt Whitman had no interest in preserving. The early efforts of a major writer are of interest and usually of value to the inquiring scholar and to the writer's actual audience—the intelligent general reader. Hence the need for assembling such early work in an organic and chronologically ordered whole so that it may be surveyed in a comprehensive fashion. Such is the purpose of this volume. I have included all the important variant readings of the stories and poems (a matter not much attended to in the past) and two tales, discovered about ten years ago by Emory Holloway, which have not been reprinted before now. The amount of my indebtedness to the researchers among Whitman's early writing is clearly evident: this volume exists only because of their curiosity and their scholarship.

Whitman's fiction and early poetry appeared (and often reappeared) in approximately twenty magazines and newspapers, some issues of which are now quite rare. The following institutions generously furnished me with photographic copies (in the case of one poem, a transcript) of most of the texts and their variants which are included in this volume: the Boston Public Library, the Library of Congress, the Long Island Historical Society, the Louisiana State University Library, the New York Historical Society Library, the New York Public Library, the Public Library of Cincinnati and Hamilton County, the Queens Borough Public Library, and the University of Texas Library.

I am indebted also to Charles E. Feinberg and Professor Emory Holloway for providing me with textual materials. Mr. Feinberg characteristically made his remarkable collection of Whitmaniana immediately available and provided me with photostats of two unique items.

A number of persons have made my task lighter through their kindness in responding to my requests, sometimes importunate, for advice and information. I especially wish to thank Professors Gay Wilson Allen, Sculley Bradley, Emory Holloway, Thomas Ollive Mabbott, and William White. Professor Bradley, in addition, carefully examined my manuscript and gave me valuable advice and criticism. Both Professors Allen and Bradley aided me importantly in establishing the form and contents of this volume; and Professor Allen also examined for me the unique files of the *Aurora* in the Paterson, New Jersey, Library. Professor White's bibliography of Whitman's fiction— Papers of the *Bibliographical Society*, LII (Fourth Quarter, 1958) 300–306—was a valuable check list.

This volume could not have been completed had not the regents and the administration of Southwest Texas State College provided me with a research grant and had not Professor Ralph Houston, Head of the Department of English, relieved me of considerable departmental duties. My typist, Miss Frances Grady, has heroically maintained her equanimity and accuracy over many months and has contributed importantly to the book's completion.

I thank my wife Chris and my son Mark for their interest, their encouragement, and their forbearance. As they know, this volume is as much theirs as it is mine.

T. L. B.

San Marcos, Texas
April 10, 1962

CONTENTS

The Fiction

APPENDICES:

Introduction

I

This volume is not intended to be a critical edition of Walt Whitman's fiction and early poetry. Its sole purpose is to provide for the first time a complete and accurate text, with variants, of Whitman's pre-*Leaves* verse and of his tales, the latter very conveniently falling into approximately the same period as that of his early poems. But I must qualify these statements. To speak of a "complete" text of the fiction and early verse is not quite exact. The reader of this volume will find in it the fragment of a temperance tale, the remainder of which may be uncovered eventually. Other of Whitman's tales may later be discovered; the same is true of Whitman's verse. Should, for example, a file of the *Long Islander* for 1838–1839 be found, it would probably bring to light poems not included in this volume. And as for this not being a critical edition, the reader will find that I have made some "critical" remarks; but these remarks appear chiefly in these introductory paragraphs. I could not resist making them.

II

Whitman's published poetry prior to the publication of *Leaves of Grass* falls, so far as is known, in the period between 1838 and 1850. Most of these poems appeared in either New York or Long Island newspapers. The earliest poem appeared in Whitman's own weekly, the *Long Islander*, and has been preserved because it was reprinted in the *Long Island Democrat*, of which there is an extant file. The last appeared in the New York *Tribune*.

The kindest remark that one can make about Whitman's early verse is that it was conventional: it was the sort of thing being printed each year by the hundreds in newspapers, magazines, and gift books. Whitman's poems are didactic in the fashion of the American school of graveyard poetry as established by Bryant and sentimental in the manner of Shelleyan self-pity and Keatsian frustration. Neither this sort of didacticism nor this sort of sentimentalism is characteristic of the later *Leaves of Grass*. Though echoes from Bryant are the most obvious in this early poetry of Whitman, one may find (in addition to some from Keats and, faintly, from Shelley) echoes from Longfellow, Emerson, Milton, Hood, and, especially, the innumerable horde of fourth-rate and unoriginal versifiers who occasionally found, as did Mrs. Lydia Sigourney, a following. Though Whitman later claimed, and probably truthfully, that Shakespeare and Homer were early passions of his, one cannot find their influence in these early poems. I suspect that Whitman was trying to appeal to the general public, an effort in which his contemporary, Poe, more nearly succeeded because of his adeptness and inventiveness in traditional metrics and in graveyard themes.

Some of the apologists for Whitman's early verse have insisted that it shows Whitman to have been quite capable of handling conventional versification in an adequate manner. My own opinion of the matter (and I invite the reader to decide for himself) is that Whitman's handling of conventional metrics was awkward and inexpert. But in 1850 Whitman abandoned subjectively sentimental themes and turned to political issues. At the same time he turned to less conventionally regular metrics, possibly in imitation of the irregular English ode, and produced his poems which, from our point on Darien, anticipated the style of the poems in *Leaves of Grass*. One of these 1850 poems was incorporated, with some revision, in *Leaves of Grass* as "Europe, the 72ᵈ and 73ᵈ Years of These States." A few lines of another 1850 poem found their way, somewhat transmuted, into "Song of Myself." But thinking of the trial lines that Whitman was already essaying in his notebooks by 1850, lines which actually bear little resemblance in thought or form to the 1850 poems, one must, I feel, stand speechless and silent.

III

The earliest of Whitman's twenty-four pieces of fiction, "Death in the School-Room," appeared in 1841 in the *Democratic Review*. The last, "The Shadow and the Light of a Young Man's Soul," appeared in the *Union Magazine* in 1848, though the *Democratic Review* reprinted as late as 1851 a tale it had carried originally nine years before. Among "Pieces in Early Youth," a division in Whitman's *Collect*, there is one tale, "Lingave's Temptation," whose original place and date of publication have not been identified. Mr. Feinberg sent me a photostat of Whitman's clipping of the original printing of the tale with pencilled-in revisions for the *Collect* version. I had hoped that the format of the clipping would enable me to locate the story in a particular journal, but it is not the format of any of the magazines or newspapers in which the other tales of Whitman were published. It is unlikely, however, that "Lingave's Temptation" was published after 1848.

A survey of first publication dates of Whitman's tales (disregarding the numerous reprintings) may be of some significance. Over a period of eight years, the original appearance of Whitman's fiction followed this pattern: four tales in 1841; seven in 1842; one in 1843; four in 1844; six in 1845; none in 1846; none in 1847; and one in 1848. The odds are against a tale being first published after 1848. It is interesting to note that while Whitman was editor of the *Brooklyn Daily Eagle* in 1846 and 1847 he published in his paper no original fiction by himself but did reprint in 1846 twelve tales (some originally imbedded tales in larger works) and in 1847 one tale. Whitman by 1846 may have become involved with the problem of expressing unconventional thoughts in unconventional metric form and may also have learned that fiction was not his forte.

In his introduction to the *Collect* section of *Specimen Days and Collect*, Whitman had the following to say about "Pieces in Early Youth": "On jaunts over Long Island, as boy and young fellow, nearly half a century ago, I heard of, or came across in my own experiences, characters, true occurrences, incidents, which I tried my 'prentice hand at recording—(I was then quite an 'abolitionist' and advocate of the 'temperance' and 'anti-capital-punishment' causes)—and publish'd during occasional visits to New York City. . . . My serious wish were to have all these crude and boyish pieces quietly dropp'd in oblivion—but to avoid the annoyance of their surreptitious issue . . . I have, with some qualms, tack'd them on here."

This present volume is in its way a "surreptitious issue" of more "crude and boyish pieces" than Whitman probably dreamed would come to light. It is impossible, as he himself seemed to have known, to speak well of Whitman's fiction. It is all very well to provide ready-made apologetics for the tales by classifying them as "Pieces in Early Youth," but after all Whitman was twenty-two when his first short story appeared and twenty-nine when the last appeared. And the fact remains that his tales were unoriginal, conventional, and poorly written. I shall not detail the faults in Whitman's fiction, for they will quickly become evident to the reader of this volume. Many of these faults may be imputed to Whitman's efforts to please the reading public's taste for the sentimental, the didactic, and the gothic in a genre for which he had not the slightest talent.

Scholars have often asserted that Whitman in his tales consciously imitated Poe or Hawthorne, who both contributed to the *Democratic Review*. But it should be remembered that Poe and Hawthorne themselves deliberately imitated—with, however, the touch of genius—the fiction of less talented writers who had succeeded in pleasing the general reader.

No doubt, as he asserted in his introductory remarks to *Collect*, Whitman based many of his tales on personal experiences and on incidents he had heard of. For example, his descriptions of Manhattan boarding houses in *Franklin Evans* were no doubt modeled on boarding houses he himself had lived in, and "Some Fact-Romances, I" (perhaps the most charming and best written of all his tales) was probably a reminiscence told him by his mother. Whitman also said in his introductory remarks to *Collect* that he was, as a young fellow trying his hand at fiction, "quite an 'abolitionist,' an advocate of the 'temperance' and 'anti-capital-punishment' causes." Either he had forgotten that he had written no abolition tales or no one yet has come across them. Whitman's opposition to capital punishment barely appeared in his stories. The temperance theme, however, was relatively prominent in the tales. Whitman was a sincere advocate of temperance but not of the "cold-water" sort except in his fiction; and his championing of total abstinence may well have been directed toward the purported reader-power of the Washingtonians. But regardless of the seriousness of the themes of some of his tales, the plain fact is that Whitman had no talent for fiction.

A number of scholars, admitting the poor quality of Whitman's fiction, have yet insisted in finding it prophetic of the major themes of *Leaves of Grass.* My only remark on this subject is that if one adumbrates the *Leaves* from Whitman's fiction one must also admit that most of Whitman's fellow contributors to journals and newspapers were potential composers and, at the least, potential admirers of *Leaves of Grass*. This was not the case, though the sentiments that Whitman expressed in his tales were the staple ingredients in the tales of his today-unheralded contemporaries.

Finally, it should be said that the ambiguity of the "Calamus" poems appears occasionally in Whitman's stories. The more one examines the tales, the more he feels, especially after encountering the original version of "The Child and the Profligate," that the "Calamus" poems may express more than simply phrenological "adhesiveness." But in view of Whitman's final achievement in *Leaves of Grass*, where the mullein and the mouse equally share the miracle of existence founded on the kelson of divine love, it is best to leave the resolution of ambiguity to Walt, not Walter, Whitman.

A NOTE ON THE TEXT

This volume, as stated in the preface, contains all of Whitman's fiction and pre-*Leaves* verse that so far have been identified. Many of these pieces long have been known as Whitman's because they were originally published as "by Walter Whitman" or "by W. Whitman." Others have been attributed to Whitman because of style, signed initials, or circumstantial evidence, and later have been found to have been reprinted elsewhere as "by Walter Whitman" or "by the author of *Franklin Evans*." Whitman's inclusion of "Pieces in Early Youth" in *Specimen Days and Collect* identified a few more. Those few pieces in this present volume whose attribution to Whitman is dubious (and this involves only three of the poems) are so indicated in their notes.

The texts and their variants in this volume have been transcribed, with four exceptions, from photographic or photostatic reproductions of the pieces as they appeared originally in either magazines or newspapers. The four exceptions are among the poems. The New York Public Library's copy of the *Home Journal* for March 30, 1892, has suffered from the ravages of time and "New Year's Day, 1848" is no longer decipherable. I was unable to locate another copy of that issue of the *Home Journal*, so I have followed the text of the poem as given in the *Uncollected Poetry and Prose*. Due to the fragility of a rare issue of a newspaper, it was advisable that the Public Library of Cincinnati make me a transcription rather than a photostat of "Isle of la Belle Riviere." Professor Gay Wilson Allen checked for me the texts in *Walt Whitman of the New York "Aurora"* of "Time to Come" and "The Death and Burial of McDonald Clarke" against the original texts of the poems in the Paterson Library's unique file of the *Aurora*.

The poems and the tales are grouped separately but are arranged in chronological order within their category. The rule for establishing the textual canon has been to accept as the honored text of a poem or tale that which can be presumed to have been the last printed version authorized by Whitman. The only exception to this practice in a few cases has been where the final printed version is an abridgement or a fragment.

All textual matters relative to each work are discussed and the variant readings, when such exist, are given in the appropriate footnotes. The footnotes to each work are numbered from "1" to "99," when necessary, and then begin at "1" again. Every poem and tale has a first footnote, if no more, giving the place and date of its publication. As a rule, "Footnote 1" contains supplementary comment valuable for someone actually about to read the text. Whenever a poem or story has had several titles, I have honored Whitman's last choice; but all variant titles are given in "Footnote 1" for the poems and in the "Appendix" for the fiction. I have recorded the rather complex history of the publication of Whitman's fiction in the Appendix. "Footnote 1" of the tales may not mention every reprint and may not give the complete citations, but the Appendix does. Since the poems were much less frequently reprinted, I have found it more convenient to deal with their complete publication history in the footnotes rather than in an appendix. Hence all the variant titles of the poems are given in the first footnote. The variant titles of the poems and tales, when such exist, are also given in the Table of Contents.

In giving variant words or phrases in the footnotes, I have enclosed a variant in quotation marks only when the variant itself contains a quotation or quoted dialogue or is a part of quoted dialogue. In regard to the poems, the footnotes ordinarily show only collated variant lines or phrases. However, in a few cases, I have given the entire variant poem in italics, following its final version, when the differences between the two versions have been so extensive as to render collation by lines or phrases burdensome to the reader.

I have taken no editorial liberties with Whitman's texts except to correct obvious typographical errors such as the omission or inversion of a letter. I have not tampered with Whitman's spelling, which is sometimes incorrect, nor with his punctuation, which is at times illogical or awkward. Whitman occasionally inserted a comma where clarity and common sense demanded no punctuation at all, and he sometimes used a semicolon where a comma was called for. In addition, he used the dash excessively and for differing purposes. Most often the dash substitutes for a parenthesis; but frequently it serves in place of a comma, whether to separate parts of a series or to separate a nonrestrictive construction from the rest of the sentence. The dash also may serve to emphasize the sentence that follows, to indicate a break in thought, or to show a new paragraph. Whitman also, especially in the *Brooklyn Eagle*, often used a series of periods (from six to over twenty) to indicate a break in thought or a new paragraph. The asterisk, employed less often, usually emphasizes what follows it. In the texts from *Collect*, Whitman consistently elided the "e" in the past forms of most regular verbs—a mannerism he first exhibited in the fourth edition of *Leaves of Grass* (1867) and which he persisted in to his death. I have made no use of *sic*, except in perhaps two footnotes. The reader of this volume will soon become habituated to Whitman's idiosyncrasies in spelling and punctuation and will recognize them as characteristic.

ABBREVIATIONS

Allen	Gay Wilson Allen, *The Solitary Singer* (1955)
Allen, Handbook	Gay Wilson Allen, *Walt Whitman Handbook* (1946)
Barrus	Clara Barrus, *Whitman and Burroughs—Comrades* (1931)
Binns	Henry Bryan Binns, *A Life of Walt Whitman* (1905)
C	*Columbian* version
Collect	Walt Whitman, "Specimen Days and Collect," *Complete Prose Works* (1892)
Correspondence	*The Correspondence of Walt Whitman* (1961), 2 vols., ed. by Edwin Haviland Miller
E	*Eagle* version
Fiedler	Leslie A. Fiedler, *Love and Death in the American Novel* (1960)
GF	*The Gathering of the Forces* (1920), 2 vols., ed. by Cleveland Rodgers and John Black
Holloway and Schwarz	*I Sit and Look Out* (1932), ed. by Emory Holloway and Vernolian Schwarz
Kennedy	William Sloane Kennedy, *The Fight of a Book for the World* (1926)
Mabbott	*The Half-Breed and Other Stories by Walt Whitman* (1927), ed. by Thomas Ollive Mabbott
NW	*New World* version
Perry	Bliss Perry, *Walt Whitman* (1906)
Rubin and Brown	Joseph Jay Rubin and Charles H. Brown, eds., *Walt Whitman of the New York "Aurora": Editor at Twenty-Two* (1950)
Traubel	Horace Traubel, ed., *With Walt Whitman in Camden* (1906–1953), 4 vols.
UPP	*The Uncollected Poetry and Prose of Walt Whitman* (1921), 2 vols., ed. by Emory Holloway

Special abbreviations occur in the footnotes to *Franklin Evans*. These are: DW ("The Death of Wind-Foot"); LJE ("Little Jane," *Eagle*, December 7, 1846); LJC ("Little Jane," *Collect*); and FC (*Fortunes of a Country-Boy; Incidents in Town—and his Adventures at the South*, *Eagle*, November 16–30, 1846).

Walt Whitman

The Early Poems and the Fiction

THE POEMS

Young Grimes[1]

When old Grimes died, he left a son—
    The graft of worthy stock;
In deed and word he shows himself
    A chip of the old block.

In youth, 'tis said, he liked not school—
    Of tasks he was no lover;
He wrote sums in a ciphering book,
    Which had a pasteboard cover.

Young Grimes ne'er went to see the girls
    Before he was fourteen;
Nor smoked, nor swore, for that he knew
    Gave Mrs. Grimes much pain.

He never was extravagant
    In pleasure, dress, or board;
His Sunday suit was of blue cloth,
    At six and eight a yard.

But still there is, to tell the truth,
    No stinginess in him;
And in July he wears an old
    Straw hat with a broad brim.

1. *Long Island Democrat*, January 1, 1840. From August 1839 until December of the same year, Whitman was a compositor and writer on the *Long Island Democrat*. While teaching school in 1840, Whitman continued to contribute to the *Democrat*. Professor Thomas O. Mabbott called my attention to the fact that the poem is a direct imitation of Albert Gorton Greene's "Old Grimes," which was first published in the Providence *Gazette* on January 16, 1822. "Old Grimes" quickly became very popular and has been reprinted and anthologized up to the present. Whitman, in his poem, imitates the meter, stanza form, and rime scheme of the older poem; and he attempts to follow the humorously genial and sympathetic style of the original. A sampling from "Old Grimes" (the fifth and sixth stanzas) in italics, which follows "Young Grimes," will illustrate the resemblance between the two poems.

"Young Grimes" was reprinted in *UPP*, I, 2–4, where the publication date is given as January 1, 1839. While this present collection was in preparation, Professor Holloway sent me a letter addressed to him on April 11, 1936, from Mr. Richard B. Sealock, Acting Curator, Long Island Collection, The Queens Borough Public Library. Mr. Sealock pointed out that the year was given incorrectly as 1839 at the head of page one of the issue of the *Long Island Democrat* containing "Young Grimes." The inside pages of the issue carry the date January 1, 1840, and the volume number, 5, agrees with that for the year 1840.

No devotee in fashion's train
    Is good old Grimes's son;
He sports no cane—no whiskers wears,
    Nor lounges o'er the town.[2]

He does not spend more than he earns
    In dissipation's round;
But shuns with care those dangerous rooms
    Where sin and vice abound.

It now is eight and twenty years
    Since young Grimes saw the light;
And no house in the land can show
    A fairer, prouder sight.

For there his wife, prudent and chaste,
    His mother's age made sweet,
His children trained in virtue's path,
    The gazer's eye will meet.

Upon a hill, just off the road
    That winds the village side,
His farm house stands, within whose door
    Ne'er entered Hate or Pride.

But Plenty and Benevolence
    And Happiness are there—
And underneath that lowly roof
    Content smiles calm and fair.

Reader, go view the cheerful scene—
    By it how poor must prove
The pomp, and tinsel, and parade,
    Which pleasure's followers love.

Leave the wide city's noisy din—
    The busy haunts of men—
And here enjoy a tranquil life,
    Unvexed by guilt or pain.

2. Holloway, in commenting on this poem (UPP, I, lxxxiv–lxxxv), suggests that Whitman "has (apparently) with gentle irony described himself." However, at the date of the composition of the poem, contrary to the younger Grimes' habit, Whit-

Old Grimes

He lived at peace with all mankind,
In friendship he was true;
His coat had pocket-holes behind,
His pantaloons were blue.

Unharmed, the sin which earth pollutes
He passed securely o'er,—
And never wore a pair of boots
For thirty years or more.

man sported a cane, wore a cravat, and had a neatly trimmed beard. The evidence is a photograph of Whitman taken in 1840 (which serves as the frontispiece of Vol. II of *UPP* and has been reproduced several times).

The Inca's Daughter[1]

Before the dark-brow'd sons of Spain,
 A captive Indian maiden stood;
Imprison'd where the moon before
 Her race as princes trod.

The rack had riven her frame that day—
 But not a sigh or murmur broke
Forth from her breast; calmly she stood,
 And sternly thus she spoke:—

"The glory of Peru is gone;
 Her proudest warriors in the fight—
Her armies, and her Inca's power
 Bend to the Spaniard's might.

"And I—a Daughter of the Sun—
 Shall I ingloriously still live?
Shall a Peruvian monarch's child
 Become the white lord's slave?

"No: I'd not meet my father's frown
 In the free spirit's place of rest,
Nor seem a stranger midst the bands
 Whom Manitou has blest."

Her snake-like eye, her cheek of fire,
 Glowed with intenser, deeper hue;
She smiled in scorn, and from her robe
 A poisoned arrow drew.

1. *Long Island Democrat*, May 5, 1840; reprinted *UPP*, I, 8–9.

"Now, paleface see! the Indian girl
    Can teach thee how to bravely die:
Hail! spirits of my kindred slain,
    A sister ghost is nigh!"

Her hand was clenched and lifted high—
    Each breath, and pulse, and limb was still'd;
An instant more the arrow fell:
    Thus died the Inca's child.

The Love That Is Hereafter[1]

O, beauteous is the earth! and fair
The splendors of Creation are:
Nature's green robe, the shining sky,
The winds that through the tree-tops sigh,
    All speak a bounteous God.

The noble trees, the sweet young flowers,
The birds that sing in forest bowers,
The rivers grand that murmuring roll,
And all which joys or calms the soul
    Are made by gracious might.

The flocks and droves happy and free,
The dwellers of the boundless sea,
Each living thing on air or land,
Created by our Master's hand,
    Is formed for joy and peace.

But man—weak, proud, and erring man,
Of truth ashamed, of folly vain—
Seems singled out to know no rest
And of all things that move, feels least
    The sweets of happiness.

Yet he it is whose little life
Is passed in useless, vexing strife,
And all the glorious earth to him
Is rendered dull, and poor, and dim,
    From hope unsatisfied.

He faints with grief—he toils through care—
And from the cradle to the bier
He wearily plods on—till Death
Cuts short his transient, panting breath,
    And sends him to his sleep.

1. *Long Island Democrat*, May 19, 1840; reprinted *UPP*, I, 9–10.

O, mighty powers of Destiny!
When from this coil of flesh I'm free—
When through my second life I rove,
Let me but find *one* heart to love,
    As I would wish to love:

Let me but meet a single breast,
Where this tired soul its hope may rest,
In never-dying faith: ah, then,
That would be bliss all free from pain,
    And sickness of the heart.

For vainly through this world below
We seek affection. Nought but wo
Is with our earthly journey wove;
And so the heart must look above,
    Or die in dull despair.

The Spanish Lady[1]

On a low couch reclining,
    When slowly waned the day,
Wrapt in gentle slumber,
    A Spanish maiden lay.

O beauteous was that lady;
    And the splendour of the place
Matched well her form so graceful,
    And her sweet, angelic face.

But what doth she lonely,
    Who ought in courts to reign?
For the form that there lies sleeping
    Owns the proudest name in Spain.

Tis the lovely Lady Inez.
    De Castro's daughter fair,
Who in the castle chamber,
    Slumbers so sweetly there.

O, better had she laid her
    Mid the couches of the dead;
O better had she slumbered
    Where the poisonous snake lay hid.

For worse than deadly serpent,
    Or mouldering skeleton,
Are the fierce bloody hands of men,
    By hate and fear urged on.

O Lady Inez, pleasant
    Be the thoughts that now have birth
In thy visions; they are last of all
    That thou shalt dream on earth.

1. *Long Island Democrat*, August 4, 1840; reprinted *UPP*, I, 12. Inez de Castro (1320?–1355), a descendant of the royal family of Castile, married below her station. King Alfonso, fearing unpleasant political repercussions as a result of

Now noiseless on its hinges
        Opens the chamber door,
And one whose trade is blood and crime
        Steals slow across the floor.

High gleams the assassin's dagger;
        And by the road that it has riven,
The soul of that fair lady
        Has passed from earth to heaven.

the mésalliance, ordered her murdered. Inez's tragic story has been retold often in European literature, ranging from Camoëns' *Lusiad* to Aphra Behn's *Agnes de Castro*.

The Columbian's Song[1]

What a fair and happy place
    Is the one where Freedom lives,
And the knowledge that our arm is strong,
    A haughty bearing gives!
For each sun that gilds the east,
When at dawn it first doth rise,
      Sets at night,
      Red and bright,
On a people where the prize
Which millions in the battle fight
Have sought with hope forlorn,
      Grows brighter every hour,
      In strength, and grace, and power,
      And the sun this land doth leave
      Mightier at filmy eve,
Than when it first arose, in the morn.

Beat the sounding note of joy!
    Let it echo o'er the hills,
Till shore and forest hear the pride,
    That a bondless bosom fills.
And on the plain where patriot sires
    Rest underneath the sod,
Where the stern resolve for liberty
    Was writ in gushing blood,
      Freeman go,
      With upright brow,
    And render thanks to God.

O, my soul is drunk with joy,
    And my inmost heart is glad,
To think my country's star will not
    Through endless ages fade,
That on its upward glorious course

1. *Long Island Democrat*, October 27, 1840; reprinted *UPP*, I, 15–16.

Our red eyed eagle leaps,
While with the ever moving winds,
     Our dawn-striped banner sweeps:
That here at length is found
     A wide extending shore,
Where Freedom's starry gleam,
Shines with unvarying beam;
     Not as it did of yore,
With flickering flash, when CAESAR fell,
Or haughty GESLER heard his knell,
     Or STUART rolled in gore.

Nor let our foes presume
     That this heart-prized union band,
Will e'er be severed by the stroke
     Of a fraternal hand.
Though parties sometime rage,
     And Faction rears its form.
Its jealous eye, its scheming brain,
     To revel in the storm:
Yet should a danger threaten,
     Or enemy draw nigh,
Then scattered to the winds of heaven,
     All civil strife would fly;
And north and south, and east and west,
     Would rally at the cry—
'Brethren arise! to battle come,
For Truth, for Freedom, and for Home,
     And for our Fathers' Memory!'

The Winding-Up[1]

Behold around us pomp and pride;
    The rich, the lofty, and the gay,
Glitter before our dazzled eyes—
    Live out their brief but brilliant day;
Then when the hour for fame is o'er,
    Unheeded pass away.

The warrior builds a mighty name,
    The object of his hopes and fears,
That future times may see it where
    Her tower aspiring Glory rears.
Desist, O, fool! think what thou'lt be
    In a few fleeting years.

Beside his ponderous age worn book
    A student shades his weary brow;
He walks Philosophy's dark path—
    That journey difficult and slow:
But in vain is all that teeming mind,[2]
    He, too, to earth must go.

The statesman's sleepless, plodding brain
    Schemes out a nation's destiny;
His is the voice that awes the crowd,
    And his, the bold, commanding eye;
But transient is his high renown—
    He like the rest must die.

1. *Long Island Democrat*, June 22, 1841; originally published in the same paper on September 22, 1840, under the title of "The End of All." This earlier version was reprinted in *UPP*, I, 13–15, where variants of the later version were listed. Stanzas three and four of "The Winding-Up" were in the reversed order in "The End of All," and there are a very few minor differences in punctuation in the two versions, the most common being the omission of some commas and the substitution of dashes for four of the commas in the later version. The verbal variants in "The End of All" are given in the footnotes that follow.

2. But vain is all that teeming mind

And beauty sweet, and all the fair,
    Who sail on fortune's sunniest wave;
The poor, with him of countless gold,
    Owner of all that mortals crave,
Alike are fated soon to lie
    Down in the silent grave.

Children of folly here behold
    How soon the fame of man is gone:
Time levels all. Trophies and names,
    Inscription that the proud have drawn
Surpassing strength—pillars and thrones
    Sink as the waves roll on.[3]

Nor think[4] when you attain your wish,
    Content will banish grief and care;
High though your stand—tho on your breast[5]
    The robes that pride[6] and splendor wear,
A secret poison in the heart
    Will stick and rankle there.

In night go view the solemn stars,
    Ever in majesty the same—
Creation's world's; how poor must seem
    The mightiest honors earth can name—
And most of all this strife[7]
    After the bubble, Fame!

3. Why, then, O, insects of an hour!
    Why, then, with struggling toil, contend
  For honors you so soon must yield,
    When Death shall his stern summons send?
  For honor, glory, fortune, wit,
    This is, to all, the end.
4. Think not
5. High though your stand, though round you thrown
6. rank   7. this silly strife

Each Has His Grief[1]

On earth are many sights of wo,[2]
    And many sounds of agony,
And many a sorrow-wither'd check,
    And many a pain-dulled eye.

The wretched weep, the poor complain,
    And luckless love pines on unknown;
And faintly from the midnight couch
    Sounds out the sick child's moan.

Each has his grief[3]—old age fears death;
    The young man's ills are pride, desire,
And heart-sickness; and in his breast
    The heat of passion's fire.

And he who runs the race of fame,
    Oft feels within a feverish dread,
Lest others snatch the laurel crown
    He bears upon his head.[4]

All, all know care;[5] and, at the close,
    All lie earth's spreading arms within—
The poor, the black-soul'd, proud, and low,
    Virtue, despair, and sin.

O, foolish, then, with pain to shrink
    From the sure doom we each must meet.
Is earth so fair—or heaven so dark—
    Or life so passing sweet?

1. *New World* (New York), November 20, 1841, at which time Whitman was working for the *New World* as a printer; originally published as "We All Shall Rest at Last" in the *Long Island Democrat*, July 14, 1840. The earlier version was reprinted in UPP, I, 10–11, where variants of the later version were noted. Some few minor changes were made in punctuation in the later version. Verbal variants in "We All Shall Rest at Last" are noted in the footnotes that follow.

No; dread ye not the fearful hour—
  The coffin, and the pall's dark gloom,
For there's a calm to throbbing hearts,
  And rest, down in the tomb.

Then our long journey will be o'er,
  And throwing off earth's load of woes,[6]
The pallid brow, the fainting heart,[7]
  Will sink in soft repose.

Nor only this: for wise men say
  That when we leave our land of care,
We float to a mysterious shore,
  Peaceful, and pure, and fair.

So, welcome death! Whene'er the time
  That the dread summons must be met,
I'll yield without one pang of fear,[8]
  Or sigh, or vain regret.

But like unto a wearied child,
  That over field and wood all day
Has ranged and struggled, and at last,
  Worn out with toil and play,

Goes up at evening to his home,
  And throws him, sleepy, tired, and sore,
Upon his bed, and rests him there,
  His pain and trouble o'er.

2. woe   3. care
4. This stanza is not in the original version.
5. grief
6. And throwing off this load of woes
7. The pallid brow, the feebled limbs
8. awe

The Punishment of Pride[1]

Once on his star-gemmed, dazzling throne,
Sat an all bright and lofty One,
    Unto whom God had given
To be the mightiest Angel-Lord
    Within the range of Heaven;
With power of knowing things to come,
To judge o'er man, and speak his doom.

O, he was pure! the fleecy snow,
Falling through air to earth below,
    Was not more undefiled:
Sinless he was as the wreathed smile
    On lip of sleeping child.
Haply, more like the snow was he,
Freezing—with all its purity.

Upon his forehead beamed a star,
Bright as the lamps of even are;
    And his pale robe was worn
About him with a look of pride,
    A high, majestic scorn,
Which showed he felt his glorious might,
His favor with the Lord of Light.

Years, thus he swayed the things of earth—
O'er human crime and human worth—
    Haughty, and high, and stern;
Nor ever, at sweet Mercy's call,
    His white neck would he turn;
But listening not to frailty's plea,
Launched forth each just yet stern decree.

At last, our Father who above
Sits throned with Might, and Truth, and Love,

1. *New World*, December 18, 1841; reprinted in the *Conservator*, XII (February 1902) 189, and *UPP*, I, 17–19. "For the *New World*" was printed above the poem, but it was evidently written about two years earlier, in 1839, when Whitman taught school for a few months at Little Bay Side near Jamaica, Long Island. In 1894, Horace Traubel interviewed a Charles A. Roe, one of Whitman's pupils at

And knows our weakness blind,
Beheld him—proud, and pitying not
　　The errors of mankind;
And doomed him, for a punishment,
To be forth from his birth-place sent.

So down this angel from on high
Came from his sphere, to live and die
　　As mortal men have done;
That he might know the tempting snares
　　Which lure each human son;
And dwell as all on earth have dwelt.
And feel the grief we all have felt.

Then he knew Guilt, while round him weaved
Their spells, pale Sickness, Love deceived,
　　And Fear, and Hate, and Wrath;
And all the blighting ills of Fate
　　Were cast athwart his path:
He stood upon the grave's dread brink,
And felt his soul with terror sink.

He learned why men to sin give way,
And how we live our passing day
　　In indolence and crime;
But yet his eye with awe looked on,
　　To see in all its prime
That godlike thing, the human mind,
A gem in black decay enshrined.

Long years in penance thus he spent,
Until the Mighty Parent sent
　　His loveliest messenger—
Who came with step so noiselessly,
　　And features passing fair;
Death was his name; the angel heard
The call, and swift to heaven he soared.

Little Bay Side. Roe stated that Whitman had his students memorize a poem entitled "The Fallen Angel" rumored to be Whitman's own. Roe still remembered the poem and recited it for Traubel. With some trivial variations, it was "The Punishment of Pride" as printed in the *New World*. See Horace Traubel, "Walt Whitman, Schoolmaster: Notes of a Conversation with Charles A. Roe, 1894," *Walt Whitman Fellowship Papers*, No. 14, April 1895, 81–87.

There in his former glory placed,
The star again his forehead graced;
    But never more that brow
Was lifted up in scorn of sin;
    His wings were folded now—
But not in pride: his port, though high,
No more spoke conscious majesty.

And O, what double light now shone
About that pure and heavenly one;
    For in the clouds which made
The veil around his seat of power,
    In silvery robes arrayed,
Hovered the seraph Charity,
And Pity with her melting eye.

Ambition[1]

One day, an obscure youth, a wanderer,
Known but to few, lay musing with himself
About the chances of his future life.
In that youth's heart, there dwelt the coal Ambition,
Burning and glowing; and he asked himself,
"Shall I, in time to come, be great and famed?"
Now soon an answer wild and mystical
Seemed to sound forth from out the depths of air;
And to the gazer's eye appeared a shape
Like one as of a cloud—and thus it spoke:

"O, many a panting, noble heart
    Cherishes in its deep recess
The hope to win renown o'er earth
    From Glory's prized caress.

"And some will win that envied goal,
    And have their deeds known far and wide;
And some—by far the most—will sink
    Down in oblivion's tide.

"But *thou*, who visions bright dost cull
    From the imagination's store,
With dreams, such as the youthful dream
    Of grandeur, love, and power,

"Fanciest that thou shalt build a name
    And come to have the nations know

1. *Brother Jonathan* (New York), January 29, 1842; reprinted in *UPP*, I, 19–20. The poem incorporates and elaborates an earlier poem, "Fame's Vanity," which appeared in the *Long Island Democrat*, October 23, 1839, and is reprinted also in *UPP*, I, 4–5. Because of the extensive alteration "Fame's Vanity" underwent in its incorporation into "Ambition," I have reprinted it in italics, following its final version.

What conscious might dwells in the brain
    That throbs beneath that brow?

"And see thick countless ranks of men
    Fix upon *thee* their reverent gaze—
And listen to the plaudits loud
    To *thee* that thousands raise?

"Weak, childish soul! the very place
    That pride has made for folly's rest;
What thoughts, with vanity all rife,
    Fill up thy heaving breast!

"At night, go view the solemn stars
    Those wheeling worlds through time the same—
How puny seem the widest power,
    The proudest mortal name![2]

"Think too, that all, lowly and rich,
    Dull idiot mind and teeming sense,
Alike must sleep the endless sleep,
    A hundred seasons hence.

"So, frail one, never more repine,
    Though thou livest on obscure, unknown;
Though after death unsought may be
    Thy markless resting stone."

And as these accents dropped in the youth's ears,
He felt him sick at heart; for many a month
His fancy had amused and charmed itself
With lofty aspirations, visions fair
Of what he *might be*. And it pierced him sore
To have his airy castles thus dashed down.

---

2. This stanza is a reworking of the final stanza of "The Winding-Up," *q.v.*

Fame's Vanity

O, many a panting, noble heart
    Cherishes in its deep recess
Th' hope to win renown o'er earth
    From Glory's priz'd caress.

And some will reach that envied goal,
    And have their fame known far and wide;
And some will sink unnoted down
    In dark Oblivion's tide.

But I, who many a pleasant scheme
    Do sometimes cull from Fancy's store,
With dreams, such as the youthful dream,
    Of grandeur, love, and power—

Shall I build up a lofty name,
    And seek to have the nations know
What conscious might dwells in the brain
    That throbs aneath this brow?

And have thick countless ranks of men
    Fix upon me their reverent gaze,
And listen to the deafening shouts,
    To me that thousands raise?

Thou foolish soul! the very place
    That pride has made for folly's rest;
What thoughts with vanity all rife,
    Fill up this heaving breast!

Fame, O what happiness is lost
    In hot pursuit of thy false glare!
Thou, whose drunk votaries die to gain
    A puff of viewless air.

So, never let me more repine,
    Though I live on obscure, unknown,
Though after death unsought may be
    My markless resting stone.

For mighty one and lowly wretch,
    Dull, idiot mind, or teeming sense
Must sleep on the same earthy couch,
    A hundred seasons hence.

The Death and Burial of McDonald Clarke

A PARODY [1]

Not a sigh was heard, not a tear was shed,
    As away to the "tombs" he was hurried,
No mother or friend held his dying head,
    Or wept when the poet was buried.

They buried him lonely; no friend stood near,
    (The scoffs of the multitude spurning,)
To weep o'er the poet's sacred bier;
    No bosom with anguish was burning.

No polish'd coffin enclosed his breast,
    Nor in purple or linen they wound him,
As a stranger he died; he went to his rest
    With cold charity's shroud wrapt 'round him.

Few and cold were the prayers they said,
    Cold and dry was the cheek of sadness,
Not a tear of grief baptised his head,
    Nor of sympathy pardon'd his madness.

---

1. New York *Aurora*, March 18, 1842; reprinted Rubin and Brown, 135. The poem (written "For the Aurora" and signed "W.") is an imitation of Charles Wolfe's very popular "The Burial of Sir John Moore at Corunna." Wolfe, an Anglo-Irish curate, first published his poem in 1817, and it can be found still in present-day anthologies. Sir John Moore died heroically during the Peninsular Campaign, leading his troops against those of Napoleon. McDonald Clarke—an eccentric Manhattan poet completely dependent for his livelihood upon the sale of his strange poems—died in poverty and madness on March 5, 1842. Whitman, who was editor of the *Aurora* from early March 1842 until about mid-April of the same year, published two sympathetic editorials on Clarke in the *Aurora* shortly after his death. See Rubin and Brown, pp. 105–110.

Whitman's parody is identical in meter, and in the form and number of stanzas, with Wolfe's poem. Whitman borrowed verbatim one line from Wolfe, which appears as the second line of his fourth stanza. For the rest he was content with a general parallel of Wolfe's ideas. *cf.* the final stanza of "The Burial of Sir John Moore":

    Slowly and sadly we laid him down,
      From the field of his fame fresh and gory;
    We carved not a line, and we raised not a stone,
      But we left him alone with his glory.

None thought, as they stood by his lowly bed,
    Of the griefs and pains that craz'd him;
None thought of the sorrow that turn'd his head,
    Of the vileness of those who prais'd him.

Lightly they speak of his anguish and woe,
    And o'er his cold ashes upbraid him,
By whatever he was that was evil below,
    Unkindness and *cruelty made* him.

Ye hypocrites! stain not his grave with a tear,
    Nor blast the fresh planted willow
That weeps o'er his grave; for while he was here,
    Ye refused him a crumb and a pillow.

Darkly and sadly his spirit has fled,
    But his name will long linger in story;
He needs not a stone to hallow his bed;
    He's in Heaven, encircled with glory.

Time to Come[1]

O, Death! a black and pierceless pall
    Hangs round thee, and the future state;
No eye may see, no mind may grasp
    That mystery of Fate.

This brain, which now alternate throbs
    With swelling hope and gloomy fear;
This heart, with all the changing hues,
    That mortal passions bear—

This curious frame of human mould,
    Where unrequited cravings play,
This brain, and heart, and wondrous form
    Must all alike decay.

The leaping blood will stop its flow;
    The hoarse death-struggle pass; the cheek
Lay bloomless, and the liquid tongue
    Will then forget to speak.

The grave will tame me; earth will close
    O'er cold dull limbs and ashy face;
But where, O, Nature, where shall be
    The soul's abiding place?

Will it e'en live? for though its light
    Must shine till from the body torn;
Then, when the oil of life is spent,
    Still shall the taper burn?

1. *Aurora*, April 9, 1842; reprinted Rubin and Brown, p. 134. This poem is a revised version of an earlier poem, "Our Future Lot," printed in the *Long Island Democrat*, October 31, 1838, and labeled "from the *Long Islander*." The poem was not signed in the *Democrat;* but Holloway—who reprinted it in UPP, I, 1–2—deduced that it was the work of Whitman on the basis of its theme and style and the fact that Whitman was owner and editor of the *Long Islander* (a weekly issued at Huntington) at the time the poem was reprinted in the *Democrat*. The *Long Islander* could not be checked, as no issues of it are known to exist. Holloway's deduction was confirmed almost thirty years later when Rubin and Brown discovered "Time to Come" "by Walter Whitman" in the *Aurora*, which Whitman was then editing. "Our Future Lot" has a claim to uniqueness as it is the earliest known published verse of Whitman; I have reprinted it in italics, following the final version.

O, powerless is this struggling brain
    To rend the mighty mystery;
In dark, uncertain awe it waits
    The common doom, to die.

Our Future Lot

This breast which now alternate burns
    With flashing hope, and gloomy fear,
Where beats a heart that knows the hue
    Which aching bosoms wear;

This curious frame of human mould,
    Where craving wants unceasing play—
The troubled heart and wondrous form
    Must both alike decay,

Then cold wet earth will close around
    Dull, senseless limbs, and ashy face,
But where, O Nature! where will be
    My mind's abiding place?

Will it ev'n live? For though its light
    Must shine till from the body torn;
Then, when the oil of life is spent,
    Still shall the taper burn?

O, powerless is this struggling brain
    To pierce the mighty mystery;
In dark, uncertain awe it waits
    The common doom—to die!

·   ·   ·   ·

Mortal! and can thy swelling soul
    Live with the thought that all its life
Is centred in this earthly cage
    Of care, and tears, and strife?

Not so; that sorrowing heart of thine
    Ere long will find a house of rest;
Thy form, re-purified, shall rise,
    In robes of beauty drest.

The flickering taper's glow shall change
To bright and starlike majesty,
Radiant with pure and piercing light
From the Eternal's eye!

Death of the Nature-Lover[1]

Not in a gorgeous hall of pride
    Where tears fall thick, and loved ones sigh,
Wished he, when the dark hour approached
    To drop his veil of flesh, and die.

Amid the thundercrash of strife,
    Where hovers War's ensanguined cloud,
And bright swords flash and banners fly
    Above the wounds, and groans, and blood.

Not there—not there! Death's look he'd cast
    Around a furious tiger's den.
Rather than in the monstrous sight
    Of the red butcheries of men.

Days speed: the time for that last look
    Upon this glorious earth has come:
The Power he served so well vouchsafes
    The sun to shine, the flowers to bloom.

Just ere the closing of the day,
    His fainting limbs he needs will have
Borne out into the fresh free air,
    Where sweet shrubs grow, and proud trees wave.

At distance, o'er the pleasant fields,
    A bay by misty vapors curled,
He gazes on, and thinks the haven
    For which to leave a grosser world.

He sorrows not, but smiles content,
    Dying there in that fragrant place,
Gazing on blossom, field, and bay,
    As on their Maker's very face.

---

1. *Brother Jonathan*, March 11, 1843, with the following editorial introduction: "The following wants but a half hour's polish to make of it an effusion of very uncommon beauty.—Ed." The poem was reprinted in *UPP*, I, 7, and in the *Con-*

The cloud-arch bending overhead,
　　There, at the setting of the sun
He bids adieu to earth, and steps
　　Down to the World Unknown.

My Departure

Not in a gorgeous hall of pride,
　　Mid tears of grief and friendship's sigh,
Would I, when the last hour has come,
　　Shake off this crumbling flesh and die.

My bed I would not care to have
　　With rich and costly stuffs hung round;
Nor watched with an officious zeal.
　　To keep away each jarring sound.

Amidst the thunder crash of war,
　　Where hovers Death's ensanguined cloud,
And bright swords flash, and banners fly,
　　Above the sickening sight of blood.

Not there—not there, would I lay down
　　To sleep with all the firm and brave;
For death in such a scene of strife,
　　Is not the death that I do crave.

But when the time for my last look
　　Upon this glorious earth should come,
I'd wish the season warm and mild,
　　The sun to shine, and flowers bloom.

Just ere the closing of the day,
　　My dying couch I then would have
Borne out in the refreshing air,
　　Where sweet shrubs grow and proud trees wave

servator, XII (January 1905) 189. An earlier and longer version of the poem appeared in the *Long Island Democrat*, November 27, 1839, with the title "My Departure." Because of the great number of variants in the two poems, I have reprinted it in italics, following the final version.

The still repose would calm my mind,
And lofty branches overhead,
Would throw around this grassy bank,
A cooling and a lovely shade.

At distance through the opening trees,
A bay by misty vapours curled,
I'd gaze upon, and think the haven
For which to leave this fleeting world.

To the wide winds I'd yield my soul,
And die there in that pleasant place,
Looking on water, sun, and hill,
As on their Maker's very face.

I'd want no human being near;
But at the setting of the sun,
I'd bid adieu to earth, and step
Down to the Unknown World—alone.

The Play-Ground[1]

When painfully athwart my brain
    Dark thoughts come crowding on,
And, sick of worldly hollowness,
    My heart feels sad or lone—

Then out upon the green I walk,
    Just ere the close of day,
And swift I ween the sight I view
    Clears all my gloom away.

For there I see young children—
    The cheeriest things on earth—
I see them play—I hear their tones
    Of loud and reckless mirth.

And many a clear and flute-like laugh
    Comes ringing through the air;
And many a roguish, flashing eye,
    And rich red cheek, are there.

O, lovely, happy children!
    I am with you in my soul;
I shout—I strike the ball with you—
    With you I race and roll.—

Methinks white-winged angels,
    Floating unseen the while,
Hover around this village green,
    And pleasantly they smile.

O, angels! guard these children!
    Keep grief and guilt away:
From earthly harm—from evil thoughts
    O, shield them night and day!

1. *Brooklyn Daily Eagle*, June 1, 1846; reprinted UPP, I, 21. The attribution of this poem to Whitman is somewhat circumstantial: it was signed "W.," it was printed as an "original" poem, and Whitman was editor of the *Eagle*. In addition, the tone, style, and diction of the poem—conventional as they are—somehow seem typically early Whitman, and a holograph of the poem contained in the Feinberg Collection certainly appears to be in Whitman's handwriting (see frontispiece).

Ode[1]

To be sung on Fort Greene; 4th of July, 1846.
Tune "The Star Spangled Banner."

1

O, God of Columbia! O, Shield of the Free!
    More grateful to you than the fanes of old story,
Must the blood-bedewed soil, the red battle-ground, be
    Where our fore-fathers championed America's glory!

Then how priceless the worth of the sanctified earth,
We are standing on now. Lo! the slopes of its girth
Where the Martyrs were buried: Nor prayers, tears, or stones,
Mark their crumbled-in coffins, their white, holy bones!

2

Say! sons of Long-Island! in legend or song,
    Keep ye aught of its record, that day dark and cheerless—
That cruel of days—when, hope weak, the foe strong,
    Was seen the Serene One—still faithful, still fearless,
Defending the worth, of the sanctified earth
We are standing on now, &c.

3

Ah, yes! be the answer. In memory still
    We have placed in our hearts, and embalmed there forever!
The battle, the prison-ship, martyrs and hill,
—O, may *it* be preserved till those hearts death shall sever!
For how priceless the worth, etc.

1. This poem, whose title seemed to include its author's name ("ODE.—BY WALTER WHITMAN"), appeared in the *Brooklyn Daily Eagle*, which Whitman was editing at the time, on July 2, 1846, in a column giving the "Order of Arrangements" for the Fourth of July Celebration at Fort Greene outside Brooklyn. The "Ode," to be sung to the tune of "The Star Spangled Banner," was seventh on the program and

4

And shall not the years, as they sweep o'er and o'er,
      Shall they not, even *here*, bring the children of ages—
To exult as their fathers exulted before,
      In the freedom achieved by our ancestral sages?
And the prayer rise to heaven, with pure gratitude given
And the sky by the thunder of cannon be riven?
Yea! yea! let the echo responsively roll
The echo that starts from the patriot's soul!

was followed by the Benediction. It has since been reprinted in the *Daily Eagle*, June 15, 1900; Peter Ross, *A History of Long Island*, Chicago and New York, 1902, where it appeared as a motto under the title of "Sons of Long Island"; *New York Times Magazine*, September 16, 1916; "Walt Whitman Centenary Number," *Daily Eagle*, May 31, 1919; *GF*, I, 75–76; *UPP*, I, 22–23.

The House of Friends[1]

> "And one shall say unto him, What are those wounds in thy hands? Then he shall answer, Those with which I was wounded in the house of my friends"—Zachariah, xiii. 6.

If thou art balked, O Freedom,
The victory is not to thy manlier foes;
From the house of thy friends comes the death stab.

Vaunters of the Free,
Why do you strain your lungs off southward?
Why be going to Alabama?
Sweep first before your own door;
Stop this squalling and this scorn
Over the mote there in the distance;
Look well to your own eye, Massachusetts—
Yours, New-York and Pennsylvania;
—I would say yours too, Michigan,
But all the salve, all the surgery
Of the great wide world were powerless there.[2]

Virginia, mother of greatness,
Blush not for being also mother of slaves.
You might have borne deeper slaves—
Doughfaces, Crawlers, Lice of Humanity—
Terrific screamers of Freedom,
Who roar and bawl, and get hot i' the face,

1. This poem appears in *Collect* as "Wounded in the House of Friends," but the present is the complete text of the original version in the New York *Tribune*, June 14, 1850, entitled "The House of Friends." The poem was intended as a protest against what Whitman thought to be a betrayal of the principles of the Democratic Party—the support given by leading Democrats to the compromise movement in Congress. Henry A. Lees, Whig editor of the Brooklyn *Daily Advertiser*, remarked apropos the poem, of which he quoted the third stanza, in his paper on June 22: "Here, now, is a specimen of the way one of the young democracy, Master Walter Whitman, lays it on the members of 'the party' whom he has had the pleasure of knowing:—Master Walter has evidently a very poor opinion of his old cronies; but who can wonder at that, after he was in the Brooklyn *Eagle* so long, and saw the operations of the Brooklyn 'democracy'? See now how he talks to 'em; we extract from a queer little poem in one of the New York paper." (*UPP*, I, 26, note.) The

But, were they not incapable of august crime,
Would quench the hopes of ages for a drink—
Muck-worms, creeping flat to the ground,
A dollar dearer to them than Christ's blessing;
All loves, all hopes, less than the thought of gain;
In life walking in that as in a shroud:[3]
Men whom the throes of heroes,
Great deeds at which the gods might stand appalled
The shriek of a drowned world,[4] the appeal of women,
The exulting laugh of untied empires,
Would touch them never in the heart,
But only in the pocket.

     Hot-headed Carolina,
Well may you curl your lip;
With all your bondsmen, bless the destiny
Which brings you no such breed as this.

     Arise, young North!
Our elder blood flows in the veins of cowards—
The gray-haired sneak, the blanched poltroon,
The feigned or real shiverer at tongues
That nursing babes need hardly cry the less for—
Are they to be our tokens always?
     Fight on, band braver than warriors,
Faithful and few as Spartans;
But fear not most the angriest, loudest malice—
Fear most the still and forked fang
That starts from the grass at your feet.[5]

Advertizer, incidentally, had published between May 18 and June 6, 1850, sixteen "Paragraph Sketches of Brooklynites" by Whitman. (*UPP*, I, 234, note.)

The "queer little poem" looks forward to *Leaves of Grass*. It has been described (Allen, 104) as "a free-verse poem (about halfway between blank verse and his later technique) . . ."

The *Collect* text omits two stanzas of the *Tribune* text. There are two or three unimportant differences in punctuation, and the later version reduces the number of capitalized words and deletes the "e" in the past forms of most regular verbs. The major variants in the *Collect* text are given in the footnotes that follow.

2. This stanza is omitted in the *Collect* version.

3. These four lines reappear, somewhat altered and scattered, in the fifth and seventh stanzas of Section 42 of "Song of Myself."

4. The shriek of the drown'd

5. This stanza is omitted in the *Collect* version.

Resurgemus[1]

Suddenly, out of its state and drowsy air, the air of slaves,[2]
Like lightning Europe le'pt forth,
Sombre, superb and terrible,
As Ahimoth, brother of Death.

God, 'twas delicious!
That brief, tight, glorious grip
Upon the throats of kings.
You liars paid to defile the People,
Mark you now:
Not for numberless agonies, murders, lusts,
For court thieving in its manifold mean forms,
Worming from his simplicity the poor man's wages;
For many a promise sworn by royal lips
And broken, and laughed at in the breaking;
Then, in their power, not for all these,
Did a blow fall in personal revenge,
Or a hair draggle in blood:
The People scorned the ferocity of kings.

But the sweetness of mercy brewed bitter destruction,
And frightened rulers come back:
Each comes in state, with his train,
Hangman, priest, and tax-gatherer,
Soldier, lawyer, and sycophant;
An appalling procession of locusts,
And the king struts grandly again.

1. The New York *Tribune*, June 21, 1850; reprinted *UPP*, I, 27–30. This poem is unique among the poems that Whitman had composed by 1850: it alone survived as a poem in *Leaves of Grass*. In the 1855 edition it was the eighth of the twelve untitled poems of which that edition was composed. In 1860, when the third edition appeared, all verbal revisions had been made and the poem, reduced in length by the cancellation and consolidation of the verses, then acquired the title, "Europe, the 72ᵈ and 73ᵈ Years of These States," which it continued to bear in subsequent editions. The 1855 *Leaves of Grass* version follows the original version in italics. In this as in two other poems of the present collection—"The House of Friends" and "Blood-Money," also of the 1850 vintage—Whitman foreshadowed his maturer style. As in *Leaves of Grass*, so in these poems, especially "Resurgemus," one finds the emphatic parallelism and contrast, and the freedom of the rhythmic line, characteristic of his

Yet behind all, lo, a Shape
Vague as the night, draped interminably,
Head, front and form, in scarlet folds;
Whose face and eyes none may see,
Out of its robes only this,
The red robes, lifted by the arm,
One finger pointed high over the top,
Like the head of a snake appears.

Meanwhile, corpses lie in new-made graves,
Bloody corpses of young men;
The rope of the gibbet hangs heavily,
The bullets of tyrants are flying,
The creatures of power laugh aloud:
And all these things bear fruits, and they are good.

Those corpses of young men,
Those martyrs that hang from the gibbets,
Those hearts pierced by the grey lead,
Cold and motionless as they seem,
Live elsewhere with undying vitality;
They live in other young men, O, kings,
They live in brothers, again ready to defy you;
They were purified by death,
They were taught and exalted.

Not a grave of those slaughtered ones,
But is growing its seed of freedom,
In its turn to bear seed,
Which the winds shall carry afar and resow,
And the rain nourish.

great poems of 1855 and later. His unconcern for the syllabic formalism and metrical
regularity of traditional verse, his dependence on the rhythm of the accented syllables
in a loosely iambic-anapestic line, are clearly perceptible as the beginnings of a new
"free verse" for the first time in "Resurgemus."

The poem deals explicitly with the European revolutionary movements of 1848:
they had failed, but the spirit of liberty still lived and would triumph ultimately over
tyranny. Implicitly, the poem alludes to the domestic situation satirized in "The
House of Friends" and expresses Whitman's faith in the final triumph of liberty in
his own country.

2. This line obviously contains three typographical errors; in the 1855 and all
later editions of *Leaves of Grass* it reads "Suddenly out of its stale and drowsy lair,
the lair of slaves."

Not a disembodied spirit
Can the weapon of tyrants let loose,
But it shall stalk invisibly over the earth,
Whispering, counseling, cautioning.

Liberty, let others despair of thee,
But I will never despair of thee:
Is the house shut? Is the master away?
Nevertheless, be ready, be not weary of watching,
He will surely return; his messengers come anon.

[*Europe, the 72ᵈ and 73ᵈ Years of These States*]

Suddenly out of its stale and drowsy lair, the lair of slaves,
Like lightning Europe le'pt forth . . . . half startled at itself,
Its feet upon the ashes and the rags . . . . Its hands tight to the
*   throats of kings.*

O hope and faith! O aching close of lives! O many a sickened heart!
Turn back unto this day, and make yourselves afresh.

And you, paid to defile the People . . . . you liars mark:
Not for numberless agonies, murders, lusts,
For court thieving in its manifold mean forms,
Worming from his simplicity the poor man's wages;
For many a promise sworn by royal lips, and broken, and laughed at
*   in the breaking,*
Then in their power not for all these did the blows strike of personal
*   revenge . . or the heads of the nobles fall;*
The People scorned the ferocity of kings.

But the sweetness of mercy brewed bitter destruction, and the
*   frightened rulers come back:*
Each comes in state with his train . . . . hangman, priest and tax-
*   gatherer . . . . soldier, lawyer, jailer and sycophant.*

Yet behind all, lo, a Shape,
Vague as the night, draped interminably, head front and form
          in scarlet folds,
Whose face and eyes none may see,
Out of its robes only this . . . . the red robes, lifted by the arm,
One finger pointed high over the top, like the head of a snake appears.

Meanwhile corpses lie in new-made graves . . . . bloody corpses
          of young men:
The rope of the gibbet hangs heavily . . . . the bullets of princes
          are flying . . . . the creatures of power laugh aloud,
And all these things bear fruits . . . . and they are good.
Those corpses of young men,
Those martyrs that hang from the gibbets . . . those hearts pierced
          by the gray lead,
Cold and motionless as they seem . . . live elsewhere with
          unslaughter'd vitality.

They live in other young men, O kings,
They live in brothers, again ready to defy you:
They were purified by death . . . . they were taught and exalted.

Not a grave of the murdered for freedom but grows seed for freedom
          . . . . in its turn to bear seed,
Which the winds carry afar and re-sow, and the rains and
          the snows nourish.

Not a disembodied spirit can the weapons of tyrants let loose,
But it stalks invisibly over the earth . . whispering counseling
          cautioning.

Liberty let others despair of you . . . . I never despair of you.

Is the house shut? Is the master away?
Nevertheless be ready . . . . be not weary of watching,
He will soon return . . . . his messengers come anon.

Sailing the Mississippi at Midnight[1]

Vast and starless, the pall of heaven
    Laps on the trailing pall below;
And forward, forward, in solemn darkness,
    As if to the sea of the lost we go.

Now drawn nigh the edge of the river,
    Weird-like creatures suddenly rise;
Shapes that fade, dissolving outlines
    Baffle the gazer's straining eyes.

Towering upward and bending forward,
    Wild and wide their arms are thrown,
Ready to pierce with forked fingers
    Him who touches their realm upon.

Tide of youth, thus thickly planted,
    While in the eddies onward you swim,
Thus on the shore stands a phantom army,
    Lining forever the channel's rim.

Steady, helmsman! you guide the immortal;
    Many a wreck is beneath you piled,
Many a brave yet unwary sailor
    Over these waters has been beguiled.

Nor is it the storm or the scowling midnight,
    Cold, or sickness, or fire's dismay—
Nor is it the reef, or treacherous quicksand,
    Will peril you most on your twisted way.

1. The text is that of *Collect*. The poem was originally published as "The Mississippi at Midnight" in the second issue of the New Orleans *Crescent*, March 6, 1848, on which paper Whitman was employed as one of the editors. The *Crescent* version of the poem was reprinted in *Notes and Fragments*, ed. Dr. Richard Maurice Bucke, London, Ontario, 1899, pp. 41–42; Emory Holloway, "Walt Whitman in New Orleans," *Yale Review*, V (October 1915) 166–183; *Publications of the Louisiana Historical Society*, VII, 102–103. Whitman had arrived in New Orleans,

But when there comes a voluptuous languor,
    Soft the sunshine, silent the air,
Bewitching your craft with safety and sweetness,
    Then, young pilot of life, beware.

The Mississippi at Midnight

How solemn! sweeping this dense black tide!
    No friendly lights i' the heaven o'er us;
A murky darkness on either side,
    And kindred darkness all before us!

Now, drawn near the shelving rim,
    Weird-like shadows suddenly rise;
Shapes of mist and phantoms dim
    Baffle the gazer's straining eyes.

River fiends, with malignant faces!
    Wild and wide their arms are thrown,
As if to clutch in fatal embraces
    Him who sails their realms upon.

Then, by the trick of our own swift motion,
    Straight, tall giants, an army vast,
Rank by rank, like the waves of ocean,
    On the shore march stilly past.

How solemn! the river a trailing pall,
    Which takes, but never again gives back;
And moonless and starless the heavens' arch'd wall,
    Responding an equal black!

Oh, tireless waters! like Life's quick dream,
    Onward and onward ever hurrying—
Like Death in this midnight hour you seem,
    Life in your chill drops greedily burying!

along with his brother Jeff, on February 25 after a journey down the Mississippi. No doubt that journey inspired the poem.

There is considerable difference in the two versions of the poem. The *Collect* version is painfully didactic and lacks a quality which the earlier version has, a quality usually absent in Whitman's early verse—the impression that the poet is sincerely reporting his emotional reaction to a real experience. The *Crescent* version is printed in italics following the final version.

Dough-Face Song[1]

—Like dough; soft; yielding to pressure; pale.—Webster's Dictionary

We are all docile dough-faces,
    They knead us with the fist,
They, the dashing southern lords,
    We labor as they list;
For them we speak—or hold our tongues,
    For them we turn and twist.

We join them in their howl against
    Free soil and "abolition,"
That firebrand—that assassin knife—
    Which risk our land's condition,
And leave no peace of life to any
    Dough-faced[2] politician.

To put down "agitation," now,
    We think the most judicious;
To damn all "northern fanatics,"
    Those "traitors" black and vicious;
The "reg'lar party usages"
    For us, and no "new issues."

Things have come to a pretty pass,
    When a trifle small as this,
Moving and bartering nigger slaves,
    Can open an abyss,
With jaws a-gape for "the two great parties;"
    A pretty thought, I wis!

1. The text is that of *Collect*. The poem was published originally as "Song for Certain Congressmen" in the New York *Evening Post*, March 2, 1850, where it was signed "Paumanok." The poem was a protest against the growing sentiment in Congress for an expedient settlement between the opponents of slavery in the North and the slaveowners in the South. The result of this, to Whitman, "dough-faced" yielding was the series of laws passed by Congress in August 1850, known as the "Compromise of 1850."

Principle—freedom!—fiddlesticks!
    We know not where they're found.
Rights of the masses—progress!—bah!
    Words that tickle and sound;
But claiming to rule o'er "practical men"
    Is very different ground.

Beyond all such we know a term
    Charming to ears and eyes,
With it we'll stab young Freedom,
    And do it in disguise;
Speak soft, ye wily dough-faces—
    That term is "compromise."

And what if children, growing up,
    In future seasons read
The thing we do? and heart and tongue
    Accurse us for the deed?
The future cannot touch us;
    The present gain we heed.

Then, all together, dough-faces!
    Let's stop the exciting clatter,
And pacify slave-breeding wrath
    By yielding all the matter;
For otherwise, as sure as guns,
    The Union it will shatter.

Besides, to tell the honest truth
    (For us an innovation,)
Keeping in with the slave power
    Is our personal salvation;
We've very little to expect
    From t' other part of the nation.

There is little difference in the two versions of the poem. A very few unimportant word changes were made in the later version, and a number of capital letters were reduced to lower case. "Dough-face" and its variants, for example, were always capitalized in the *Post* text. The verbal variants in "Song for Certain Congressmen" are given in the following footnotes.

2. Dough-Face

Besides it's plain at Washington
  Who likeliest wins the race,[3]
What earthly chance has "free soil"
  For any good fat place?
While many a daw has feather'd his nest,
  By his creamy and meek dough-face.

Take heart, then, sweet companions,
  Be steady, Scripture Dick!
Webster, Cooper, Walker,
  To your allegiance stick!
With Brooks, and Briggs and Phoenix,
  Stand up through thin and thick!

We do not ask a bold brave front;
  We never try that game;
'Twould bring the storm upon our heads,
  A huge mad storm of shame;
Evade it, brothers—"compromise"[4]
  Will answer just the same. PAUMANOK

3. chase 4. subterfuge

Blood-Money[1]

"Guilty of the body and the blood of Christ"

1

Of olden time, when it came to pass
That the beautiful god, Jesus, should finish his work on earth,
Then went Judas, and sold the divine youth,
And took pay for his body.

Curs'd was the deed, even before the sweat of the clutching hand
        grew dry;
And darkness frown'd upon the seller of the like of God,[2]
Where, as though earth lifted her breast to throw him from her,
        and heaven refused him,
He hung in the air, self-slaughter'd.

The cycles, with their long shadows, have stalk'd silently forward,
Since those ancient days—many a pouch enwrapping meanwhile
Its fee, like that paid for the son of Mary.

1. The text followed here is that of *Collect*. The year 1843 affixed to the poem by Whitman as the date of its composition is probably erroneous. It was first published, under the same title, in the New York *Tribune Supplement*, March 22, 1850, and was reprinted in the *Evening Post* on the following April 30. It seems clearly to have been inspired by indignation at Webster's speech in Congress on March 7, 1850, when he championed the proposed Fugitive Slave Law. The poem is a logical sequel to the earlier "Song for Certain Congressmen." (But see, in the illustrations contained in this volume, the curious markings made by Whitman when he revised the earlier text.)

"Blood-Money" interestingly anticipates to a degree the parallelism so characteristic of *Leaves of Grass*. "The run-on lines show how far the poet still is from the characteristic style of *Leaves of Grass*. He is experimenting with phrasal or clausal units; not yet 'thought rhythm.' But his arrangement of the verse is a step in that direction" (Allen, *Handbook*, p. 394).

The differences in the *Collect* and the *Tribune* versions are few. There are three or four minor differences in punctuation, and, in the earlier text, all epithets referring to Christ are capitalized. The remaining few variants are given in the footnotes that follow.

2. the seller of a Son of God

And still goes one, saying,[3]
"What will ye give me, and I will deliver this man unto you?"[4]
And they make the covenant, and pay the pieces of silver.

2

Look forth, deliverer,
Look forth, first-born of the dead,
Over the tree-tops of Paradise;
See thyself in yet-continued bonds,
Toilsome and poor, thou bear'st man's form again,
Thou art reviled, scourged, put into prison,
Hunted from the arrogant equality of the rest;
With staves and swords throng the willing servants of authority,
Again they surround thee, mad with devilish spite;
Toward thee stretch the hands of a multitude, like vultures' talons,
The meanest spit in thy face, they smite thee with their palms;
Bruised, bloody, and pinion'd is thy body,
More sorrowful than death is thy soul.

Witness of anguish, brother of slaves,
Not with thy price closed the price of thine image:
And still Iscariot plies his trade.

April, 1843   PAUMANOK

3. Again goes one, saying
4. No quotation marks in the original.

New Year's Day, 1848[1]

A morning fair: A noontide dubious:
Then gathering clouds obscure the Sun:
Then rain in torrents falls, subsiding soon
Into a gentle dropping. By eve the sun
Sinks into a cloudless west; and a mild breeze
With pleasant motion stirs the atmosphere.
Next in the blue vault above do moon and stars
Vie in bright emulation to destroy the gloom of night.

Such was our New Year's Day, and eventide!
Was it not an index of each passing Year,
Within whose seasons circumstance and change
Ever with Hope and Happiness war?
One now superior: anon the other:
And as succeeds pleasure or pain or joy or sorrow,
Clouding the firmament of each heart,
Raindrops of melancholy dim the eyes,
To shortly dry, hiding the Past and Present
'Neath bright starry thoughts—
Suggestive of a Future aye serene.

Day of a coming year promising change,
Yet full of promises, we need but watch
And pray for guardianship to come
Over caprices and all foolish ways!
So shall bright sunshine in advancing days
And starry invitations lead to Heavenly praise.

1. *Home Journal* (New York), March 30, 1892; reprinted UPP, I, 23–24.
The poem was preceded in the *Home Journal* by these remarks: "The following
verses were written by Walt Whitman in 1848, in the album of a lady, from which
a friend of the *Home Journal* copied them. They do not appear in any of the poet's
published collections, but are interesting as a specimen of his early essays in verse."
  Though some verse falsely represented as being "undiscovered poems" by Whitman was published in 1892 after the death of the poet, "New Year's Day, 1848" is
very possibly authentic. The rough blank verse, the absence of parody based on the
unpublished *Leaves of Grass*, the innocuous contents, and the fact that Whitman
was in the environs of New York for most of 1848 and hence able in the flesh to in-
scribe an album are all in favor of the poem's authenticity.

Isle of La Belle Riviere[1]

Bride of the swart Ohio;
Nude, yet fair to look upon,
Clothed only with the leaf,
As was innocent Eve of Eden.
The son of grim old Alleghany,
And white-breasted Monongahela
Is wedded to thee, and it is well.
His tawny thighs cover thee
In the vernal time of spring,
And lo! in the autumn is the fruitage.
Virgin of Nature, the holy spirit of the waters enshroud thee,
And thou art pregnant with the fruits
Of the field and the vine.
But like the sabine maid of old,
The lust of Man hath ravished thee
And compelled thee to pay tribute to the
Carnal wants of earth.
Truth and romance make up thy
Strange, eventful history,
From the eye of the red man;
Who bowed at thy shrine and worshiped thee,
To the dark days of that traitor
Who linked thine innocent name to infamy,
Farewell, Queen of the waters
I have slept upon thy breast in the innocence of a babe,
But now I leave thee
To the embraces of thine acknowledged lord.

At Blennerhassett—aged 30

1. This poem was first published in the Cincinnati *Post*, April 30, 1892 (reprinted *UPP*, I, 24–25), where it was preceded by the following:
"Parkersburg, Va., April 30— (Special.)—It is well known that the late Walt Whitman made a pilgrimage down the Ohio Valley in the year 1849; that he stopped on Blennerhassett Island for a brief season (a spot almost world-famous in song, story and history as the home of the exiled Blennerhassett, and as the scene of Aaron Burr's machinations for the destruction of this Republic); that he drank from the historic old well of Blennerhassett, and that he retained pleasant recollections of his pilgrimage long afterward.
"But it is not so well-known, in fact, it is scarcely known at all, that he com-

posed a characteristic poem while on his visit to the old island which appears in The Post for the first time. The original draft of the poem was left at the home of Whitman's entertainer, old Farmer Johnson, who then lived on the island. The poet took a copy, and The Post representative has a copy of the original, so that these three are the only known copies of the poem in existence, if indeed the copy which Whitman took exists anywhere.

"The original draft of the poem has lain unnoticed all these years between the leaves of an old Bible. It is written in the irregular, scrawling hand of the much-abused poet on a sheet of old-fashioned foolscap paper. It is just such a piece of venerable chirography as would set a Browning student clean daft and throw a Concord blue-stocking into a fit of hysterics.

"The death of Whitman recalled the fact of his visit to the island, and the present proprietoter [sic] of Blennerhassett, Mr. Amos Gordon, having heard something about Whitman and his poem on the island, began a search for it, and finally found it. As an old friend, The Post representative was the only person permitted to copy it, and here it is:"

"Isle of La Belle Riviere" is certainly a journalistic hoax. Whitman made a "pilgrimage" down the Ohio Valley in 1848, two-and-a-half months before his twenty-ninth birthday, enroute to New Orleans and the *Crescent*. After leaving Brooklyn, he barely got to Wheeling, West Virginia, in time to get on the steamboat *St. Cloud* and proceed downstream. There was no time for a visit to Blennerhassett Island, even of the most unleisurely sort. The only other time that Whitman came near Blennerhassett Island was early fall of 1879, and he was then on a through sleeping car from New York to St. Louis. See Charles E. Feinberg, "A Whitman Collector Destroys a Whitman Myth," *Papers*, Bibliographical Society of America, 52 (1958) II, 78–81.

The poem itself bears no resemblance in diction, style, or sentiment to the early poems preceding or following the ostensible date of 1849. And did he who made "The Mississippi at Midnight" make "Isle of La Belle Riviere"? The whole poem seems an amusing but inept burlesque of the style and popularly assumed contents of *Leaves of Grass;* the *Post*'s special correspondent called it "a characteristic poem." The "tawny thighs" of the Ohio covering the island seems based on the sexual imagery of the *Leaves;* but "tawny thighs" is the sort of term a person unacquainted with the *Leaves* might use in burlesque, unaware that Whitman's term would refer to the genitalia. The mention of the "innocent Eve of Eden" has no parallel in either the early poems or in the *Leaves;* but once again, it would suggest itself to a person acquainted with the *Leaves* chiefly through hearsay. The classical allusion to the "Sabine maid" is atypical of both the early poems and the *Leaves*. Other lines in the poem may be cited as burlesques of the later Whitman, especially the last three lines of the poem; but certainly one must not forget that the special *Post* correspondent said that the original draft of the poem "is just such a piece of venerable chirography as would set a Browning student clean daft and throw a Concord blue-stocking into a fit of hysterics." Did he intend, as a lark, to set Whitman students "clean daft"? Neither the original draft of the poem nor Whitman's copy, "if indeed the copy . . . exists anywhere," has been found.

Another certainly spurious poem which saw print soon after Whitman's death was published in the New Orleans *Item*, untitled, April 2, 1892 (*UPP*, I, 30–31). It was, according to the so-called special dispatch from Duluth, Minnesota, "a fragment of a poem by the late Walt Whitman, written while in this city a year ago . . . The good gray poet was quite impressed with Duluth . . . and after leaving he sent his friend the following, which has remained unprinted until now." As Holloway remarks, the poem is probably "a puerile attempt at burlesque." And that the poem was a hoax is supported by Thomas O. Mabbott's discovery—" 'Whitman's' Lines on Duluth," *American Literature* III (November, 1931) 316–317—that the special dispatch was originally published (along with the poem) as a letter signed "Mendax" in the Duluth *Daily News*, March 30, 1892. Mabbott suggests that "the correspondent of the *Item* failed to note the significance of the signature, 'fallacious.' " The interested reader may peruse the entire poem in *UPP*, but a few sample lines will clearly show the intent to parody:

> The nations hear thy message;
> A fateful word; oh, momentous
> Audition! The murmur of waves
> Bearing heavy freighted argosies; the sigh
> Of gently stirring life in the birth-beds
> Of not o'er distant grain fields . . .

The style of the fragment is not at all Whitman's and, of course, Whitman had been, as he put it, "house-tied" in Camden for several years by 1891.

Walt Whitman

The Early Poems and the Fiction

THE FICTION

Death in the School-Room (A FACT)[1]

TING-A-LING-LING-LING! went the little bell on the teacher's desk of a village-school one morning, when the studies of the earlier part of the day were about half completed. It was well understood that this was a command for silence and attention; and when these had been obtain'd, the master spoke. He was a low thick-set man, and his name was Lugare.

"Boys," said he, "I have had a complaint enter'd, that last night some of you were stealing fruit from Mr. Nichols's garden. I rather think I know the thief. Tim Barker, step up here, sir."

The one to whom he spoke came forward. He was a slight, fair-looking boy of about thirteen; and his face had a laughing, good-humor'd expression, which even the charge now preferr'd against him, and the stern tone and threatening look of the teacher, had not entirely dissipated. The countenance of the boy, however, was too unearthly fair for health; it had, notwithstanding its fleshy, cheerful look, a singular cast as if some inward disease, and that a fearful one, were seated within. As the stripling stood before that place of judgment—that place so often made the scene of heartless and coarse brutality, of timid innocence confused, helpless childhood

1. The text followed here is that of *Collect*. "Death in the School-Room" first appeared in *The United States Magazine and Democratic Review* (hereafter given as the *Democratic Review*) for August, 1841. Except for a very few trivial changes in punctuation, the elision of the "e" in the past forms of most regular verbs, and the deletion of the next-to-the-last sentence (see note 3), in the original, the *Collect* version does not differ from the *Democratic* version.

So far as is known, "Death in the School-Room" was Whitman's first fiction to be published. Professor C. Carroll Hollis of the University of Detroit called my attention to an interesting account in a little-known book of Whitman's alleged reaction to his first published tale. *Pen Pictures of Modern Authors*, ed. William Shepard [William S. Walsh], New York, 1882, contains a chapter on Whitman which includes an account of him in his Pfaff days by Jay Charlton [J. C. Goldsmith] which originally appeared in the *Danbury News* (Connecticut), according to the editor, though the date of the original publication is not given. Charlton says (pp. 163–164) that the way Whitman "came to consider himself a poet was due to a prose sketch he wrote, describing a death in a schoolroom. The piece was vividly written and widely copied. That was when he and Joe Otterson (to be remembered as the 'Bayard' of Wilke's *Spirit of the Times*) were setting type in a New York printing office. Walt was elated at the success of his sketch."

According to Kennedy, p. 55, Whitman called the article in *Pen Pictures* a compound of "nonsense, lies and rot." That Whitman was somewhat proud of "Death in the School-Room" seems indicated in a letter written to Nathan Hale, Jr., editor of the *Boston Miscellany*. Attempting to place a story in Hale's journal, Whitman called attention to the favor with which his tales in the *Democratic Review* had been received. However, he mentioned by name only "Death in the School-Room." See *Correspondence* I, 26. See also footnote 1, "The Tomb Blossoms" (pages 88–89), for reference to a didactic purpose in "Death in the School-Room."

outraged, and gentle feelings crush'd—Lugare looked on him with a frown which plainly told that he felt in no very pleasant mood. (Happily a worthier and more philosophical system is proving to men that schools can be better govern'd than by lashes and tears and sighs. We are waxing toward that consummation when one of the old-fashion'd school-masters, with his cowhide, his heavy birch-rod, and his many ingenious methods of child-torture, will be gazed upon as a scorn'd memento of an ignorant, cruel, and exploded doctrine. May propitious gales speed that day!)[2]

"Were you by Mr. Nichols's garden-fence last night?" said Lugare.

"Yes, sir," answer'd the boy, "I was."

"Well, sir, I'm glad to find you so ready with your confession. And so you thought you could do a little robbing, and enjoy yourself in a manner you ought to be ashamed to own, without being punish'd, did you?"

"I have not been robbing," replied the boy quickly. His face was suffused, whether with resentment or fright, it was difficult to tell. "And I didn't do anything last night, that I am ashamed to own."

"No impudence!" exclaim'd the teacher, passionately, as he grasp'd a long and heavy ratan: "give me none of your sharp speeches, or I'll thrash you till you beg like a dog."

The youngster's face paled a little; his lip quiver'd, but he did not speak.

"And pray, sir," continued Lugare, as the outward signs of wrath disappear'd from his features; "what were you about the garden for? Perhaps you only receiv'd the plunder, and had an accomplice to do the more dangerous part of the job?"

"I went that way because it is on my road home. I was there again afterwards to meet an acquaintance; and—and— But I did not go into the garden, nor take anything away from it. I would not steal,—hardly to save myself from starving."

"You had better have stuck to that last evening. You were seen, Tim Barker, to come from under Mr. Nichols's garden-fence, a little after nine o'clock, with a bag full of something or other over your shoulders. The bag had every appearance of being filled with fruit, and this morning the melon-beds are found to have been completely clear'd. Now, sir, what was there in that bag?"

Like fire itself glow'd the face of the detected lad. He spoke not a word. All the school had their eyes directed at him. The perspiration ran down his white forehead like rain-drops.

"Speak, sir!" exclaimed Lugare, with a loud strike of his ratan on the desk.

2. The parentheses do not appear in the original version.

The boy look'd as though he would faint. But the unmerciful teacher, confident of having brought to light a criminal, and exulting in the idea of the severe chastisement he should now be justified in inflicting, kept working himself up to a still greater and greater degree of passion. In the meantime, the child seem'd hardly to know what to do with himself. His tongue cleav'd to the roof of his mouth. Either he was very much frighten'd, or he was actually unwell.

"Speak, I say!" again thunder'd Lugare; and his hand, grasping his ratan, tower'd above his head in a very significant manner.

"I hardly can, sir," said the poor fellow faintly. His voice was husky and thick. "I will tell you some—some other time. Please let me go to my seat—I a'n't well."

"Oh yes; that's very likely;" and Mr. Lugare bulged out his nose and cheeks with contempt. "Do you think to make me believe your lies? I've found you out, sir, plainly enough; and I am satisfied that you are as precious a little villain as there is in the State. But I will postpone settling with you for an hour yet. I shall then call you up again; and if you don't tell the whole truth then, I will give you something that'll make you remember Mr. Nichols's melons for many a month to come:—go to your seat."

Glad enough of the ungracious permission, and answering not a sound, the child crept tremblingly to his bench. He felt very strangely, dizzily—more as if he was in a dream than in real life; and laying his arms on his desk, bow'd down his face between them. The pupils turn'd to their accustom'd studies, for during the reign of Lugare in the village-school, they had been so used to scenes of violence and severe chastisement, that such things made but little interruption in the tenor of their way.

Now, while the intervening hour is passing, we will clear up the mystery of the bag, and of young Barker being under the garden fence on the preceding night. The boy's mother was a widow, and they both had to live in the very narrowest limits. His father had died when he was six years old, and little Tim was left a sickly emaciated infant whom no one expected to live many months. To the surprise of all, however, the poor child kept alive, and seem'd to recover his health, as he certainly did his size and good looks. This was owing to the kind offices of an eminent physician who had a country-seat in the neighborhood, and who had been interested in the widow's little family. Tim, the physician said, might possibly outgrow his disease; but everything was uncertain. It was a mysterious and baffling malady; and it would not be wonderful if he should in some moment of apparent health be suddenly taken away. The poor widow was at first in a continual state of uneasiness; but several years had now pass'd, and none of the impending evils had fallen upon the boy's head. His mother seem'd to feel confident that he would live, and be a help and an honor to her old age; and the two struggled on together, mutually happy in each other, and enduring much of poverty and discomfort without repining, each for the other's sake.

Tim's pleasant disposition had made him many friends in the village, and among the rest a young farmer named Jones, who, with his elder brother, work'd a large farm in the neighborhood on shares. Jones very frequently made Tim a present of a bag of potatoes or corn, or some garden vegetables, which he took from his own stock; but as his partner was a parsimonious, high-tempered man, and had often said that Tim was an idle fellow, and ought not to be help'd because he did not work, Jones generally made his gifts in such a manner that no one knew anything about them, except himself and the grateful objects of his kindness. It might be, too, that the widow was loth to have it understood by the neighbors that she received food from anyone; for there is often an excusable pride in people of her condition which makes them shrink from being consider'd as objects of "charity" as they would from the severest pains. On the night in question, Tim had been told that Jones would send them a bag of potatoes, and the place at which they were to be waiting for him was fixed at Mr. Nichols's garden-fence. It was this bag that Tim had been seen staggering under, and which caused the unlucky boy to be accused and convicted by his teacher as a thief. That teacher was one little fitted for his important and responsible office. Hasty to decide, and inflexibly severe, he was the terror of the little world he ruled so despotically. Punishment he seemed to delight in. Knowing little of those sweet fountains which in children's breasts ever open quickly at the call of gentleness and kind words, he was fear'd by all for his sternness, and loved by none. I would that he were an isolated instance in his profession.

The hour of grace had drawn to its close, and the time approach'd at which it was usual for Lugare to give his school a joyfully-receiv'd dismission. Now and then one of the scholars would direct a furtive glance at Tim, sometimes in pity, sometimes in indifference or inquiry. They knew that he would have no mercy shown him, and though most of them loved him, whipping was too common there to exact much sympathy. Every inquiring glance, however, remain'd unsatisfied, for at the end of the hour, Tim remain'd with his face completely hidden, and his head bow'd in his arms, precisely as he had lean'd himself when he first went to his seat. Lugare look'd at the boy occasionally with a scowl which seem'd to bode vengeance for his sullenness. At length the last class had been heard, and the last lesson recited, and Lugare seated himself behind his desk on the platform, with his longest and stoutest ratan before him.

"Now, Barker," he said, "we'll settle that little business of yours. Just step up here."

Tim did not move. The school-room was as still as the grave. Not a sound was to be heard, except occasionally a long-drawn breath.

"Mind me, sir, or it will be the worse for you. Step up here, and take off your jacket!"

The boy did not stir any more than if he had been of wood. Lugare shook with passion. He sat still a minute, as if considering the best way to wreak his vengeance. That minute, passed in death-like silence, was a fearful one to some of the children, for their faces whiten'd with fright. It seem'd, as it slowly dropp'd away, like the minute which precedes the climax of an exquisitely-performed tragedy, when some mighty master of the histrionic art is treading the stage, and you and the multitude around you are waiting, with stretch'd nerves and suspended breath, in expectation of the terrible catastrophe.

"Tim is asleep, sir," at length said one of the boys who sat near him.

Lugare, at this intelligence, allow'd his features to relax from their expression of savage anger into a smile, but that smile look'd more malignant if possible, than his former scowls. It might be that he felt amused at the horror depicted on the faces of those about him; or it might be that he was gloating in pleasure on the way in which he intended to wake the slumberer.

"Asleep! are you, my young gentleman!" said he; "let us see if we can't find something to tickle your eyes open. There's nothing like making the best of a bad case, boys. Tim, here, is determin'd not to be worried in his mind about a little flogging, for the thought of it can't even keep the little scoundrel awake."

Lugare smiled again as he made the last observation. He grasp'd his ratan firmly, and descended from his seat. With light and stealthy steps he cross'd the room, and stood by the unlucky sleeper. The boy was still as unconscious of his impending punishment as ever. He might be dreaming some golden dream of youth and pleasure; perhaps he was far away in the world of fancy, seeing scenes, and feeling delights, which cold reality never can bestow. Lugare lifted his ratan high over his head, and with the true and expert aim which he had acquired by long practice, brought it down on Tim's back with a force and whacking sound which seem'd sufficient to awake a freezing man in his last lethargy. Quick and fast, blow follow'd blow. Without waiting to see the effect of the first cut, the brutal wretch plied his instrument of torture first on one side of the boy's back, and then on the other, and only stopped at the end of two or three minutes from very weariness. But still Tim show'd no signs of motion; and as Lugare, provoked at his torpidity, jerk'd away one of the child's arms, on which he had been leaning over the desk, his head dropp'd down on the board with a dull sound, and his face lay turn'd up and exposed to view. When Lugare saw it, he stood like one transfix'd by a basilisk. His countenance turn'd to a leaden whiteness; the ratan dropp'd from his grasp; and his eyes, stretch'd wide open, glared as at some monstrous spectacle of horror and death. The sweat started in great globules seemingly from every pore in his face; his skinny lips contracted, and show'd his teeth; and when he at length stretch'd forth his arm, and with the end of one of his fingers touch'd the child's cheek, each limb quiver'd like the tongue of a snake; and his strength seemed as though it would momentarily fail him. The boy was dead. He had probably been so for some time, for his eyes were turn'd up, and his body was quite cold.[3] Death was in the school-room, and Lugare had been flogging A CORPSE.[4]

3. While he was editor of the *Brooklyn Daily Eagle*, Whitman reprinted this tale in his newspaper on December 24, 1847. The *Eagle* text followed the *Democratic* text but ended the story with this sentence.

4. In the *Democratic* text this concluding sentence is preceded by the following sentence: "The widow was now childless too." When "Death in the School-Room" was reprinted in the *Ladies Garland* (Philadelphia), September 1841, this sentence was rendered as "The widow was now childless indeed," but this change of "too" to "indeed" was certainly an editorial emendation.

Wild Frank's Return[1]

As the sun, one August day some fifty years ago, had just pass'd the meridian of a country town in the eastern section of Long Island,[2] a single traveler came up to the quaint low-roof'd village tavern, open'd its half-door, and enter'd the common room. Dust cover'd the clothes of the wayfarer, and his brow was moist with sweat. He trod in a lagging, weary way;[3] though his form and features told of an age not more than nineteen or twenty years. Over one shoulder was slung a sailor's jacket, and in his hand he carried a little bundle. Sitting down on a rude bench, he told a female who made her appearance behind the bar, that he would have a glass of brandy and sugar. He took off the liquor at a draught: after which he lit and began to smoke a cigar, with which he supplied himself from his pocket—stretching out one leg, and leaning his elbow down on the bench, in the attitude of a man who takes an indolent lounge.

"Do you know one Richard Hall that lives somewhere here among you?" said he.

"Mr. Hall's is down the lane that turns off by that big locust tree," answer'd the woman, pointing to the direction through the open door; "it's about half a mile from here to his house."

The youth, for a minute or two, puff'd the smoke from his mouth very leisurely in silence. His manner had an air of vacant self-sufficiency, rather strange in one of so few years.

"I wish to see Mr. Hall," he said at length—"Here's a silver sixpence, for any one who will[4] carry a message to him."

"The folks[5] are all away. It's but a short walk, and your limbs are young," replied the female, who was not altogether pleased with the easy way of making himself at home, which mark'd her shabby-looking customer. That individual, however, seem'd to give small attention to the hint, but lean'd and puff'd his cigar-smoke as leisurely as before.

1. The text followed here is the revised version of *Collect*. The story first appeared in the *Democratic Review* for November 1841. As usual, the "e" in the past forms of most regular verbs is elided in the 1882 version, and a few minor changes in punctuating and paragraphing are made. The more important differences in the two versions are textual, and the variant readings of the original text are given in the footnotes that follow.

2. The main incidents of this and another story, 'Death in the School-Room,' contributed by the same writer to a preceding number of the Democratic Review, were of actual occurrence; and in the native town of the author, the relation of them often beguiles the farmer's winter-fireside. [Whitman's Note]

3. with a lagging, weary pace

4. "who'll"   5. "boys"

"Unless," continued the woman, catching a second glance at the six-pence; "unless old Joe is at the stable, as he's very likely to be. I'll go and find out for you." And she push'd open a door at her back, stepp'd[6] through an adjoining room into a yard, whence her voice was the next moment heard calling the person she had mention'd, in accents by no means remarkable for their melody or softness.

Her search was successful. She soon return'd with him who was to act as messenger—a little, wither'd, ragged old man—a hanger-on there, whose unshaven face told plainly enough the story of his intemperate habits—those deeply seated habits, now too late to be uprooted, that would ere long lay him in a drunkard's grave. The youth[7] inform'd him what the required service was, and promised him the reward as soon as he should return.

"Tell Richard Hall that I am[8] going to his father's house this afternoon. If he asks who it is that wishes him here, say the person sent no name," continued the stranger, sitting up from his indolent posture, as the feet of old Joe were about leaving the door-stone, and his blear'd eyes turned to catch the last sentence of the mandate.

"And yet, perhaps you may as well," added he,[9] communing a moment with himself: "you may tell him his brother Frank, Wild Frank, it is, who wishes him to come."

The old man departed on his errand, and he who call'd himself Wild Frank, toss'd his nearly smoked cigar out of the window, and folded his arms in thought.

No better place than this, probably, will occur to give a brief account of some former events in the life of the young stranger, resting and waiting at the village inn. Fifteen miles east of that inn lived a farmer named Hall, a man of good repute, well-off in the world, and head of a large family. He was fond of gain—required all his boys to labor in proportion to their age; and his right hand man, if he might not be called favorite, was his eldest son Richard. This eldest son, an industrious, sober-faced young fellow, was invested by his father with the powers of second in command; and as strict and swift obedience was a prime tenet in the farmer's domestic government, the children all tacitly[10] submitted to their brother's sway—all but one, and that was Frank. The farmer's wife was a quiet woman, in rather tender health; and though for all her offspring she had a mother's love, Frank's kiss ever seem'd sweetest to her lips. She favor'd[11] him more than the rest—perhaps, as in a hundred similar instances, for his being so often at fault, and so often blamed. In truth, however, he seldom receiv'd more blame than he deserv'd, for he was a capricious, high-

6. stepping   7. young man   8. "I'm"   9. added the youth
10. quietly   11. loved

temper'd lad, and up to all kinds of mischief. From these traits he was known in the neighborhood by the name of Wild Frank.

Among the farmer's stock there was a fine young blood mare—a beautiful creature, large and graceful, with eyes like dark-hued jewels, and her color that of the deep night. It being the custom of the farmer to let his boys have something about the farm that they could call their own, and take care of as such, Black Nell, as[12] the mare was called, had somehow or other fallen to Frank's share. He was very proud of her, and thought as much of her comfort as his own. The elder brother, however, saw fit to claim for himself, and several times to exercise, a privilege of managing and using Black Nell, notwithstanding what Frank consider'd his prerogative. On one of these occasions a hot dispute arose, and after much angry blood, it was referr'd to the farmer for settlement. He decided in favor of Richard, and added a harsh lecture to his other son. The farmer was really unjust; and Wild Frank's face paled with rage and mortification. That furious temper which he had never been taught to curb, now swell'd like an overflowing torrent. With difficulty restraining the exhibition of his passions, as soon as he got by himself he swore that not another sun should roll by and find him under that roof. Late at night he silently arose,[13] and turning his back on what he thought an inhospitable home, in mood in which the child should never leave the parental roof, bent his steps toward the city.

It may well be imagined that alarm and grief pervaded the whole of the family, on discovering Frank's departure. And as week after week melted away and brought no tidings of him, his poor mother's heart grew wearier and wearier. She spoke not much, but was evidently sick in spirit. Nearly two years had elaps'd when about a week before the incidents at the commencement of this story, the farmer's family were joyfully surprised by receiving a letter from the long absent son. He had been to sea, and was then in New York, at which port his vessel had just arrived. He wrote in a gay strain; appear'd to have lost the angry feeling which had caused his flight from home; and said he heard in the city that Richard had married, and settled several miles distant,[14] where he wished him all good luck and happiness. Wild Frank wound up his letter by promising, as soon as he could get through the imperative business of his ship, to pay a visit to his parents and native place.[15] On Tuesday of the succeeding week, he said he would be with them.

Within half an hour after the departure of old Joe, the form of that ancient personage was seen slowly wheeling round the locust-tree at the end

12. for so   13. In the night he silently rose
14. several miles from home   15. to his home and native place

of the lane, accompanied by a stout young man in primitive homespun apparel. The meeting between Wild Frank and his brother Richard, though hardly of that kind which generally takes place between persons so closely related, could not exactly be call'd distant or cool either.[16] Richard press'd his brother to go with him to the farm house, and refresh and repose himself for some hours at least, but Frank declined.

"They will all expect me home this afternoon," he said, "I wrote to them I would be there to-day."

"But you must be very tired, Frank," rejoin'd the other; "won't you let some of us harness up and carry you? Or if you like—" he stopp'd a moment, and a trifling suffusion spread over his face; "if you like, I'll put the saddle on Black Nell—she's here at my place now, and you can ride home like a lord."

Frank's face color'd a little, too. He paused for a moment in thought—he was really foot-sore, and exhausted with his journey that hot day—so he accepted his brother's offer.

"You know the speed of Nell, as well as I," said Richard; "I'll warrant when I bring her here you'll say she's in good order as ever." So telling him to amuse himself for a few minutes as well as he could, Richard left the tavern.

Could it be that Black Nell knew her early master?[17] She neigh'd and rubb'd her nose on his shoulder; and as he put his foot in the stirrup and rose on her back, it was evident that they were both highly pleased with their meeting. Bidding his brother farewell, and not forgetting old Joe, the young man set forth on his journey to his father's house. As he left the village behind, and came upon the long monotonous road before him, he thought on the circumstances of his leaving home—and he thought, too, on his course of life, how it was being frittered away and lost. Very gentle influences, doubtless,[18] came over Wild Frank's mind then, and[19] he yearn'd to show his parents that he was sorry for the trouble he had cost them. He blamed himself for his former follies, and even felt remorse that he had not acted more kindly to Richard, and gone to his house. Oh, it had been a sad mistake of the farmer that he did not teach his children to love one another. It was a foolish thing that he prided himself on governing[20] his little flock well, when sweet affection, gentle forbearance, and brotherly faith, were almost unknown among them.

16. was hardly of that kind which generally takes place between persons so closely related; neither could it be called distant or cool.
17. old master
18. "Doubtless" has been added in the later text.
19. for   20. on, of governing

The day was now advanced, though the heat pour'd down with a strength little less oppressive than at noon. Frank had accomplish'd the greater part of his journey; he was within two miles[21] of his home. The road here led over a high, tiresome hill, and he determined to stop on the top of it and rest himself, as well as give the animal he rode a few minutes' breath. How well he knew the place! And that mighty oak, standing just outside the fence on the very summit of the hill, often had he reposed under its shade. It would be pleasant for a few minutes to stretch his limbs there again as of old, he thought to himself; and he dismounted from the saddle and led Black Nell under the tree. Mindful of the comfort of his favorite, he took from his little bundle, which he had strapped behind him on the mare's back, a piece of strong cord,[22] four or five yards in length, which he tied to the bridle, and wound and tied the other end, for security, over[23] his own wrist; then throwing himself at full length upon the ground, Black Nell was at liberty to graze around him, without danger of straying away.

It was a calm scene, and a pleasant. There was no rude sound—hardly even a chirping insect—to break the sleepy silence of the place. The atmosphere had a dim, hazy cast, and was impregnated with overpowering heat. The young man lay there minute after minute, as time glided away unnoticed; for he was very tired, and his repose was sweet to him. Occasionally he raised himself and cast a listless look at the distant landscape, veil'd as it was by the slight mist. At length his repose was without such interruptions. His eyes closed, and though at first they open'd languidly again at intervals, after a while they shut altogether. Could it be that he slept? It was so indeed. Yielding to the drowsy influences about him, and to his prolong'd weariness of travel,[24] he had fallen into a deep, sound slumber. Thus he lay; and Black Nell, the original cause of his departure from his home—by a singular chance,[25] the companion of his return—quietly cropp'd the grass at his side.

An hour nearly pass'd away, and yet the young man slept on. The light and heat were not glaring now; a change had come over earth and heaven.[26] There were signs of one of those thunderstorms[27] that in our climate spring up and pass over so quickly and so terribly. Masses of vapor loom'd up in the horizon, and a dark shadow settled on the woods and fields. The leaves of the great oak rustled together over the youth's head.

21. three miles 22. small, strong cord 23. round
24. "Of travel" has been added in the later version.
25. fatality
26. over the aspect of the scene.
27. sudden thunder-storms

Clouds flitted swiftly in the sky, like bodies of armed men coming up to battle at the call of their leader's trumpet. A thick rain-drop fell now and then, while occasionally hoarse mutterings of thunder sounded in the distance; yet the slumberer was not arous'd.[28] It was strange that Wild Frank[29] did not awake. Perhaps his ocean life had taught him to rest undisturbed amid the jarring of elements. Though the storm was now coming on its fury, he slept like a babe in its cradle.[30]

Black Nell had ceased grazing, and stood by her sleeping master with ears erect, and her long mane and tail waving in the wind. It seem'd quite dark, so heavy were the clouds. The blast blew[31] sweepingly, the lightning flash'd, and the rain fell in torrents. Crash after crash of thunder seem'd to shake the solid earth. And Black Nell, she stood now, an image of beautiful terror, with her fore feet thrust out, her neck arch'd, and her eyes glaring[32] balls of fear. At length, after a dazzling and lurid glare, there came a peal—a deafening crash—as if the great axle was rent.[33] God of Spirits! the startled mare sprang off like a ship in an ocean-storm! Her eyes were blinded with light;[34] she dashed madly down the hill, and plunge after plunge—far, far away—swift as an arrow—dragging the hapless body of the youth[35] behind her!

In the low, old-fashion'd dwelling of the farmer there was a large family group. The men and boys had gather'd under shelter at the approach of the storm; and the subject of their talk was the return of the long absent son. The mother spoke of him, too, and her eyes brighten'd with pleasure as she spoke. She made all the little domestic preparations—cook'd his favorite dishes—and arranged for him his own bed, in its own old place. As the tempest mounted to its fury[36] they discuss'd the probability of his getting soak'd by it; and the provident dame had already selected some dry garments for a change. But the rain was soon over, and nature smiled again in her invigorated beauty. The sun shone out as it was dipping in the west. Drops sparkled on the leaf-tips—coolness and clearness were in the air.

The clattering of a horse's hoofs came to the ears of those who were gather'd there. It was on the other side of the house that the wagon road led; and they open'd the door and rush'd in a tumult of glad anticipations,[37]

---

28. Between this sentence and the next, which begins a new paragraph, the following passage intervenes in the original:

> Lo! thus in the world you may see men steeped in lethargy while a mightier tempest gathers over them. Even as the floods are about to burst—as the warning caution is sent forth, they close their eyes, and dream idly, and smile while they dream. Many a throned potentate, many a proud king with his golden crown, will start wildly in the midst of the thundercrash, and the bright glaring of the storm, and wonder that he saw it not when it was coming.

through the adjoining room to the porch. What a sight it was that met them there! Black Nell stood a few feet from the door, with her neck crouch'd down; she drew her breath long and deep, and vapor rose from every part of her reeking body. And with eyes starting from their sockets, and mouths agape with stupefying terror, they beheld on the ground near her a mangled, hideous mass—the rough semblance of a human form—all batter'd and cut, and bloody. Attach'd to it was the fatal cord, dabbled over with gore. And as the mother gazed—for she could not withdraw her eyes—and the appalling truth came upon her mind, she sank down without shriek or utterance, into a deep, deathly swoon.

29. the young man
30. The storm was now coming on in its fury.
31. came   32. glittering
33. as if the great axle was rent; it seemed to shiver the very central foundations, and every object appeared reeling like a drunken man.
34. with terror   35. the sleeper
36. was at its fury
37. "In a tumult of glad anticipations," not present in 1841, was added in the text of *Collect*.

The Child and the Profligate[1]

JUST after sunset,[2] one evening in summer—that pleasant hour when the air is balmy, the light loses its glare, and all around is imbued with soothing quiet—on the door-step of a house there sat an elderly woman waiting the arrival of her son. The house was in a straggling village some fifty miles from New York city.[3] She who sat on the door step was a widow; her white cap cover'd locks of gray, and her dress, though clean, was exceedingly homely. Her house—for the tenement she occupied was her own—was very little and very old. Trees cluster'd around it so thickly as almost to hid its color—that blackish gray color which belongs to old wooden houses that have never been painted; and to get in it you had to enter a little rickety gate and walk through a short path, border'd by carrot beds and beets and other vegetables. The son whom she was expecting was her only child. About a year before he had been bound apprentice to a rich farmer in the place, and after finishing his daily task he was in the

1. The text followed here is that of *Collect*. The publication record of this tale gives it a certain distinction. Only one other story was reprinted more often in Whitman's lifetime: "Death in the School-Room," which appeared in print on six occasions. Only one other story was reprinted as often in Whitman's lifetime: "A Legend of Life and Love," which also appeared in print on four occasions. But "The Child and the Profligate" is truly unique as the only one of Whitman's tales that was radically revised for publication prior to its inclusion in *Collect*. The story was first printed in the *New World*, where Whitman was working as a compositor, on November 20, 1841, under the title of "The Child's Champion"; and its theme was then the regenerative power of love, specifically the love of a young man for a boy. Under its present title in the *Columbian Magazine* for October 1844 it had become a blatant temperance tale, which it remained when reprinted in the *Brooklyn Eagle* in January 1847, near the end of Whitman's editorship of that paper, and in *Collect*, though its didacticism is muted in the latter version. The *Columbian* was not a temperance journal *per se*, but its version invoked the past reputation of Whitman as a temperance writer in the by-line following the title: "By Walter Whitman, Author of 'The Merchant's Clerk'" (*Franklin Evans*), and by reproducing, as a motto, the first stanza of the two-stanza epigraph from the head of Chapter XVI of *Franklin Evans*. As usual, the *Collect* text differs from the earlier texts in the deletion of the "e" in the past forms of most regular verbs and by minor changes in punctuation. The *Columbian* version separates the extremely long paragraphs of the *New World* text into shorter paragraphs, and this paragraph division is followed in the *Eagle* and *Collect*. The significant variants from the *Collect* text appear in the notes below, identified by NW (*New World*), C (*Columbian*), and E (*Eagle*).
2. In the E and C versions, this paragraph is the fourth and is preceded by these three introductory paragraphs:

> Among the victims of the passion for strong drink the greater part become so, I have observed, not from any ignorance of the danger of the path they pursue, but from weakness and irresolution of mind. To the abstemious it is almost impossible to convey an idea of the strength of the desire, formed,

habit of spending half an hour at his mother's. On the present occasion the shadows of night had settled heavily before the youth made his appearance. When he did, his walk was slow and dragging, and all his motions were languid, as if from great weariness. He open'd the gate, came through the path, and sat down by his mother in silence.

"You are sullen to-night, Charley," said the widow, after a moment's[4] pause, when she found that he return'd no answer to her greeting.

As she spoke she put her hand fondly on his head; it seem'd moist as if it had been dipp'd in the water. His shirt, too, was soak'd; and as she pass'd her fingers down his shoulder she felt a sharp twinge in her heart, for she knew that moisture to be the hard wrung sweat of severe toil, exacted from her young child (he was but thirteen years old)[5] by an unyielding task-master.

"You have work'd hard to-day, my son."

"I've been mowing."

The widow's heart felt another pang.

"Not *all day*,[6] Charley?" she said, in a low voice; and there was a slight quiver in it.

---

after a while, in a habitual drinker. No one can know, except him who has realized it himself. The world points with contempt at the inebriate, and laughs him to scorn that he does not turn from the error of his ways. But oh, if the agony of his struggles could be seen—if the vain and impotent efforts he makes to disentangle himself from the thraldom of his tyrant—if the sharp shame, the secret tears, the throes of mortification and conscious disgrace—were apparent to those who condemn so severely, one little drop of sorrow might certainly be mingled with their anger.

Now and then, though rarely, it does happen that something occurs which turns the tide and converts the drinker with the feelings I have mentioned into a reformed man. And it is strange to observe how small and trivial are frequently the causes of this change. A word merely, or an unimportant action, or a casual incident not out of the ordinary routine, forms the starting point whence the hitherto miserable one commences a reformation which ere long presents him to the world with a clearer head and purer soul. Such a word, it may be—such an incident—stirs up the fountains of thought, brings back memories long passed away and awakens the man to beautiful and pathetic recollections of an earlier and more innocent age. Thus fully awakened, and with the genial influence of the time in all its sway over him, if the crisis turns for good, it will surely be consummated for good. But should it turn to wickedness again, God have mercy on the fated being!

The incidents of my little narrative are simple and unromantic enough, and yet I hope they will not be found without interest. I tell no tale of fiction either. There are those now in this metropolis who will peruse the tale and acknowledge in their own minds' consciousness of its unadorned truth.

3. from the great city, whose spires and ceaseless clang rise up, where the Hudson pours forth its waters. *NW*

4. minute's *NW*

5. Charley is twelve in *NW*, fourteen in *E*.

6. No italics in *NW*.

"Yes mother, all day," replied the boy; "Mr. Ellis said he couldn't afford to hire men, for wages are so high. I've swung the scythe ever since an hour before sunrise. Feel of my hands."

There were blisters on them like great lumps. Tears started in the widow's eyes. She dared not trust herself with a reply, though her heart was bursting with the thought that she could not better his condition. There was no earthly means of support on which she had dependence enough to encourage her child in the wish she knew he was forming— the wish not utter'd for the first time—to be freed from his bondage.

"Mother," at length said the boy, "I can stand it no longer. I cannot and will not stay at Mr. Ellis's. Ever since the day I first went into his house I've been a slave; and if I have to work so much longer I know I shall run off and go to sea or somewhere else. I'd as leave be in my grave as there." And the child burst into a passionate fit of weeping.

His mother was silent, for she was in deep grief herself. After some minutes had flown, however, she gather'd sufficient self-possession to speak to her son in a soothing tone, endeavoring to win him from his sorrows and cheer up his heart. She told him that time was swift—that in the course of a few years he would be his own master—that all people have their troubles —with many other ready arguments which, though they had little effect in calming her own distress, she hoped would act as a solace to the disturb'd temper of the boy. And as the half hour to which he was limited had now elaps'd, she took him by the hand and led him to the gate, to set forth on his return. The youth seemed pacified, though occasionally one of those convulsive sighs that remain after a fit of weeping, would break from his throat. At the gate he threw his arms about his mother's neck; each press'd a long kiss on the lips of the other, and the youngster bent his steps towards his master's house.

As her child pass'd out of sight the widow return'd, shut the gate and enter'd her lonely room. There was no light in the old cottage that night— the heart of its occupant was dark and cheerless. Love, agony, and grief,[7] and tears and convulsive wrestlings were there. The thought of a beloved son condemned to labor—labor that would break down a man—struggling from day to day under the hard rule of a soulless gold-worshipper; the knowledge that years must pass thus; the sickening idea of her own

7. Sore agony and grief NW

8. In NW "without repose" does not appear and this sentence is followed by the following passage: "O, you, who, living in plenty and peace, fret at some little misfortune or some trifling disappointment—behold this spectacle, and blush at your unmanliness! Little do you know of the dark trials (compared to yours as night's great veil to a daylight cloud) that are still going on around you; the pangs of hunger—the faintness of the soul at seeing those we love trampled down, without our having the

poverty, and of living mainly on the grudged charity of neighbors—thoughts, too, of former happy days—these rack'd the widow's heart, and made her bed a sleepless one without repose.[8]

The boy bent his steps to his employer's, as has been said. In his way down the village street he had to pass a public house, the only one the place contain'd; and when he came off against it he heard the sound of a fiddle—drown'd, however, at intervals, by much laughter and talking. The windows were up, and, the house standing close to the road, Charles thought it no harm to take a look and see what was going on within. Half a dozen footsteps brought him to the low casement, on which he lean'd his elbow, and where he had a full view of the room and its occupants. In one corner was an old man, known in the village as Black Dave—he it was whose musical performances had a moment before drawn Charles's attention to the tavern; and he it was who now exerted himself in a violent manner to give, with divers flourishes and extra twangs, a tune very popular among that thick-lipp'd race whose fondness for melody is so well known. In the middle of the room were five or six sailors, some of them quite drunk, and others in the earlier stages of that process, while on benches around were more sailors, and here and there a person dress'd in landsman's[9] attire.[10] The men[11] in the middle of the room were dancing; that is, they were going through certain contortions and shufflings, varied occasionally by exceedingly hearty stamps upon the sanded floor. In short the whole party were engaged in a drunken frolic, which was in no respect different from a thousand other drunken frolics, except, perhaps, that there was less than the ordinary amount of anger and quarreling. Indeed everyone seem'd in remarkably good humor.

But what excited the boy's attention more than any other object was an individual, seated on one of the benches opposite, who, though evidently enjoying the spree as much as if he were an old hand at such business, seem'd in every other particular to be far out of his element. His appearance was youthful. He might have been twenty-one or two years old. His countenance was intelligent, and had the air of city life and society. He was dress'd not gaudily, but in every respect fashionably; his coat being of the finest broadcloth, his linen delicate and spotless as snow, and his whole aspect that of one whose counterpart may now and then be seen upon

---

power to aid them—the wasting away of the body in sickness incurable—and those dull achings of the heart when the consciousness comes upon the poor man's mind, that while he lives he will in all probability live in want and wretchedness."

9. landsmen's NW, C, E

10. The sentence continues, "but hardly behind the sea gentlemen in uproar and mirth" C and E; "uproariousness and mirth" NW

11. "The individuals" in all other versions.

the pave in Broadway of a fine afternoon.[12] He laugh'd and talk'd with the rest, and it must be confess'd his jokes—like the most of those that pass'd current there—were by no means distinguish'd for their refinement or purity. Near the door was a small table, cover'd with decanters and glasses, some of which had been used, but were used again indiscriminately, and a box of very thick and very long cigars.

One of the sailors—and it was he who made the largest share of the hubbub—had but one eye. His chin and cheeks were cover'd with huge, bushy whiskers, and altogether he had quite a brutal appearance. "Come, boys," said this gentleman, "come, let us take a drink. I know you're all a getting dry;" and he clench'd his invitation with an appalling oath.[13]

This politeness[14] was responded to by a general moving of the company toward the table holding the before-mention'd decanters and glasses. Clustering there around, each one help'd himself to a very handsome portion of that particular liquor which suited his fancy; and steadiness and accuracy being at that moment by no means distinguishing traits of the arms and legs of the party, a goodly amount of the fluid was spill'd upon the floor. This piece of extravagance excited the ire of the personage who gave the "treat;" and that ire was still further increas'd when he discover'd two or three loiterers who seem'd disposed to slight his request to drink. Charles, as we have before mention'd, was looking in at the window.[15]

"Walk up, boys! walk up! If there be any skulker among us,[16] blast my eyes if he shan't go down on his marrow bones and taste the liquor we have spilt![17] Hallo!" he exclaim'd as he spied Charles; "hallo, you chap in the window, come here and take a sup."

As he spoke he stepp'd to the open casement, put his brawny hands under the boy's arms,[18] and lifted him into the room bodily.

"There, my lads," said he, turning to his companions, "There's a new recruit for you. Not so coarse a one, either," he added as he took a fair view of the boy, who, though not what is called pretty, was fresh and manly looking, and large for his age.

"Come, youngster, take a glass," he continued. And he pour'd one nearly full of strong brandy.

12. his whole aspect a counterpart to those which may be nightly seen in the dress circles of our most respectable theatres. NW

13. This paragraph is rendered in the following fashion in NW:

"Come, boys," said one of the sailors, taking advantage of a momentary pause in the hubbub to rap his enormous knuckles on the table, and call attention to himself; the gentleman in question had but one eye, and two most extensive whiskers. "Come, boys, let's take a drink, I know you're all getting dry, so curse me if you shant have a suck at my expense."

C follows the Collect text except that it concludes with "So, curse me if you sha'n't have a suck at my expense."

Now Charles was not exactly frighten'd, for he was a lively fellow, and had often been at the country merry-makings, and at the parties of the place;[19] but he was certainly rather abash'd at his abrupt introduction to the midst of strangers. So, putting the glass aside, he look'd up with a pleasant smile in his new acquaintance's face.

"I've no need for anything now," he said, "but I'm just as much obliged to you as if I was."

"Poh! man, drink it down," rejoin'd the sailor, "drink it down—it won't hurt you."

And, by way of showing its excellence, the one-eyed worthy drain'd it himself to the last drop. Then filling it again, he renew'd his efforts[20] to make the lad go through the same operation.

"I've no occasion. Besides, *my mother has often pray'd me not to drink*, and I promised to obey her."[21]

A little irritated by his continued refusal, the sailor, with a loud oath, declared that Charles should swallow the brandy, whether he would or no. Placing one of his tremendous paws on the back of the boy's head, with the other he thrust the edge of the glass to his lips, swearing at the same time, that if he shook it so as to spill its contents the consequences would be of a nature by no means agreeable to his back and shoulders. Disliking the liquor, and angry at the attempt to overbear him, the undaunted child lifted his hand and struck the arm of the sailor with a blow so sudden that the glass fell and was smash'd to pieces on the floor; while the brandy was about equally divided between the face of Charles, the clothes of the sailor, and the sand. By this time the whole of the company had their attention drawn to the scene. Some of them laugh'd when they saw Charles's undisguised antipathy to the drink; but they laugh'd still more heartily when he discomfited the sailor. All of them, however, were content to let the matter go as chance would have it—all but the young man of the black coat, who has been spoken of.[22]

What was there in the words which Charles had spoken that carried the mind of the young man back to former times—to a period when he was more pure and innocent than now? "*My mother has often pray'd me not to*

14. This polite invitation NW, C   15. This sentence is not in NW.

16. "Don't let there be any skulker among us, or" NW, C, E

17. "And gobble up the rum we've spilt." NW

18. armpits NW

19. the country merry-makings, and with the young men of the place who were very fond of him NW

20. Hospitable efforts NW

21. 'I've no occasion; besides, it makes my head ache, and I have promised my mother not to drink any,' was the boy's answer. NW

22. who had before been spoken of. NW who has before been spoken of. C, E

drink!" Ah, how the mist of months roll'd aside, and presented to his soul's eye the picture of *his* mother, and a prayer of exactly similar purport! Why was it, too, that the young man's heart moved with a feeling of kindness toward the harshly treated child?[23]

Charles stood, his cheek flush'd and his heart throbbing, wiping the trickling drops from his face with a handkerchief. At first the sailor, between his drunkenness and his surprise, was much in the condition of one suddenly awaken'd out of a deep sleep, who cannot call his consciousness about him. When he saw the state of things, however, and heard the jeering laugh of his companions, his dull eye lighting up with anger, fell upon the boy who had withstood him. He seized Charles with a grip of iron, and with the side of his heavy boot[24] gave him a sharp and solid kick. He was about repeating the performance—for the child hung like a rag in his grasp—but all of a sudden his ears rang, as if pistols were snapp'd[25] close to them; lights of various hues flicker'd in his eye, (he had but one, it will be remember'd,) and a strong propelling power caused him to move from his position, and keep moving until he was brought up by the wall. A blow, a cuff given in such a scientific manner that the hand from which it proceeded was evidently no stranger to the pugilistic art, had been suddenly planted in the ear of the sailor. It was planted by the young man[26] of the black coat. He had watch'd with interest the proceeding of the sailor and the boy—two or three times he was on the point of interfering; but when the kick was given, his rage was uncontrollable. He sprang from his seat in the attitude of a boxer—struck the sailor in a manner to cause those

---

23. The *NW* version of this paragraph is as follows:
    Why was it that from the first moment of seeing him, the young man's heart had moved with a strange feeling of kindness toward the boy? He felt anxious to know more of him—he felt that he should love him. O, it is passing wondrous, how in the hurried walks of life and business, we meet with young beings, strangers, who seem to touch the fountains of our love, and draw forth their swelling waters. The wish to love and to be loved, which the forms of custom, and the engrossing anxiety for gain, so generally smother, will sometimes burst forth in spite of all obstacles; and, kindled by one, who, till the hour was unknown to us, will burn with a lovely and pure brightness. No scrap is this of sentimental fiction; ask your own heart, reader, and your own memory, for endorsement to its truth.
    Except for one or two minor word changes, the *C* and *E* versions were those of the paragraph as it later appeared in *Collect* but with the addition of the following lines, derived chiefly from the original text: "Was it that his associations had hitherto been among the vile, and the contrast was now so strikingly great? Even in the hurried walks of life and business may we meet with beings who seem to touch the fountains of our love, and draw forth their swelling waters! The wish to love and be beloved, which the forms of custom and the engrossing anxiety for gain so generally smother, will sometimes burst forth in spite of all obstacles; and kindled by one who, till the hour, was unknown to us, will burn with a permanent and pure brightness!"
    24. He seized the child with a grip of iron; he bent Charles half way over, and

unpleasant sensations which have been described—and would probably have follow'd up the attack,[27] had not Charles, now thoroughly terrified, clung around his legs and prevented his advancing.

The scene was a strange one, and for the time quite a silent one.[28] The company had started from their seats, and for a moment held breathless but strain'd positions. In the middle of the room stood the young man, in his not at all ungraceful attitude—every nerve out, and his eyes flashing brilliantly.[29] He seem'd rooted like a rock; and clasping him, with an appearance of confidence in his protection, clung[30] the boy.

"You scoundrel!"[31] cried the young man, his voice thick with passion,[32] "dare to touch the boy again, and I'll thrash[33] you till no sense is left in your body."

The sailor, now partially recover'd, made some gestures of a belligerent nature.[34]

"Come on, drunken brute!" continued the angry youth; "I wish you would! You've not had half what you deserve!"

Upon sobriety and sense more fully taking their power in the brains of the one-eyed mariner, however, that worthy determined in his own mind that it would be most prudent to let the latter drop. Expressing therefore his conviction to that effect, adding certain remarks to the purport that he "meant no harm to the lad," that he was surprised at such a gentleman being angry at "a little piece of fun,"[35] and so forth—he proposed that the company should go on with their jollity just as if nothing had happen'd. In truth, he of the single eye was not a bad fellow at heart, after all; the fiery

---

with the side of his heavy foot *NW*

25. had snapped *NW*   26. young stranger *NW*

27. He sprung from his seat like a mad tiger. Assuming, unconsciously, however, the attitude of a boxer, he struck the sailor in a manner to cause those unpleasant sensations just described; and he would probably have followed up his attack in a method by no means consistent with the sailor's personal ease *NW*

   He sprang from his seat, and assuming, unconsciously however, the attitude of a boxer, he struck the sailor in a manner to cause those unpleasant sensations which have been described. And he would probably have followed up the attack in a manner by no means consistent with the sailor's personal safety *C, E*

28. This sentence does not appear in *E*.

29. The company started from their seats and held startled but quiet positions; in the middle of the room stood the young man, in his not at all ungraceful posture, every nerve strained, and his eyes flashing very brilliantly. *NW*

30. hung *NW, C, E*

31. "Dare! you scoundrel!" *NW, C, E*

32. agitation *NW*   33. "batter" *NW*

34. "You be d———d," said the sailor, now partially recovered, and he made some gestures of a belligerent nature. *E*

35. "getting so 'up about a little piece of fun' " *NW*

enemy whose advances he had so often courted that night, had stolen away his good feelings, and set busy devils at work within him, that might have made his hands do some dreadful deed, had not the stranger interposed.

In a few minutes the frolic of the party was upon its former footing. The young man sat down upon one of the benches, with the boy by his side, and while the rest were loudly laughing and talking, they two convers'd together.[36] The stranger learn'd from Charles all the particulars of his simple story—how his father had died years since—how his mother work'd hard for a bare living—and how he himself, for many dreary months, had been the servant[37] of a hard-hearted, avaricious master. More and more interested, drawing the child close to his side, the young man listen'd to his plainly told history—and thus an hour pass'd away.

It was now past midnight. The young man told Charles that on the morrow he would take steps to relieve him from his servitude—that for the present night the landlord would probably give him a lodging at the inn—and little persuading did the host need for that.

As he retired to sleep, very pleasant thoughts filled the mind of the young man—thoughts of a worthy action perform'd—thoughts, too, newly awakened ones, of walking in a steadier and wiser path than formerly.

That roof, then, sheltered two beings that night—one of them innocent and sinless of all wrong—the other—oh, to that other what evil had not been present, either in action or to his desires![38]

Who, was the stranger? To those that, from ties of relationship or otherwise, felt an interest in him, the answer to that question was not pleasant to dwell upon. His name was Langton[39]—parentless—a dissipated young man—a brawler—one whose too frequent companions were row-

36. held communion together. NW   37. bond-child NW

38. In NW, the matter of this and the two preceding paragraphs is rendered in this fashion:

> It was now past midnight. The young man told Charles that on the morrow he would take steps to have him liberated from his servitude; for the present night, he said, it would perhaps be best for the boy to stay and share his bed at the inn; and little persuading did the child need to do so. As they retired to sleep, very pleasant thoughts filled the mind of the young man; thoughts of a worthy action performed; of unsullied affection; thoughts, too—newly awakened ones—of walking in a steadier and wiser path than formerly. All his imaginings seemed to be interwoven with the youth who lay by his side; he folded his arms around him, and, while he slept, the boy's cheek rested on his bosom. Fair were those two creatures in their unconscious beauty—glorious, but yet how differently glorious! One of them was innocent and sinless of all wrong: the other—O to that other, what evil had not been present, either in action or to his desires!

39. Lankton NW

40. The New-York police officers were not altogether strangers to his countenance; and certain reporters who note the transactions there, had more than once re-

dies, blacklegs, and swindlers. The New York police offices were not strangers to his countenance.[40] He had been bred to the profession of medicine; besides, he had a very respectable income, and his house was in a pleasant street on the west side of the city. Little of his time, however, did Mr. John Langton spend at his domestic hearth; and the elderly lady who officiated as his housekeeper was by no means surprised to have him gone for a week or a month at a time, and she knowing nothing of his whereabouts.

Living as he did, the young man was an unhappy being. It was not so much that his associates were below his own capacity—for Langton, though sensible and well bred, was not highly talented or refined—but that he lived without any steady purpose, that he had no one to attract him to his home, that he too easily allow'd himself to be tempted—which caused his life to be, of late, one continued scene of dissatisfaction. This dissatisfaction he sought to drive away[41] by the brandy bottle, and mixing in all kinds of parties where the object was pleasure. On the present occasion he had left the city a few days before, and was passing his time at a place near the village where Charles and his mother lived. He fell in, during the day,[42] with those who were his companions of the tavern spree; and thus it happen'd that they were all together. Langton hesitated not to make himself at home with any associate that suited his fancy.

The next morning the poor widow rose from her sleepless cot; and from that lucky trait in our nature which makes one extreme follow another, she set about her toil with a lighten'd heart. Ellis, the farmer, rose, too, short as the nights were, an hour before day; for his god was gain, and a prime article of his creed was to get as much work as possible from every one around him.[43] In the course of the day Ellis was called upon by

---

ceived gratuities for leaving out his name from the disgraceful notoriety of their columns. *NW*

The New York police officers were not altogether strangers to his countenance; and certain reporters, who notice the proceedings there, had more than once received a fee for leaving out his name from the disgraceful notoriety of their columns. *C, E*

41. to drive away (ah, foolish youth!) *NW, C, E*

42. He had that day fallen in *NW*

43. In all earlier versions, a long passage intervenes at this point between this sentence and the next. The *NW* version of the passage is given below:

> He roused up all his people, and finding that Charles had not been home the preceding night, he muttered threats against him, and calling a messenger, to whom he hinted that any minutes which he stayed beyond a most exceeding short period, would be subtracted from his breakfast time, dispatched him to the widow's to find what was her son about.
>
> What was he about? With one of the brightest and earliest rays of the warm sun a gentle angel entered his apartment, and hovering over the sleepers on invisible wings, looked down with a pleasant smile and blessed them. Then noiselessly taking a stand by the bed, the angel bent over the boy's face, and whispered strange words into his ear: thus it came that he had

young Langton, and never perhaps in his life was the farmer puzzled more than at the young man's proposal—his desire to provide for the widow's family, a family that could do him no pecuniary good,[44] and his willingness to disburse money for that purpose.[45] The widow, too, was called upon, not only on that day, but the next and the next.

It needs not that I should particularize the subsequent events of Lang-

beautiful visions. No sound was heard but the slight breathing of those who slumbered there in each others arms; and the angel paused a moment, and smiled another and a doubly sweet smile as he drank in the scene with his large soft eyes. Bending over again to the boy's lips, he touched them with a kiss, as the languid wind touches a flower. He seemed to be going now—and yet he lingered. Twice or thrice he bent over the brow of the young man— and went not. Now the angel was troubled; for he would have pressed the young man's forehead with a kiss, as he did the child's; but a spirit from the Pure Country, who touches anything tainted by evil thoughts, does it at the risk of having his breast pierced with pain, as with a barbed arrow. At that moment a very pale bright ray of sunlight darted through the window and settled on the young man's features. Then the beautiful spirit knew that permission was granted him: so he softly touched the young man's face with his, and silently and swiftly wafted himself away on the unseen air.

The C and E versions of this passage are identical and follow the original version very closely except that the young man and Charles are perhaps sleeping in separate beds, the angel's "doubly sweet smile" is evoked merely by the sight of Charles alone, and Charles dreams the whole incident. The significant lines in the C–E version follow:

What was he about? He had a beautiful dream—and thus it was in seeming.

With one of the brightest and earliest rays of the warm sun a gentle angel entered his apartment, and hovered over him, and looked down with a pleasant smile, and blessed him. And the child thought his benefactor, the young man, was nigh, sleeping also. Noiselessly taking a stand by the bed, the angel bent over the boy's face and whispered strange words into his ear; it seemed to him like soft and delicate music. So the angel, pausing a moton's and the boy's history—how the reformation of the profligate might be dated to begin from that time—how he gradually sever'd the guilty ties that had so long gall'd him—how he enjoy'd his own home again—how the friendship of Charles and himself grew not slack with time—and how, when in the course of seasons he became head of a family of his own, he would shudder at the remembrance of his early dangers and his escapes.[46]

ment, and smiling another and a doubly sweet smile, and drinking in the scene with his large soft eyes, bent over again to the boy's lips and touched them with a kiss, as the languid wind touches a flower. He seemed to be going now, and yet he lingered.

44. his desire to provide for a boy who could do him no pecuniary good *NW*

45. These two sentences follow in all of the early versions:

In that department of Ellis's structure where the mind was, or ought to have been situated, there never had entered the slightest thought assimilating to those which actuated the young man in his proceedings in this business. Yet Ellis was a church member and a county officer.

c and *E* substitute "benevolent movements" for "proceedings in this business."

46. how he enjoyed his own home, and loved to be there, and why he loved to be there; how the close knit love of the boy and him grew not slack with time; and how, when at length he became head of a family of his own, he would shudder when he thought of his early danger and escape. *NW*

The *c* and *E* versions of this paragraph follow that of *Collect* except that they add this final line:

Often, in the bustle of day and the silence of night, would he bless the utterance of those words, "*My mother prayed me not to drink!*"

All of the early versions add a brief concluding paragraph addressed to the reader:

Loved reader, own you the moral of this simple story? Draw it forth— pause a moment, ere your eye wanders to a more bright and eloquent page— and dwell upon it. *NW, E*

Loved reader, own you the moral interwoven in this simple story? Let your children read it. To them draw forth the moral—pause a moment ere your eye wander to a different page—and dwell upon it. *c*

Bervance: or, Father and Son[1]

ALMOST incredible as it may seem, there is more truth than fiction in the following story. Whatever of the latter element may have been added, is for the purpose of throwing that disguise around the real facts of the former, which is due to the feelings of a respectable family. The principal parties alluded to have left the stage of life many years since; but I am well aware there are not a few yet alive, who, should they, as is very probable, read this narration, will have their memories carried back to scenes and persons of a much more substantial existence than the mere creation of an author's fancy. I have given it the form of a confession in the first person, partly for the sake of convenience, partly of simplicity, but chiefly because such was the form in which the main incidents were a long time ago repeated to me by my own informant. It is a strange story—the true solution of which will probably be found in the supposition of a certain degree of unsoundness of mind, on the one part, manifesting itself in the morbid and unnatural paternal antipathy; and of its reproduction on the other, by the well known though mysterious law of hereditary transmission.

W. W.

My appointed number of years has now almost sped. Before I sink to that repose in the bosom of our great common mother, which I have so long and earnestly coveted, I will disclose the story of a life which one fearful event has made, through all its latter stages, a continued stretch of wretchedness and remorse. There may possibly be some parents to whom it may serve as a not useless lesson.

I was born, and have always lived, in one of the largest of our Atlantic cities. The circumstances of my family were easy; I received a good education, was intended by my father for mercantile business, and upon attaining the proper age, obtained from him a small but sufficient capital; and in the course of a few years from thus starting, found myself sailing smoothly on the tide of fortune. I married; and, possessed of independence and domestic comfort, my life was a happy one indeed. Time passed on; we had several children; when about twenty years after our

1. "Bervance; or, Father and Son" first appeared in the *Democratic Review*, December 1841, and apparently was not reprinted in Whitman's lifetime.

marriage my wife died. It was a grievous blow to me, for I loved her well; and the more so of late, because that a little while before, at short intervals, I had lost both my parents.

Finding myself now at that period of life when ease and retirement are peculiarly soothing, I purchased an elegant house in a fashionable part of the city; where, surrounding myself and my family with every resource that abundance and luxury can afford for happiness, I settled myself for life—a life which seemed to promise every prospect of a long enjoyment. I had my sons and daughters around me; and objecting to the boarding-school system, I had their education conducted under my own roof, by a private tutor who resided with us. He was a mild, gentlemanly man, with nothing remarkable about his personal appearance, unless his eyes might be called so. They were gray—large, deep, and having a softly beautiful expression, that I have never seen in any others; and which, while they at times produced an extraordinary influence upon me, and yet dwell so vividly in my memory, no words that I can use could exactly describe. The name of the tutor was Alban.

Of my children, only two were old enough to be considered anything more than boys and girls. The eldest was my favorite. In countenance he was like the mother, whose first-born he was; and when she died, the mantle of my affections seemed transferred to him, with a sadly undue and unjust degree of preference over the rest. My second son, Luke, was bold, eccentric, and high-tempered. Strange as it may seem, notwithstanding a decided personal resemblance to myself, he never had his father's love. Indeed, it was only by a strong effort that I restrained and concealed a positive aversion. Occasions seemed continually to arise wherein the youth felt disposed to thwart me, and make himself disagreeable to me. Every time I saw him, I was conscious of something evil in his conduct or disposition. I have since thought that a great deal of all this existed only in my own imagination, warped and darkened as it was, and disposed to look upon him with an "evil eye." Be that as it may, I was several times made very angry by what I felt sure were intended to be wilful violations of my rule, and contemptuous taunts toward me for that partiality to his brother which I could not deny. In the course of time, I grew to regard the heedless boy with a feeling almost amounting—I shudder to make the confession —to hatred. Perhaps, for he was very cunning, he saw it, and, conscious that he was wronged, took the only method of revenge that was in his power.

I have said that he was eccentric. The term is hardly strong enough to mark what actually was the case with him. He occasionally had spells which approached very nearly to complete derangement. My family physician spoke learnedly of regimen, and drugs, and courses of treatment which, if carefully persevered in, might remove the peculiarity. He said, too, that cases of that kind were dangerous, frequently terminating in confirmed insanity. But I laughed at him, and told him his fears were idle. Had it been my favorite son instead of Luke, I do not think I would have passed by the matter so contentedly.

Matters stood as I have described them for several years. Alban, the tutor, continued with us; as fast as one grew up, so as to be beyond the need of his instructions, another appeared in the vacant place. The whole family loved him dearly, and I have no doubt he repaid their affection; for he was a gentle-hearted creature, and easily won. Luke and he seemed always great friends. I blush now, as I acknowledge that this was the only thing by which Alban excited my displeasure.

I shall pass over many circumstances that occurred in my family, having no special relation to the event which, in the present narrative, I have chiefly in view. One of my favorite amusements was afforded by the theatre. I kept a box of my own, and frequently attended, often giving my family permission also to be present. Luke I seldom allowed to go. The excuse that I assigned to myself and to others was, that he was of excitable temperament, and the acting would be injurious to his brain. I fear the privilege was withheld quite as much from vindictiveness toward him, and dislike of his presence on my own part. So Luke himself evidently thought and felt. On a certain evening—(were it last night, my recollection of it all could not be more distinct)—a favorite performer was to appear in a new piece; and it so happened that every one of us had arranged to attend—every one but Luke. He besought me earnestly that he might go with the rest—reminded me how rarely such favors were granted him—and even persuaded Alban to speak to me on the subject.

"Your son," said the tutor, "seems so anxious to partake of this pleasure, and has set his mind so fully upon it, that I really fear, sir, your refusal would excite him more than the sight of the play."

"I have adopted a rule," said I, "and once swerving from it makes it no rule at all."

"Mr. Bervance will excuse me," he still continued, "if I yet persevere in asking that you will allow Luke this indulgence, at least for this one evening. I am anxious and disturbed about the boy,—and should even consider it as a great personal favor to myself."

"No, sir," I answered, abruptly, "it is useless to continue this conversation. The young man cannot go, either from considerations of his pleasure or yours."

Alban made no reply; he colored, bowed slightly, and I *felt* his eye fixed upon me with an expression I did not at all like, though I could not analyze it. I was conscious, however, that I had said too much; and if the tutor had not at that moment left the room, I am sure I should have apologized for my rudeness.

We all went to the theatre. The curtain had hardly risen, when my attention was attracted by sone one in the tier above, and right off against my box, coming noisily in, talking loudly, and stumbling along, apparently on purpose to draw the eyes of the spectators. As he threw himself into a front seat, and the glare of the lamps fell upon his face, I could hardly believe my eyes when I saw it was Luke. A second and third observation were necessary to convince me. There he sat, indeed. He looked over to where I was seated, and while my sight was riveted upon him in unbounded astonishment, he deliberately rose—raised his hand to his head—lifted his hat, and bowed low and long—a cool sarcastic smile playing on his features all the time,—and finally breaking into an actual laugh, which even reached my ears. Nay—will it be believed!—the foolish youth had even the effrontery to bring down one of the wretched outcasts who are met with there, and seated himself full in our view—he laughing and talking with his companion so much to the annoyance of the house, that a police officer was actually obliged to interfere! I felt as if I should burst with mortification and anger.

At the conclusion of the tragedy we went home. Reader, I cannot dwell minutely on what followed. At a late hour my rebellious boy returned. Seemingly bent upon irritating me to the utmost, he came with perfect nonchalance into the room where I was seated. The remainder of that night is like a hateful dream in my memory, distinct and terrible, though shadowy. I recollect the sharp, cutting, but perfectly calm rejoinders he made to all my passionate invectives against his conduct. They worked me up to phrensy, and he smiled all the more calmly the while. Half maddened by my rage, I seized him by the collar, and shook him. My pen almost refuses to add—but justice to myself demands it—the Son felled the Father to the earth with a blow! Some blood even flowed from a slight wound caused by striking my head, as I fell against a projecting corner of furniture—and the hair that it matted together was gray!

What busy devil was it that stepped noiselessly round the bed, to which I immediately retired, and kept whispering in my ears all that endless night? Sleep forsook me. Thoughts of a deep revenge—a fearful redress—but it seemed to me hardly more fearful than the crime—worked within my brain. Then I turned, and tried to rest, but vainly. Some spirit from the abodes of ruin held up the provocation and the punishment continually before my mind's eye. The wretched youth had his strange fits: those fits were so thinly divided from insanity, that who should undertake to define the difference? And for insanity was there not a prison provided, with means and appliances, confinement, and, if need be, chains and scourges? For a few months it would be nothing more than wholesome that an unnatural child, a brutal assaulter of his parent, should taste the discipline of such a place. Before my eyes closed, my mind had resolved on the scheme—a scheme so cruel, that as I think of it now, my senses are lost in wonder that any one less than fiend could have resolved to undertake it.

The destinies of evil favored me. The very next morning Luke had one of his strange turns, brought on, undoubtedly, by the whirl and agitation of the previous day and night. With the smooth look and the quiet tread with which I doubt not Judas looked and trod, I went into his room and enjoined the attendants to be very careful of him. I found him more violently affected than at any former period. He did not know me; I felt glad that it was so, for my soul shrank at its own intentions, and I could not have met his conscious eye. At the close of the day, I sent for a physician; not him who generally attended my family, but one of those obsequious gentlemen who bend and are pliant like the divining-rod, that is said to be attracted by money. I sent, too, for some of the officers of the lunatic asylum. Two long hours we were in conversation. I was sorry, I told them, very sorry; it was a dreadful grief to me; the gentlemen surely could not but sympathize in my distress; but I felt myself called upon to yield my private feelings. I felt it best for my unhappy son to be, for a time at least, removed to the customary place for those laboring under his miserable disease. I will not say what other measures I took—what *tears* I shed. Oh, to what a depth may that man be sunk who once gives bad passions their swing! The next day, Luke was taken from my dwelling to the asylum, and confined in what was more like a dungeon, than a room for one used to all the luxurious comforts of life.

Days rolled on. I do not think any one suspected aught of what really was the case. Evident as it had been that Luke was not a favorite of mine, no person ever thought it possible that a father could place his son in a mad-house, from motives of any other description than a desire to have him cured. The children were very much hurt at their brother's unfortunate situation. Alban said nothing; but I knew that he sorrowed in secret. He frequently sought, sometimes with success, to obtain entrance to Luke; and after a while began to bring me favorable reports of the young man's recovery. One day, about three weeks after the event at the theatre, the tutor came to me with great satisfaction on his countenance. He had just returned from Luke, who was now as sane as ever. Alban said he could hardly get away from the young man, who conjured him to remain, for solitude there was a world of terror and agony. Luke had besought him, with tears streaming down his cheeks, to ask me to let him be taken from that place. A few days longer residence there, he said, a conscious witness of its horrors, and he should indeed be its fit inmate for ever.

The next morning I sent private instructions to the asylum, to admit no person in Luke's apartment without an order from me. Alban was naturally very much surprised, as day after day elapsed, and I took no measures to have my son brought home. Perhaps, at last, he began to suspect the truth; for in one of the interviews we had on the subject, those mild and beautiful eyes of his caused mine to sink before them, and he expressed a determination, dictated as he said by an imperious duty, in case I did not see fit to liberate the youth, to take some decided steps himself. I talked as smoothly and as sorrowfully as possible—but it was useless.

"My young friend, I am sure," said he, "has received all the benefits he can possibly derive from the institution, and I do not hesitate to say, any longer continuance there may be followed by dangerous—even fatal consequences. I cannot but think," and the steadfast look of that gray eye settled *at* me, as if it would pierce my inmost soul, "that Mr. Bervance desires to see his unlucky child away from so fearful an abode; and I have no doubt that I shall have his approval in any proper and necessary measures for that purpose."

I cursed him in my heart, but I felt that I had to submit. So I told him that if in two days more Luke did not have any relapse, I would then consider it safe to allow him to be brought home.

The swift time flew and brought the evening of the next day. I was alone in the house, all the family having gone to a concert, which I declined attending, for music was not then suited to my mood. The young people stayed later than I had expected; I walked the floor till I was tired, and then sat down on a chair. It was a parlor at the back of the house, with long, low windows opening into the garden. There and then, in the silence of the place, I thought for the first time of the full extent of the guilt I had lately been committing. It pressed upon me, and I could not hide from my eyes its dreadful enormity. But it became too painful, and I rose, all melted with agonized yet tender emotions, and determined to love my injured boy from that hour as Father should love Son. In the act of rising, my eyes were involuntarily cast toward a large mirror, on the chimney-piece. Was it a reflection of my own conscience, or a horrid reality? My blood curdled as I saw there an image of the form of my son—my cruelly treated Luke—but oh, how ghastly, how deathly a picture! I turned, and there was the original of the semblance. Just inside one of the windows stood the form, the pallid, unwashed, tangly-haired, rag-covered form of Luke Bervance. And that look of his—there was no deception there—it was the vacant, glaring, wild look of a *maniac*.

"Ho, ho!"

As I listened, I could hardly support myself, for uncontrollable horror.

"My son, do you not know me? I am your father," I gasped.

"You are Flint Serpent. Do you know *me*, Flint? A little owl screeched in my ear, as I came through the garden, and said you would be glad to see me, and then laughed a hooting laugh. Speak low," he continued in a whisper; "big eyes and bony hands are out there, and they would take me back again. But you will strike at them, Flint, and scatter them, will you not? Sting them with poison; and when they try to seize me, knock them down with your heart, will you not?"

"Oh, Christ! what a sight is this!" burst from me, as I sank back into the chair from which I had risen, faint with agony. The lunatic started as I spoke, and probably something like recollection lighted up his brain for a moment. He cast a fierce look at me:

"Do you like it?" he said, with a grim smile; "it is of your own doing. You placed me in a mad-house. I was not mad; but when I woke, and breathed *that* air, and heard the sounds, and saw what is to be seen *there*— Oh, now I am mad! Curse you! it is your work. Curse you! Curse you!"

I clapped my hands to my ears, to keep out the appalling sounds that seemed to freeze my very blood. When I took them away, I heard the noise of the street door opening, and my children's voices sounding loud and happily. Their maniac brother heard them also. He sprang to the window.

"Hark!" he said; "they are after me, Flint. Keep them back. Rather than go there again, I would jump into a raging furnace of fire!" He glided swiftly into the garden, and I heard his voice in the distance. I did not move, for every nerve seemed paralyzed.

"Keep them back, Flint! It is all your work! Curse you!"

When my family came into the apartment, they found me in a deep swoon, which I fully recovered from only at the end of many minutes.

My incoherent story, the night, and the strangeness of the whole affair, prevented any pursuit that evening, though Alban would have started on one, if he had had any assistance or clue. The next morning, the officers of the asylum came in search of the runaway. He had contrived a most cunning plan of escape, and his departure was not found out till day-light.

My story is nearly ended. We never saw or heard of the hapless Luke more. Search was extensively made, and kept up for a long time; but no tidings were elicited of his fate. Alban was the most persevering of those who continued the task, even when it became hopeless. He inserted advertisements in the newspapers, sent emissaries all over the country, had handbills widely distributed, offering a large reward; but all to no purpose. The doom, whatever it was, of the wretched young man, is shrouded in a mantle of uncertainty as black as the veil of the outer darkness in which his form had disappeared on that last memorable night; and in all likelihood it will now never be known to mortal.

A great many years have gone by since these events. To the eyes of men, my life and feelings have seemed in no respect different from those of thousands of others. I have mixed with company—laughed and talked— eaten and drunk; and, now that the allotted term is closing, must prepare to lay myself in the grave. I say I have lived many years since then, and have laughed and talked. Let no one suppose, however, that time has banished the phantoms of my busy thoughts, and allowed me to be happy. Down in the inward chamber of my soul there has been a mirror—large, and very bright. It has pictured, for the last thirty years, a shape, wild and haggard, and with tangly hair—the shape of my maniac son. Often, in the midst of society, in the public street, at my own table, and in the silent watches of the night, that picture stands out in glaring brightness; and, without a tongue, tells me that it is all my work, and repeats that terrible cursing which, the last time the tyrant and victim stood face to face together, rang from the lips of the Son, and fell like a knell of death on the ear of the Father.

The Tomb Blossoms[1]

A PLEASANT, fair-sized country village—a village embosomed in trees, with old churches, one[2] tavern, kept by a respectable widow—long, single-storied farm-houses, their roofs mossy, and their chimneys smoke black—a village with much grass and shrubbery, and no mortar, no bricks, no pavements, no gas—no newness![3] that is the place for him who wishes life in its flavor and in its bloom. Until of late, my residence has been in such a spot.[4]

Men of cities! what is there in all your boasted pleasure—your fashions, parties, balls, and theatres, compared to the simplest of the delights we country folk enjoy? Our pure air making the blood leap with buoyant health; our labor and our exercise; our freedom from the sickly vices that taint the town; our not being racked with notes due, or the fluctuations of prices, or the breaking of banks; our manners of sociality, expanding the heart, and reacting with a wholesome effect upon the body; can any thing,[5] which citizens possess, balance these?

One Saturday, after paying a few days' visit to[6] New-York, I returned to my quarters at[7] the country inn. The day was hot, and my journey a disagreeable one.[8] Out of humor with myself and every thing[9] around me, when I came to my travel's end, I refused to partake of the comfortable supper which my landlady had prepared for me; and returning the good

---

1. The text followed here is that which appeared in *Voices from the Press; A Collection of Sketches, Essays, and Poems*, by practical printers, ed. by James J. Brenton (New York, Charles B. Norton, 1850). James Brenton was the editor of the *Long Island Democrat*, Jamaica, Long Island, and a former employer of Whitman. A number of Whitman's poems and essays were printed in Brenton's newspaper in 1838, 1839, and 1840 (see Allen, p. 548, note 108). In "Notices of Contributors" to *Voices from the Press* the following is said of Whitman:

> Whitman, Walter, was born at West Hills, in the town of Huntington, L. I. At the age of thirteen he was placed an apprentice to the printing business in the office of the "Patriot," a weekly paper then published in Brooklyn. The establishment passing into other hands, he found himself, at the age of sixteen, teaching school on Long Island. He continued in this occupation three or four years, intermitted only by establishing the "Long Islander," at Huntington, L. I., which he sold out at the end of the first year. While teaching a school near Jamaica, he wrote a sketch entitled "Death in a School Room," for the purpose of making odious the use of the rod in the school. It was published originally in the "Democratic Review," and was very popular.
> Mr. W.'s literary career commenced with sketches of that character, in the "Democratic Review," "American Review," and other periodicals. He soon, however, became connected with the press, and edited the "Aurora," "Sunday Times," "Brooklyn Eagle," and "New Orleans Crescent." Mr. W. is

woman's look of wonder at such an unwonted event, and her kind inquiries about my health, with a sullen silence I took my lamp, and went my way to my room. Tired and head throbbing, in less than a score[10] of minutes after I threw myself upon my bed, I was steeped in the soundest slumber.

When I awoke, every vein and nerve felt fresh and free. Soreness and irritation had been swept away, as it were, with the curtains of the night; and the accustomed tone had returned again. I arose and threw open my window. Delicious! It was a calm, bright Sabbath morning in May. The dew drops glittered on the grass; the fragrance of the apple blossoms, which covered the trees, floated up to me; and the notes of a hundred birds discoursed music to my ear. By the rays just shooting up in the eastern verge, I knew that the sun would be risen in a moment. I hastily dressed myself, performed my ablutions, and sallied forth to take a morning walk.

Sweet, yet simple[11] scene! No one seemed stirring. The placid influence of the day was even now spread around, quieting every thing,[12] and hallowing every thing.[13] I sauntered slowly onward, with my hands folded behind me. I passed round the edge of a hill, on the rising elevation and top of which was the burial ground. On my left, through an opening in the trees, I could see at some distance the ripples of our beautiful bay; on my right, was the large ancient field for the dead. I stopped and leaned my back against the fence, with my face turned toward the white marble stones a few rods before me. All I saw was far from new to me; and yet I pondered upon it. The entrance to that place of tombs was a kind of arch—a rough-hewn and hardy piece of architecture, that had stood winter and summer over the

an ardent politician of the radical democratic school, and lately established the "Daily Freeman," in Brooklyn, to promulgate his favorite "Free Soil" and other reformatory doctrines.

"The Tomb Blossoms" originally appeared in the *Democratic Review*, January 1842. The *Voices from the Press* version eliminates considerable capitalization, alters punctuation (not always happily), and divides one overlong paragraph. In addition, the later version omits some phrases and changes some of the wording of the original text. The verbal variants of the *Democratic* version are given in the footnotes that follow.

2. *one*
3. and no mortar, nor bricks, nor pavements, nor gas—no *newness:*
4. in such a place.   5. anything   6. at   7. in
8. In the original, the following lines intervene between this sentence and the next: "I had been forced to stir myself beyond comfort, and despatch my affairs quickly, for fear of being left by the cars. As it was, I arrived panting and covered with sweat, just as they were about to start. Then for many miles I had to bear the annoyance of the steam-engine smoke; and it seemed to me that the vehicles kept swaying to and fro on the track, with a more than usual motion, on purpose to distress my jaded limbs."
9. everything   10. half a score   11. Sweet, yet sleepy
12. everything   13. everything.

gate there, for many years.[14] O! fearful arch! if there were for thee a voice to utter what has passed beneath and near thee—if the secrets of the earthy dwelling that to thee are known could be disclosed—whose ear might listen to the appalling story and its possessor not go mad with terror?

Thus thought I; and strange enough, such imagining marred not in the least the sunny brightness which spread alike over my mind and over the landscape. Involuntarily as I mused, my look was cast to the top of the hill. I saw a figure moving. Could some one beside myself be out so early, and among the tombs? What creature odd enough in fancy to find pleasure there, and at such a time? Continuing my gaze, I saw that the figure was a woman.

She seemed to move with a slow and a feeble step, passing and repass-ing constantly between two and the same graves, which were within half a rod of each other. She would bend down and appear to busy herself a few moments with the one; then she would rise and go to the second, and bend there and employ herself as at the first. Then to the former one, and then to the second again. Occasionally the shape[15] would pause a moment, and stand back a little, and look steadfastly down upon the graves, as if to see whether her work were done well. Thrice I saw her walk with a tottering gait, and stand midway between the two, and look alternately at each. Then she would go to one and arrange something, and come back to the midway place, and gaze first on the right and then on the left, as before. The figure evidently had some trouble to arrange things[16] to her mind. Where I stood I could hear no noise of her foot-fall;[17] nor could I see accu-rately enough to tell what she was doing. Had a superstitious man beheld the spectacle, he would possibly have thought that some spirit of the dead, allowed the night before to burst its cerements, and wander forth in the darkness, had been belated in returning, and was now perplexed to find its coffin-house again.

Curious to know the woman's employment,[18] I undid the simple fasten-ings of the gate, and walked over the rank wet grass towards her. As I came near I recognized her for an old, a very old inmate of the poor-house, named Delaree. Stopping a moment, while I was yet several yards from her, and before she saw me, I tried to call to recollection certain particulars of her history which I had heard a great while past. She was a native of one of the West India Islands, and, before I who gazed at her was born, had, with her husband, come hither to settle and gain a livelihood. They were

14. for many, many years.   15. the figure
16. in suiting things   17. footfalls
18. Curious to know what was the woman's employment,
19. their destitute abode

poor, most miserably poor. Country people, I have noticed, seldom like foreigners. So this man and his wife, in all probability, met much to discourage them. They kept up their spirits, however, until at last their fortunes became desperate. Famine and want laid iron fingers upon them. They had no acquaintance; and to beg they were ashamed. Both were taken ill; then the charity that had been so slack came to their abode,[19] but came too late. Delaree died, the victim of poverty. The woman recovered after awhile; but for many months was quite an invalid, and was sent to the alms-house, where she had ever since remained.

This was the story of the aged creature before me; aged with the weight of seventy winters. I walked up to her. By her feet stood a large rude basket, in which I beheld leaves and buds. The two graves which I had seen her passing between so often were covered with flowers—the earliest but sweetest flowers of the season. They were fresh, and wet, and very fragrant—those soul-offerings.[20] And this, then, was her employment.[21] Flowers frail and passing, grasped by the hand of age, and scattered upon a tomb! White hairs and pale blossoms, and stone tablets of Death!

"Good morning, mistress," said I, quietly.

The withered female turned her eyes to mine and acknowledged my greeting in the same spirit wherewith it was given.

"May I ask whose graves they are that you remember so kindly?"

She looked up again—probably catching, from my manner, that I spoke in no spirit of rude inquisitiveness—and answered:

"My husband's."

A manifestation of fanciful taste, thought I, this tomb-ornamenting, which she probably brought with her from abroad. Of course but one of the graves could be her husband's; and one, likely, was that of a child, who had died and been placed[22] by its father.

"Whose else?" I asked.

"My husband's," replied the aged widow.

Poor creature! her faculties were becoming dim. No doubt her sorrows and her length of life had worn both mind and body nearly to the parting.

"Yes, I know," continued I, mildly: "but there are two graves. One is your husband's and the other is—"

I paused for her to fill the blank.

She looked at me for a minute, as if in wonder at my perverseness; and then answered as before.

20. those delicate soul-offerings.
21. This sentence is followed in the original by the following exclamation: "Strange!"
22. and been laid away

"My husband's. None but Gilbert's."[23]

"And is Gilbert buried in both?" said I.

She appeared as if going to answer, but stopped again, and did not. Though my curiosity was now somewhat excited, I forebore to question her farther,[24] feeling that it might be to her a painful subject. I was wrong, however. She had been rather agitated at my intrusion, and her powers flickered for a moment. They were soon steady again, and, perhaps gratified with my interest in her affairs, she gave me in a few brief sentences the solution of the mystery. When her husband's death occurred, she was herself confined to a sick bed, which she did not leave for a long while after he was buried. Still longer days passed before she had permission, or even strength, to go into the open air. When she did, her first efforts were essayed to reach Gilbert's grave. What a pang sunk to her heart when she found it could not be pointed out to her! With the careless indifference which is shown to the corpses of outcasts, poor Delaree had been thrown into a hastily dug hole, without any one noting it, or remembering which it was. Subsequently, several other paupers were buried in the same spot; and the sexton could only show two graves to the disconsolate woman, and tell her that her husband's was positively one of the twain. During the latter stages of her recovery she had looked forward to the consolation of coming to his tomb as to a shrine, and wiping her tears there; and it was bitter that such could not be. The miserable widow even attempted to obtain the consent of the proper functionaries that the graves might be opened, and her anxieties put at rest! When told that this could not be done, she determined in her soul that at least the remnant of her hopes and intentions should not be given up. Every Sunday morning, in the mild seasons, she went forth early, and gathered fresh flowers, and dressed both[25] the graves. So she knew that the right one was cared for, even if another shared that care. And lest she should possibly bestow the most of this testimony of love on him whom she knew not, but whose spirit might be looking down invisible in the air, and smiling upon her, she was ever careful to have each tomb adorned in an exactly similar manner. In a strange land, and among a strange race, she said, it was like communion with her own people to visit that burial-ground.[26]

"If I could only know which to bend over when my heart feels heavy," thus finished the sorrowing being as she rose to depart, "then it would be a happiness. But, perhaps, I am blind to my dearest mercies. God, in his great wisdom, may have sent that I cannot be sure[27] which grave was his,

---

23. "my Gilbert's"   24. further   25. *both*   26. burial-mound.
27. "may have sent that I should not know"

lest grief over it should become too common a luxury for me, and melt me away."

I offered to accompany her, and support her feeble steps; but she preferred that it should not be so. With languid feet she moved on. I watched her pass through the gate and under the arch; I saw her turn, and in a little while she was hidden from my view. Then I carefully parted the flowers upon one of the graves, and sat down there, and leaned my face in my open hands and thought—

What a wondrous thing is human love![28] Oh! Thou whose mighty attribute is the incarnation of love, I bless Thee that Thou didst make this fair disposition in our hearts,[29] and didst root it there so deeply that it is stronger than all else, and can never be torn out! Here is this aged wayfarer—a woman of trials and griefs—decrepid,[30] sore, and steeped in poverty—the most forlorn of her kind, and yet, through all the storms[31] of misfortune, and the dark cloud of years settling upon her, the memory of her love hovers like a beautiful spirit amid the gloom, and never deserts her, but abides with her while life abides. Yes! this[32] creature loved; this wrinkled, skinny, gray-haired crone had her heart to swell with passion, and her pulses to throb, and her eyes to sparkle. Now, nothing remains but a lovely remembrance, coming as of old, and stepping in its accustomed path, not to perform its former object, or its former duty—but from long habit. Nothing[33] but that! Ah! is not that a great deal?

And the buried man—he was happy to have passed away as he did. The woman—she was the one to be pitied. Without doubt she wished many times that she were laid beside him. And not only she, thought I, as I cast my eyes on the solemn memorials around me: but at the same time there were thousands else on earth who panted for the long repose, as a tired child for the night. The grave—the grave. What foolish man calls it a dreadful place? It is a kind friend, whose arms shall compass us round about, and while we lay our heads upon his bosom, no care, temptation nor corroding passion shall have power to disturb us. Then the weary spirit shall no more be weary; the aching head and aching heart will be strangers to pain; and the soul that has fretted and sorrowed away its little life on earth will sorrow not any more. When the mind has been roaming abroad in the crowd, and returns sick and tired of hollow hearts, and of human deceit—let us think of the grave and death, and they will seem like soft and pleasant music. Such thoughts then soothe and calm our pulses; they open a peaceful prospect before us.

28. woman's love!   29. in the human heart   30. decrepit
31. storm   32. *this*   33. *Nothing*

There have of late frequently come to me times when I do not dread the grave—when I could lie down, and pass my immortal part through the valley and shadow,[34] as composedly as I quaff water after a tiresome walk. For what is there of terror in taking our rest? What is there here below to draw us with such fondness? Life is the running of a race—a most weary race, sometimes. Shall we fear the goal, merely because it is shrouded in a cloud?

I rose, and carefully replaced the parted flowers, and bent my steps homewards.

If there be any sufficiently interested in the fate of the aged woman, that they wish to know farther[35] about her, for those I will add that ere long her affection was transferred to a region where it might receive the reward of its constancy and purity. Her last desire, and it was complied with—was that she should be placed midway between the two graves.

34. This opening portion of this sentence is rendered in the following fashion in the original: "I do not dread the grave. There is many a time when I could lay down, and pass my immortal part through the valley of the shadow,"

35. further

The Last of the Sacred Army[1]

THE memory of the WARRIORS of our FREEDOM!—let us guard it with a holy care. Let the mighty pulse which throbs responsive in a nation's heart at utterance of that nation's names of glory, never lie languid when their deeds are told or their example cited. To him of the Calm Gray Eye, selected by the Leader of the Ranks of Heaven as the instrument for a people's redemption;—to him, the bright and brave, who fell in the attack at Breed's;—to him, the nimble-footed soldier of the swamps of Santee;—to the young stranger from the luxuries of his native France;—to all who fought in that long weary fight for disenthralment from arbitrary rule—may our star fade, and our good angel smile upon us no more, if we fail to chamber them in our hearts, or forget the method of their dear-won honor!

For the fame of these is not as the fame of common heroes. The mere gaining of battles—the chasing away of an opposing force—wielding the great energies of bodies of military—rising proudly amid the smoke and din of the fight—and marching the haughty march of a conqueror,—all this, spirit-stirring as it may be to the world, would fail to command the applause of the just and discriminating. But such is not the base whereon American warriors found their title to renown. *Our* storied names are those of the Soldiers of Liberty; hardy souls, incased in hardy bodies—untainted with the effeminacy of voluptuous cities, patient, enduring much for principle's sake, and wending on through blood, disease, destitution, and prospects of gloom, to attain the Great Treasure.

Years have passed; the sword-clash and the thundering of the guns have died away; and all personal knowledge of those events—of the fierce incentives to hate, and the wounds, and scorn, and the curses from the injured, and the wailings from the prisons—lives now but in the memory of a few score gray-haired men; whose number is, season after season, made thinner and thinner by death. Haply, long, long will be the period ere our beloved country shall witness the presence of such or similar scenes again. Haply, too, the time is arriving when War, with all its train of sanguinary horrors, will be a discarded custom among the nations of earth. A newer and better philosophy—teaching how evil it is to hew down and slay ranks of fellow-men, because of some disagreement between their respective rulers—is

1. "The Last of the Sacred Army" first appeared in the *Democratic Review*, March 1842, and was reprinted without change in the same journal, November 1851. The reader will recognize it, however, with some dismay, in a transmuted form as the dream episode in Chapter XX of *Franklin Evans.*

melting away old prejudices upon this subject, as warmth in spring melts the frigid ground.

The lover of his race—did he not, looking abroad in the world, see millions whose swelling hearts are all crushed into the dust beneath the iron heel of oppression; did he not behold how kingcraft and priestcraft stalk abroad over fair portions of the globe, and forge the chain, and rivet the yoke; and did he not feel that it were better to live in one flaming atmosphere of carnage than slavishly thus—would offer up nightly prayers that this new philosophy might prevail to the utmost, and the reign of peace never more be disturbed among mankind.

On one of the anniversaries of our national independence, I was staying at the house of an old farmer, about a mile from a thriving country town, whose inhabitants were keeping up the spirit of the occasion with great fervor. The old man himself was a thumping patriot. Early in the morning, my slumbers had been broken by the sharp crack of his ancient musket, (I looked upon that musket with reverence, for it had seen service in *the* war,) firing salutes in honor of the day. I am free to confess, my military propensities were far from strong enough (appropriate as they might have been considered at such a time) to suppress certain peevish exclamations toward the disturber of my sweet repose. In the course of the forenoon, I attended the ceremonials observed in the village; sat, during the usual patriotic address, on the same bench with a time-worn veteran that had fought in the contest now commemorated; witnessed the evolutions of the uniform company; and returned home with a most excellent appetite for my dinner.

The afternoon was warm and drowsy. I ensconced myself in my easy-chair, near an open window; feeling in that most blissful state of semi-somnolency, which it is now and then, though rarely, given to mortals to enjoy. I was alone, the family of my host having gone on some visit to a neighbor. The bees hummed in the garden, and among the flowers that clustered over the window frame; a sleepy influence seemed to imbue everything around; occasionally the faint sound of some random gun-fire from the village would float along, or the just perceptible music of the band, or the tra-a-a-ra of a locust. But these were far from being jars to the quiet spirit I have mentioned.

Insensibly, my consciousness became less and less distinct; my head leaned back; my eyes closed; and my senses relaxed from their waking vigilance. I slept.

* * * How strange a chaos is sometimes the outset to a dream!— There was the pulpit of the rude church, the scene of the oration—and in it a grotesque form whom I had noticed as the drummer in the band, beating away as though calling scattered forces to the rescue. Then the speaker of

the day pitched coppers with some unshorn hostler boys; and the grave personage who had opened the services with prayer, was half stripped and running a foot-race with a tavern loafer. The places and the persons familiar to my morning excursion about the country town, appeared as in life; but in situations all fantastic and out of the way.

After a while, what I beheld began to reduce itself to more method. With the singular characteristic of dreams, I knew—I could not tell how—that thirty years elapsed from the then time, and I was among a new generation. Beings by me never seen before, and some with shrivelled forms, bearing an odd resemblance to men whom I had known in the bloom of manhood, met my eyes.

Methought I stood in a splendid city. It seemed a gala day. Crowds of people were swiftly wending along the streets and walks, as if to behold some great spectacle or famous leader.

"Whither do the people go?" said I to a Shape who passed me, hurrying on with the rest.

"Know you not," answered he, "that the Last of the Sacred Army may be seen to-day?"

And he hastened forward, apparently fearful lest he might be late.

Among the dense ranks, I noticed many women, some of them with infants in their arms. Then there were boys, beautiful creatures, struggling on, with a more intense desire even than the men. And as I looked up, I saw at some distance, coming toward the place where I stood, a troop of young females, the foremost one bearing a wreath of fresh flowers. The crowd pulled and pushed so violently, that this party of girls were sundered from one another, and she who carried the wreath being jostled, her flowers were trampled to the ground.

"O, hapless me!" cried the child; and she began to weep.

At that moment, her companions came up; and they looked frowningly when they saw the wreath torn.

"Do not grieve, gentle one," said I to the weeping child. "And you," turning to the others, "blame her not. There bloom more flowers, as fair and fragrant as those which lie rent beneath your feet."

"No," said one of the little troop, "it is now too late."

"What mean you?" I asked.

The children looked at me in wonder.

"For whom did you intend the wreath?" continued I.

"Heard you not," rejoined one of them, "that to-day may be seen the Last of *His* Witnesses? We were on our way to present this lovely wreath—and she who should give it, was to say, that fresh and sweet, like it, would ever be His memory in the souls of us, and of our countrymen."

And the children walked on.

Yielding myself passively to the sway of the current, which yet continued to flow in one huge human stream, I was carried through street after street, and along many a stately passage, the sides of which were lined by palace-like houses. After a time, we came to a large open square, which seemed to be the destination—for there the people stopped. At the further end of this square stood a magnificent building, evidently intended for public purposes; and in front of it a wide marble elevation, half platform and half porch. Upon this elevation were a great many persons, all of them in standing postures, except one, an aged, very aged man, seated in a throne-like chair. His figure and face showed him to be of a length of years seldom vouchsafed to his kind; and his head was thinly covered with hair of a silvery whiteness.

Now, near me stood one whom I knew to be a learned philosopher; and to him I addressed myself for an explanation of these wonderful things.

"Tell me," said I, "who is the ancient being seated on yonder platform."

The person to whom I spoke stared in my face surprisedly.

"Are you of this land," said he, "and have not heard of him—the Last of the Sacred Army?"

"I am ignorant," answered I, "of whom you speak, or of what Army."

The philosopher stared a second time; but soon, when I assured him I was not jesting, he began telling me of former times, and how it came to be that this white-haired remnant of a past age was the object of so much honor. Nor was the story new to me—as may it never be to any son of America.

We edged our way close to the platform. Immediately around the seat of the ancient soldier stood many noble-looking gentlemen, evidently of dignified character and exalted station. As I came near, I heard them mention a *name*—that name which is dearest to our memories as patriots.

"And you saw the Chief with your own eyes?" said one of the gentlemen.

"I did," answered the old warrior.

And the crowd were hushed, and bent reverently, as if in a holy presence.

"I would," said another gentleman, "I would you had some relic which might be as a chain leading from our hearts to his."

"I have such a relic," replied the aged creature; and with trembling fingers he took from his bosom a rude medal, suspended round his neck by a string. "This the Chief gave me," continued he, "to mark his good-will for some slight service I did The Cause."

"And has it been in *his* hands?" asked the crowd, eagerly.

"Himself hung it around my neck," said the veteran.

Then the mighty mass was hushed again, and there was no noise— but a straining of fixed eyes, and a throbbing of hearts, and cheeks pale with excitement—such excitement as might be caused in a man's soul by some sacred memorial of one he honored and loved deeply.

Upon the medal were the letters "G. W."

"Speak to us of him, and of his time," said the crowd.

A few words the old man uttered; but few and rambling as they were, the people listened as to the accents of an oracle.

Then it was time for him to stay there no longer. So he rose, assisted by such of the bystanders whose rank and reputation gave them a right to the honor, and slowly descended. The mass divided, to form a passage for him and his escort, and they passed forward. And as he passed, the young boys struggled to him, that they might take his hand, or touch his garments. The women, too, brought their infants, to be placed for a moment in his arms; and every head was uncovered.

I noticed that there was little shouting, or clapping of hands—but a deep-felt sentiment of veneration seemed to pervade them, far more honorable to its object than the loudest acclamations.

In a short time, as the white-haired ancient was out of sight, the square was cleared, and I stood in it with no companion but the philosopher.

"Is it well," said I, "that such reverence be bestowed by a great people on a creature like themselves? The self-respect each one has for his own nature might run the risk of effacement, were such things often seen. Besides, it is not allowed that man pay worship to his fellow."

"Fear not," answered the philosopher; "the occurrences you have just witnessed spring from the fairest and manliest traits in the soul. Nothing more becomes a nation than paying its choicest honors to the memory of those who have fought for it, or labored for its good. By thus often bringing up their examples before the eyes of the living, others are incited to follow in the same glorious path. Do not suppose, young man, that it is by sermons and oft-repeated precepts we form a disposition great or good. The model of one pure, upright character, living as a beacon in history, does more benefit than the lumbering tomes of a thousand theorists.

"No: it is well that the benefactors of a state be so kept alive in memory and in song, when their bodies are mouldering. Then will it be impossible for a people to become enslaved; for though the strong arm of their old defender come not as formerly to the battle, his spirit is there, through the power of remembrance, and wields a better sway even than if it were of fleshly substance."

* * * The words of the philosopher sounded indistinctly to my ears

—and his features faded, as in a mist. I awoke; and looking through the window, saw that the sun had just sunk in the west—two hours having passed away since the commencement of my afternoon slumber.

The Last Loyalist[1]

"She came to me last night,
The floor gave back no tread."

THE story I am going to tell is a traditional reminiscence of a country place, in my rambles about which I have often passed the house, now unoccupied, and mostly in ruins, that was the scene of the transaction.[2] I cannot, of course, convey to others that particular kind of influence which is derived from my being so familiar with the locality, and with the very people whose grandfathers or fathers were contemporaries of the actors in the drama I shall transcribe. I must hardly expect, therefore, that to those who hear it thro'[3] the medium of my pen, the narration will possess as life-like and interesting a character as it does to myself.

On a large and fertile neck of land that juts out in the Sound, stretching to the east[4] of New York city, there stood, in the latter part of the last century, an old-fashion'd country-residence. It had been built by one of the first settlers of this section of the New World; and its occupant was originally owner of the extensive tract lying adjacent to his house, and pushing into the bosom[5] of the salt waters. It was during the troubled times which mark'd our American Revolution that the incidents oc-

1. The text followed here is that of *Collect*. The tale first appeared under the title of "The Child-Ghost; a Story of the Last Loyalist" in the *Democratic Review* for May 1842. As usual, the later version elides the "e" in the past forms of most regular verbs and makes some minor changes in punctuation and paragraphing. In addition, the later version omits some passages, chiefly Macbethean or chauvinistic, and alters some of the wording of the original text. The important variants of the *Democratic* version appear in the footnotes that follow.

2. In the original version, this sentence introduces the second paragraph, which is preceded by the following opening paragraph:

Were it not from the evidence of my own ears and observation, I could hardly believe that any considerable number of persons exist among us, who give credence to accounts of spectres and disembodied spirits appearing from the dead;—yet there are many such people, especially in our country places. Though the schools are gradually thrusting aside these superstitious relics of a by-gone time, it will perhaps be long before their influence is effectually rooted out. Guilt or ignorance, working through imagination, has magic power; and the ideal forms through which terror is thus stricken, produces a panic in the minds of their victims, as real as if those forms were of perceptible substance.

3. through

4. which stretches to the south-east   5. the very bosom

curr'd which are the foundation of my story. Some time before the commencement of the war, the owner, whom I shall call Vanhome, was taken sick and died. For some time before his death he had lived a widower; and his only child,[6] a lad of ten years old, was thus left an orphan. By his father's will this child was placed implicitly under the guardianship of an uncle, a middle-aged man, who had been of late a resident in the family. His care and interest, however, were needed but a little while —not two years elaps'd[7] after the parents were laid away to their last repose before another grave had to be prepared for the son—the child[8] who had been so haplessly deprived of their fostering care.

The period now arrived when the great national convulsion burst forth. Sounds of strife and the clash of arms, and the angry voices of disputants, were borne along by the air, and week after week grew to still louder[9] clamor. Families were divided; adherents to the crown, and ardent upholders of the rebellion, were often found in the bosom of the same domestic circle. Vanhome, the uncle spoken of as guardian to the young heir, was a man who lean'd to the stern, the high-handed and the severe. He soon became known among the most energetic of the loyalists. So decided[10] were his sentiments that, leaving the estate which he had inherited[11] from his brother and nephew, he join'd the forces of the British king. Thenceforward, whenever his old neighbors heard of him, it was as being engaged in the cruelest outrages, the boldest inroads, or the most determin'd attacks upon the army of his countrymen or their peaceful settlements.[12]

Eight years brought the rebel States and their leaders to that glorious epoch when the last remnant of a monarch's rule was to leave their shores —when the last waving of the royal standard was to flutter as it should be haul'd down from the staff, and its place fill'd by the proud testimonial of our warriors' success.

Pleasantly over the autumn fields shone the November sun, when a horseman, of somewhat military look, plodded slowly along the road that led to the old Vanhome farmhouse. There was nothing peculiar in his attire, unless it might be a red scarf which he wore tied round his waist. He was a dark-featured, sullen-eyed man; and as his glance was thrown rest-

6. and his child, an only one
7. In the original version, this sentence opens in the following fashion: "As if to verify the truth of the ancient proverb, which declares that evils, when once started on their path, follow each other thick and fast—not two years elapsed"
8. the fair and lovely child   9. to louder and still louder
10. So violent   11. had so fortunately inherited
12. At this point in the original version, this paragraph follows:

lessly to the right and left, his whole manner appear'd to be that of a person moving amid familiar and accustom'd scenes. Occasionally he stopp'd, and looking long and steadily at some object that attracted his attention, mutter'd to himself, like one in whose breast busy thoughts were moving. His course was evidently to the homestead itself, at which in due time he arrived. He dismounted, led his horse to the stables, and then, without knocking, though there were evident signs of occupancy around the building, the traveler made his entrance as composedly and boldly as though he were master of the whole establishment.

Now the house being in a measure deserted for many years,[13] and the successful termination of the strife rendering it probable that the Vanhome estate would be confiscated to the new government, an aged, poverty-stricken couple had been encouraged by the neighbors to take possession as tenants of the place. Their name was Gills; and these people the traveler found upon his entrance were likely to be his host and hostess. Holding their right as they did by so slight a tenure, they ventur'd to offer no opposition when the stranger signified his intention of passing several hours there.

The day wore on, and the sun went down in the west; still the interloper, gloomy and taciturn,[14] made no signs of departing. But as the evening advanced[15] (whether the darkness was congenial to his sombre thoughts, or whether it merely chanced so) he seem'd to grow more affable and communicative,[16] and informed Gills that he should pass the night there, tendering him at the same time ample remuneration, which the latter accepted with many thanks.

"Tell me," said he to his aged host, when they were all sitting around the ample hearth, at the conclusion of their evening meal, "tell me something to while away the hours."

"Ah! sir," answered Gills, "this is no place for new or interesting events.[17] We live here from year to year, and at the end of one we find ourselves at about the same place which we filled in the beginning."

"Can you relate nothing, then?" rejoin'd the guest, and a singular smile pass'd over his features; "can you say nothing about your own place?—this house or its former inhabitants, or former history?"

Though pleasant for an American mind to dwell upon the traits,—the unshaken patriotism, the lofty courage, and the broad love of liberty exhibited by our fathers in their memorable struggle, I shall pass over the relation.

13. Now it happened that the house being in a measure deserted for many years
14. These two adjectives do not appear in the earlier text.
15. But as the night fell
16. The rest of the sentence past this point does not appear in the original.
17. "events to happen."

The old man glanced across to his wife, and a look expressive of sympathetic feeling started in the face of each.

"It is an unfortunate story, sir," said Gills, "and may cast a chill upon you, instead of the pleasant feeling which it would be best to foster when in strange walls."

"Strange walls!" echoed he of the red scarf, and for the first time since his arrival he half laughed, but it was not the laugh which comes from a man's heart.

"You must know, sir," continued Gills, "I am myself a sort of intruder here. The Vanhomes—that was the name of the former residents and owners—I have never seen; for when I came to these parts the last occupant[18] had left to join the red-coat soldiery. I am told that he is to sail with them for foreign lands, now that the war is ended, and his property almost certain to pass into other hands."

As the old man went on, the stranger cast down his eyes, and listen'd with an appearance of great interest, though a transient smile or a brightening of the eye would occasionally disturb the serenity of his deportment.

"The old owners[19] of this place," continued the white-haired narrator, "were well off in the world, and bore a good name among their neighbors. The brother of Sergeant Vanhome, now the only one of the name, died ten or twelve years since, leaving a son—a child so small that the father's will made provision for his being brought up by his uncle, whom I mention'd but now as of the British army. He was a strange man, this uncle; disliked by all who knew him; passionate, vindictive, and, it was said, very avaricious, even from his childhood.

"Well, not long after the death of the parents, dark stories began to be circulated about cruelty and punishment and whippings and starvation inflicted by the new master upon his nephew. People who had business at the homestead would frequently, when they came away, relate the most fearful things of its manager, and how he misused his brother's child. It was half hinted that he strove to get the youngster out of the way in order that the whole estate might fall into his own hands. As I told you before, however, nobody liked the man; and perhaps they judged him too uncharitably.

"After things had gone on in this way for some time, a countryman, a

18. "the last Mr. Vanhome"
19. "The old occupants"
20. In the original version, the next sentence begins a new paragraph.
21. "tired and sleepy"   22. "whacking sound"
23. "the succeeding night"
24. "which at that time were beginning"

laborer, who was hired to do farm-work upon the place, one evening observed that the little orphan Vanhome was more faint and pale even than usual, for he was always delicate, and that is one reason why I think it possible that his death, of which I am now going to tell you, was but the result of his own weak constitution, and nothing else.[20] The laborer slept that night at the farmhouse. Just before the time at which they usually retired to bed, this person, feeling sleepy[21] with his day's toil, left the kitchen hearth and wended his way to rest. In going to his place of repose he had to pass a chamber—the very chamber where you, sir, are to sleep to-night—and there he heard the voice of the orphan child uttering half-suppress'd exclamations as if in pitiful entreaty. Upon stopping, he heard also the tones of the elder Vanhome, but they were harsh and bitter. The sound[22] of blows followed. As each one fell it was accompanied by a groan or shriek, and so they continued for some time. Shock'd and indignant, the countryman would have burst open the door and interfered to prevent this brutal proceeding, but he bethought him that he might get himself into trouble, and perhaps find that he could do no good after all, and so he passed on to his room.

"Well, sir, the following day the child did not come out among the work-people as usual. He was taken very ill. No physician was sent for until the next afternoon; and though one arrived in the course of the night,[23] it was too late—the poor boy died before morning.

"People talk'd threateningly upon the subject, but nothing could be proved against Vanhome. At one period there were efforts made to have the whole affair investigated. Perhaps that would have taken place, had not every one's attention been swallow'd up by the rumors of difficulty and war, which were then beginning[24] to disturb the country.

"Vanhome joined the army of the king. His enemies said that he feared to be on the side of the rebels, because if they were routed his property would be taken from him. But events have shown that, if this was indeed what he dreaded, it has happen'd to him from the very means which he took to prevent it."

The old man paused. He had quite wearied himself with so long talking. For some minutes there was unbroken silence.[25]

Presently the stranger signified his intention of retiring for the night.

25. In the original version, this paragraph is succeeded by the following:
   "Did you say that Vanhome had left this land and sailed for Europe?" at length asked the stranger; who, when Gills concluded, had raised his face, pale, and with eyes glittering like one in great perturbation.
   "So we hear," returned the old man.
   Again there was silence, which no one seemed inclined to break.

He rose, and his host took a light for the purpose of ushering him to his apartment.[26]

When Gills return'd to his accustom'd situation in the large arm-chair by the chimney hearth, his ancient helpmate had retired to rest. With the simplicity of their times, the bed stood in the same room where the three had been seated during the last few hours; and now the remaining two talk'd together about the singular events of the evening. As the time wore on, Gills show'd no disposition to leave his cosy chair; but sat toasting his feet, and bending over the coals.[27] Gradually the insidious heat and the lateness of the hour began to exercise their influence over the old man. The[28] drowsy indolent feeling which every one has experienced in getting thoroughly heated through by close contact with a glowing fire, spread in each vein and sinew, and relax'd its tone. He lean'd back in his chair and slept.

For a long time his repose went on quietly and soundly. He could not tell how many hours elapsed; but, a while after midnight, the torpid senses of the slumberer were awaken'd by a startling shock. It was a cry as of a strong man in his agony—a shrill, not very loud cry, but fearful, and

26. This paragraph is followed, in the original text, by this scene:

"What of this chamber which you mentioned?" said the traveller, pausing as he stood with his back to the fire, and looking not into the face of the old man, but as it were into vacancy.

The host started, and it was evident the question had awakened agitating thoughts in his mind; for his face blanched a little, and his glance turned feverishly from object to object.

"It is said," answered he, in a low stealthy tone, "that the spirit of the little orphan child haunts that chamber in the silent hours of night!"

The stranger wheeled, and looked full into the face of the speaker. A convulsive spasm passed over his features, and from his eyes came the flashing of condensed rage and hideous terror.

"Hell!" uttered he, furiously, "am I to be taunted by ghosts, and placed amid the spectres of puling brats? Find me, hoary thief!—find me some other sleeping place; else will I have you dragged forth and lashed—lashed before the whole regiment!"

His cheeks were white with excitement; ferocity gleamed in every look and limb; and the frightened Gills and his wife shrank back in very fear that he would do them some bodily harm. They thought him mad; his words were so incoherent and strange.

But not quicker passed away is the lightning's flash—not in the swiftest night-storm does a cloud flit more quickly over the face of the moon—than was the clearing up of the stranger's countenance, and the clothing of his face again in its former mantle of indifference.

"Forgive me!" said he, with a bland smile, "I am too hasty. In truth, I have a horror of these superstitious stories; they fret me. But no matter. Do not think I am so silly as to *fear* this child-spirit you have spoken of. Such nonsense is for the ignorant and the credulous. Again I ask pardon for my rudeness. Let me now be shown to this chamber—this *haunted* chamber. I am weary. Good night, mistress!"

And without waiting for an answer, he of the red scarf hastily pushed

creeping into the blood like cold, polish'd steel.[29] The old man raised himself in his seat and listen'd, at once fully awake. For a minute, all was the solemn stillness of midnight. Then rose that horrid tone again, wailing and wild, and making the hearer's hair to stand on end.[30] One moment more, and the trampling of hasty feet sounded in the passage outside. The door was thrown open, and the form of the stranger, more like a corpse than living man, rushed into the room.[31]

"All white!" yell'd the conscience-stricken creature[32]—"all white, and with the grave-clothes around him. One shoulder was bare, and I saw," he whisper'd, "I saw blue streaks upon it. It was horrible, and I cried aloud. He stepp'd toward me! He came to my very bedside; his small hand almost touch'd[33] my face. I could not bear it, and fled."

The miserable man bent his head down upon his bosom; convulsive rattlings shook his throat; and his whole frame waver'd to and fro like a tree in a storm. Bewilder'd and shock'd, Gills look'd at his apparently deranged guest, and knew not what answer to make, or what course of conduct to pursue.[34]

the old man through the door, and they passed to the sleeping room.

27. bending over the coals—an enjoyment that was to his mind very pleasant and satisfactory.

28. That   29. cold, sharp, polished steel.

30. In the original version, the following lines intervene between this sentence and the next: "As it floated along to the chamber—borne through the darkness and stillness—it brought to the mind of Gills thoughts of the howlings of damned spirits, and the death-rattle of murdered men, and the agonies of the drowning, and the hoarse croak of the successful assassin.

"He sat paralyzed in his chair. Then came an interval; and then another of those terrible shrieks."

31. In the original, this paragraph follows at this point:

"He is there!" said the quivering wretch, pointing with his finger, and speaking in low hoarse tones; "he is there, in his little shroud! And he smiled and looked gently upon me with those blue eyes of his—O, how much sharper than a thousand frowns!"

The man shook, like one in a great ague, and his jaws clashed against each other.

32. continued the miserable, conscience-stricken creature

33. "his small hand was raised, and almost touched"

34. The following lines intervene between this paragraph and the next in the original version:

"Do you not believe it?" furiously exclaimed the stranger, with a revulsion of feeling, in consistence with his character; "do you think me a child, to be frightened by a bugbear?—Come!" continued he, seizing the alarmed old man by the shoulder; "Come hither, and let your own eyes be blasted with the sight!"

And dragging the unresisting Gills, he strode to the door, and dashed it open with a loud and echoing clang.

The house was one of that old fashioned sort, still to be met with occasionally in country villages, the ground floor of which was comprised of

Thrusting out his arms and his extended fingers, and bending down his eyes, as men do when shading them from a glare of lightning, the stranger[35] stagger'd from the door, and, in a moment further, dash'd madly through the passage which led through the kitchen into the outer road. The old man heard the noise of his falling footsteps,[36] sounding fainter and fainter in the distance, and then, retreating, dropp'd his own exhausted limbs into the chair from which he had been arous'd so terribly. It was many minutes before his energies recover'd their accustomed tone again. Strangely enough, his wife, unawaken'd by the stranger's ravings, still slumber'd on as profoundly as ever.

Pass we on to a far different scene[37]—the embarkation of the British troops for the distant land whose monarch was never more to wield the sceptre over a kingdom lost by his imprudence and tyranny. With frowning brow and sullen pace the martial ranks moved on. Boat after boat was filled, and, as each discharged its complement in the ships that lay heaving their anchors in the stream, it return'd, and was soon filled with another load. And at length it became time for the last soldier to lift his eye and take a last glance at the broad banner of England's pride, which flapp'd its folds from the top of the highest staff on the Battery.[38]

As the warning sound of a trumpet called together all who were laggards—those taking leave of friends, and those who were arranging their own private affairs, left until the last moment—a single horseman was seen furiously dashing down the street. A red scarf tightly encircled his waist. He made directly for the shore, and the crowd there gather'd started back in wonderment as they beheld his dishevel'd appearance and ghastly face. Throwing himself violently from his saddle, he flung the bridle over the animal's neck, and gave him a sharp cut[39] with a small riding whip. He made for the boat; one minute later, and he had been left. They were push-

two rooms, divided by a hall—the door of each room being off against the other; so that the old man and his companion had a full view of the adjoining apartment. Though there was no light there, Gills fancied he could see everything distinctly.

In one corner stood the bed from which the stranger had started—its coverlets and sheets all tumbled and half dragged down on the floor. A few feet on one side of its head, was the hearth-stone; and the sight thereon, as Gills strained his eyes to behold it, was drunk in with chilling terror to his heart.

Upon that hearth-stone stood the form of a boy, some ten years old. His face was wan and ghastly, but very beautiful; his hair light and wavy; and he was apparelled in the habiliments of the tomb. As the appalled Gills looked, he felt that the eyes of the pale child were fixed upon him and his companion—fixed, not as in anger, but with a gentle sorrow. From one shoulder the fearful dress had fallen aside, and the appearance of gashes

ing the keel from the landing—the stranger sprang—a space of two or three feet already intervened—he struck on the gunwale—and the Last Soldier of King George had left the American shores.

and livid streaks were visible.

"See you?" harshly shrieked the stranger, as if maddened by the sight; "I have not dreamed—he is there, in his snowy robes—he comes to mock me. And look you!" he crouched and recoiled, "does he not step this way again? I shall go mad! If he but touches me with that little hand, I am mad! Away, spectre! boy-phantom, away! or I die too upon this very floor!"

35. he   36. flying footsteps
37. a far different and almost as thrilling a scene
38. This additional line concludes this paragraph in the original version:
Proud spectacle! May the flag which was planted in the place of the blood-red cross, waft out to the wind for ages and ages yet—and the nations of earth number not one so glorious as that which claims the star-gemmed symbol of liberty for its token!
39. a cut

Reuben's Last Wish[1]

IF the reader supposes that I am going to tell a story full of plot, interest, and excitement, let him peruse no farther than these two or three lines—for he will be disappointed. A simple tale—a narration not half so strange as people frequently see exemplified in their ordinary walks—is all I have to offer. Yet, as the greatest and profoundest truths are often most plain to the senses of men—in the same resemblance, my "Reuben" may haply teach a moral and plant a seed of wholesome instruction.

Not many weeks since, I happened to be in a country village, sixty miles, more or less, to the north of our great new world metropolis, New York. Towards sundown, I heard from the keeper of the inn where I was staying, that there was to be a temperance lecture in the place that night. The scene of the meeting was the school house; and having no other means of employing my time, I determined to attend.

At the appointed hour, I did so. The lecture itself was rather a prosy affair, but fortunately short; when it concluded, several persons, apparently residents thereabout, rose and made remarks, partly advice and partly transcripts of facts which had come under their observation. One of the speakers, a man considerably advanced in life, I listened to with much interest. After the exercises were over, I took occasion to introduce myself, and converse for some time with this man; and upon what I heard him say in the public meeting—the particulars he furnished me at our private interview—and, also, the additional facts I gathered from the people of the place, the subsequent day—I have based the narrative which follows.

Franklin Slade, a handsome, healthy American farmer, possessed at the age of thirty years, a comfortable estate, a fair reputation, a tolerably well filled purse—and could boast that he owed no debts which he was not able to pay on the instant. He had a prudent, good tempered wife, and two children, sons, one eight years old and the other three.

Through one of the thousand painted snares, which ministers of sin ever stand ready to tempt frailty withal, Slade, about this period, fell into a habit of tippling. At first, he would indulge himself but rarely, and that

1. Professor Emory Holloway announced the discovery of this tale and of a fragment of a longer work also by Whitman, *The Madman*, in *American Literature*, XXVII (January 1956) 577–78. "Reuben's Last Wish" appeared in a New York temperance newspaper, the *Washingtonian*, May 21, 1842. Holloway gives the date

to a limited degree; but the fatal taste grew upon him, and in the course of years, the man was a *drunkard*, habitual and confirmed.

Franklin Slade, a bloated, red faced fellow, at the age of forty years, had his estate mortgaged for half its value—no man cared for his good will —his purse held not a dollar—and creditors insulted him daily. The once ruddy cheek of his wife was withered and pale from much sorrow; and her eye had lost its accustomed brightness. His eldest son, Slade had struck in a fit of drunken passion; the boy was high tempered—he left his father's house—shipped as a sailor to some far distant port—and thenceforward they never heard of him again. Little Reuben, the other son, was an invalid, and, (the bitter truth may as well be told,) an invalid through his father's wretched sensuality. Some time previous, the child being with Slade several miles away, the farmer drank so deeply, that he soon felt in no condition to get home. Reuben was kept out the whole night—a cold, rainy one. He was naturally delicate, and the exposure produced an effect on him from which he never recovered.

There is something very solemn in the sickness of children. The ashiness, and the moisture on the brow, and the film over the eye balls—what man can look upon the sight, and not feel his heart awed within him? Children, I have noticed too, increase in beauty as their illness deepens. The angels, it may be, are already vesting them with the garments they shall wear in the Pleasant Land.

Slade, to do him justice, was deeply grieved that the fruits of his folly fell thus upon the innocent Reuben, whom he loved much. Yet his infatuation had rooted so deeply, that he desisted in no respect from his dissolute practices. He scoffed at the efforts of the temperance advocates, who were becoming numerous and successful in the town—as they occasionally strove to bring him to their faith, and besought him to sign the pledge. His son very often joined his voice for the same purpose; entreaties and arguments, however, were alike futile.

Visiting, whenever his strength permitted, the meetings of the Temperance people, and reading and talking frequently upon the subject, Reuben before long entered with much enthusiasm into the new movement. He was an intelligent lad—and that he had seen what an evil thing drunkenness was, may well be imagined from the facts already given.

"I would," said the child one day to his mother, "I would have this paper bordered prettily with silk, and a fine ribbon bow at the top."

As May 2, which is the date given on page one of the *Washingtonian*, the page on which "Reuben's Last Wish" begins. However, page two carries the date May 21, and meetings of local temperance societies are reported for such dates as May 13 and May 18.

He held in his hand a Temperance pledge, with a picture at the top, and a blank space at the bottom for the names of signers.

"You are whimsical, my dear," said the matron, as she took the paper; "why do you desire so needless a thing done?"

"I hardly know myself," answered he, "yet please do it, mother. Ask me not why—let it be a whim."

And he smiled faintly.

And the sickening thought came over the woman's soul, that ere long she would probably not have the pleasant trouble of listening to the poor fellow's vagaries. She stepped hastily from the room, weeping.

In a day or two the Temperance pledge was edged tastily with a border of blue silk, and at each end, a piece of ribbon of the same color. The child was pleased: he took it and put it aside.

Days, months rolled on. The dwelling of Slade was a substantial old farm-house, a pleasant place, in the rear of which stretched a large garden. As it was now the season of advanced spring, the trees began to bud out and bloom there—the flowers to put forth their beautiful tints—and the grass donned its darkest green. Birds sang there too—the robin, and the black bird, and the fanciful bob-o-link.

In the middle of the garden was a fine, grassy patch, shaded by a stupendous tree: leaning against the trunk of the tree had been built a long, wide, rustic seat. It was very fair, that spot—dreamy, warm, and free from annoyance of any kind.

Reuben, frequently walking here among the flowers and shrubs, would admire this grass plot, and stop, and resting himself on the seat, would remain a long hour enjoying the delight of the scene—not such delight as children are generally fond of, romping, and playing, and laughing—but a noiseless, motionless delight, in keeping with the place.

Still the days rolled on—and Reuben grew no better, but worse. Physicians seemed of little benefit. The only method of producing a favorable effect upon his spirits—and that was merely temporary—seemed to be to let him have quite his own way in all his fancies and his actions. Still he was never querulous or fretful.

One notion of the sick boy—though an odd one, they acquiesced in it —was to have a kind of couch made for him; and when he was too weak for walking about, to have it carried in the garden, on the favorite grass plot, that he might rest on it there.

For a time they kept somebody by him while he lay thus, lest his illness might take a fatal turn.—As, however, nothing of that kind occured, and he lingered day after day without alteration, they relaxed somewhat from having a watcher by his garden bed. Now and then they would leave him, though not long—for a mother's affection is to her child like a needle to its magnet—though it may vibrate aside a little on occasions, it ever settles back again, truly and constantly.

Reuben, indeed, preferred being alone. He would get them to bring him large bunches of flowers, roses, and the fragrant carnation, and the delicate lily—which he would arrange fancifully about him: then, when he grew tired of such simple pastime, he would sink back, and lie long, long minutes, gazing on the bright sky above, and watching the changes of the clouds as they melted from tint to tint, and changed from form to form.

It grew at length to be, that the very birds, that had their nests thereabout, or sought fruit from the neighboring trees, became accustomed to the presence of Reuben, and hopped down upon his couch, and would rest upon his extended hand. They sometimes sat upon the branches over him, and would sing blithely and long—which was very sweet to the little invalid.

One morning it happened that the child fell asleep while he lay alone upon his bed in the garden. And while he slept, he dreamed a beautiful dream. He thought that he, after passing, he could not tell how, for a great way through the air, landed at last on the borders of a fair country, where he wandered about for some time. The place was more delightful than ever entered the imagination of man, with fadeless verdure, and bright day, and summer eternal. By and by he entered a city, thronged with people, such as it charmed his eyes to behold—all clothed in raiment like the fleecy clouds, and each with a glittering star upon his forehead. Here he was accosted by a Being, even more splendid than the others, and told in tones of soft music, that he should not be sick any more as on earth, but be taken to the presence of the Great King. Then he was conducted by the Being, who led the way, holding his hand, through many bright avenues and shining halls—and at last ushered into a mighty space, whose limits the gazer's eye could not scan, filled with millions of the winged ones—and in the midst a throne, whence light flashed like double lightning.

And then the sleeper awoke.

Several persons were standing around him. One, the village doctor, had apparently been holding his wrist—for he let it fall as soon as Reuben opened his eyes. The boy felt strangely faint, yet he smiled as he saw his parents, and briefly told them his vision. His mother was sobbing aloud.

"My son," she cried, in uncontrollable agony; "my son! you die!"

And the father bowed him low, as a tree by the tempest—and thick tears rippled between the fingers which he held before his eyes. O, it is a fearful thing to see a *man* in desperate grief!

Reuben comprehended the truth; else why that cloud—that dark consciousness shadowing his soul? He lay drowsily; a few drops of sweat started upon his forehead, and he began to grow insensible to perception or feeling of any kind. It was a state somewhat resembling sleep, yet different from it—it was without pain—it was DEATH.

For what moved the child thus uneasily and sped his eyes from one to another? With some effort he turned himself, raised his arm to his pillow, and drew something from underneath it, he unrolled a paper edged with silk, of the hue of the clouds overhead.

All was the silence of the grave. The dying boy slowly lifted the tremulous forefinger of his right hand, as he held the document in his left—that finger quivered for a moment in the air—the eyes of the child, now becoming glassy with death damp, were fixedly cast toward his father's face; he smiled pleasantly—and as an indistinct gurgle sounded from his throat, the uplifted finger calmly settled downward, and rested, pointing upon the blank space at the bottom of the Temperance pledge.

And so he passed away.

When the solemnity of the scene, and the impressiveness of the closing incident, which for a while awed them motionless and silent, allowed other influences to act, they looked, and saw Reuben lying before them a cold corpse. His finger was pointed still. A gentle look lingered upon his face; the perfume of flowers filled the air; and from the western sky came a ray of light, left by the departing sun, investing the spot, as it were, with a halo of glory.

A Legend of Life and Love[1]

UPON[2] the banks of a pleasant river once[3] stood a cottage, the residence of an ancient man whose limbs were feeble with the weight of years, and of former sorrow. In his appetites easily gratified, like the simple race of the people among whom he lived, every want was supplied by a few fertile acres. Those acres were tilled and tended by two brothers, grandsons of the old man, and dwellers also in the cottage. The parents of the boys lay buried in a tomb[4] nearby.

Nathan, the elder, had hardly seen his twentieth summer. He was a beautiful youth. Glossy hair clustered upon his head, and his cheeks were very brown from sunshine and the air.[5] Though the eyes of Nathan were soft and liquid, like a girl's, and his lips[6] curled with a voluptuous swell, exercise and labor had developed his limbs into noble and manly proportions. The bands of hunters as they met sometimes to start off together after game upon the neighboring hills, could hardly show one among their number who in comeliness, strength or activity, might compete with the youthful Nathan.

Mark was but a year younger than his brother. He, too, had great beauty.

In the course of time the ancient sickened, and knew that he was to die. Before the approach of the fatal hour, he called before him the two youths, and addressed them thus:

"The world, my children, is full of deceit. Evil men swarm in every place, and sorrow and disappointment are the fruits of intercourse with them. So wisdom is wary.

"And as the things of life are only shadows, passing like the darkness

---

1. The text is that printed in the *Brooklyn Eagle*, which Whitman was editor of at the time, on June 11, 1846. The story was first published in the *Democratic Review*, July 1842. Except for some minor differences in paragraphing and punctuation, the variants in the *Democratic Review* are given in the notes that follow.
2. In the original version, this paragraph is preceded by the following paragraph:
A very cheerless and fallacious doctrine is that which teaches to deny the yielding to natural feelings, righteously directed, because the consequences may be trouble and grief, as well as satisfaction and pleasure. The man who lives on from year to year, jealous of ever placing himself in a situation where the chances can possibly turn against him—ice, as it were, surrounding his heart, and his mind too scrupulously weighing in a balance the results of giving way to any of those propensities his Creator has planted in his heart—may be a philosopher, but can never be a happy man.
3. "Once" is not in the original version.
4. grave   5. and open air   6. cheeks

of a cloud, twine no bands of love about your hearts. For love is the ficklest of the things of life. The object of our affection dies, and we thenceforth languish in agony; or perhaps the love we covet dies, and that is more painful yet.

"It is well never to confide in any man. It is well to keep aloof from the follies and impurities of earth. Let there be no links between you and others. Let not any being control you through your dependence upon him for a portion of your happiness. This my sons I have learned by bitter experience, is a teaching of truth."

Within a few days afterwards, the old man was placed away in the marble tomb of his kindred, which was built on a hill by the shore.

Now the injunctions given to Nathan and his brother—injunctions frequently impressed upon them[7] by the same monitorial voice—were pondered over by each youth in his inmost heart. They had always habitually respected their grandsire; whatever came from his mouth, therefore, seemed as the words of an oracle not to be gainsayed.

Soon the path of Nathan chanced to be sundered from that of Mark.

And the trees leaved out, and then in autumn cast their foliage; and in due course leaved out again and again, and many times again—and the brothers met not yet.

Two-score years and ten! what changes worked over earth in such a space of two score years and ten!

As the sun, as hour ere his setting, cast long slanting shadows to the eastward, two men, withered and with hair thin and snowy, came wearily up from opposite directions, and stood together at a tomb built on a hill by the borders of a fair river. Why do they start, as each cast[8] his dim eyes toward the face of the other? Why do tears drop down their cheeks, and their forms tremble even more than with the feebleness of age? They are the long separated brethren, and they enfold themselves in one another's arms.

"And yet," said Mark, after a few moments, stepping back and gazing earnestly upon his companion's form and features, "And yet it wonders me that *thou* art my brother. There should be a brave and beautiful youth, with black curls upon his head, and not those pale emblems of decay. And my brother should be straight and nimble—not bent and tottering as thou."

The speaker cast a second searching glance—a glance of discontent.

"And I," rejoined Nathan, "I might require from *my* brother, not such shrivelled limbs as I see, and instead of that cracked voice, the full swelling music of the[9] morning heart—but that half a century is a fearful melter

---

7. upon them before   8. casts   9. "a"

of comeliness and of strength; for half a century it is, dear brother, since my hand touched thine, or my gaze rested upon thy face."

Mark sighed and answered not.

Then, in a little while, they made inquiries of what had befallen either during the time past. Seated upon the marble by which they had met, Mark briefly told his story.

"I bethink me, brother, many, many years have indeed passed over since the sorrowful day when our grandsire, dying, left us to seek our fortunes amid a wicked and a seductive world.

"His last words, as thou, doubtless, dost remember, advised us against the snares that should beset our subsequent journeyings. He portrayed the dangers which lie in the path of love; he impressed upon our minds the folly of placing confidence in human honor; and warned us to keep aloof from too close communion with our kind. He then died, but his instructions live, and have ever been present in my memory.

"Dear Nathan, why should I conceal from you that at that time I loved? My simple soul, unfitted[10] with the wisdom of our aged relative, had yielded to the delicious folly, and the brown eyed Eva was my young heart's choice. O brother, even now, the feeble and withered thing I am, dim recollections, pleasant passages, come forth around me, like the joy of old dreams! A boy again, and in the confiding heart of the boy, I walk with Eva by the river's bank.[11] And the gentle creature blushes at my protestations of love, and leans her cheek upon my neck. The regal sun goes down in the West; we gaze upon the glory of the clouds that attend his setting, and while we look at their fantastic changes, a laugh sounds,[12] clear like a flute, and merry as the jingling of silver bells. It is the laugh of Eva!"

The eye of the old man glistened with unwonted brightness. He paused, sighed, the brightness faded away, and he went on with his narration.

"As I said, the dying lessons of him whom we reverenced were treasured in my soul. I could not but feel their truth. I feared that if I again stood beside the maiden of my love, and looked upon her face, and listened to her words, the wholesome axioms might be blotted from my thought. So I determined to act as became a man; from that hour I never have beheld the brown-eyed Eva.

"I went amid the world. Acting upon the wise principles which our aged friend taught us, I looked upon everything with suspicious eyes. Alas! I found it but too true that iniquity and deceit are the ruling spirits of men.

10. "ungifted"   11. "banks"   12. "sounds out"

"Some called me cold, calculating and unamiable; but it was their own unworthiness that made me appear so to their eyes. I am not—you know, my brother—I am not, naturally, of proud and repulsive manner; but I was determined never to give my friendship merely to be blown off again, it might chance, as a feather by the wind; nor interweave my course of life with those that very likely would draw all the advantage of the connexion, and leave me no better than before.

"I engaged in traffic. Success attended me. Enemies said that my good fortune was the result of chance, but I knew it the fruit of the judicious system of caution which governed me in matters of business, as well as of social intercourse.

"My brother, thus have I lived my life. Your look asks me if I have been happy. Dear brother, truth impels me to say *no*. Yet assuredly, if few glittering pleasures ministered to me on my journey, equally few were the disappointments, the hopes blighted, the trusts betrayed, the faintings of soul, caused by the dereliction[13] of those in whom I had laid up treasures.

"Ah, my brother, the world is full of misery!"

The disciple of a wretched faith ceased his story, and there was silence a while.

Then Nathan spake:

"In the early years," he said, "I too loved a beautiful woman. Whether my heart was more frail than thine, or affection had gained a mightier power over me, I could not part from her I loved without the satisfaction of a farewell kiss. We met—I had resolved to stay but a moment—for I had laid out[14] my future life after the fashion thou hast described thine.

"How it was I know not, but the moments rolled on to hours; and still we stood with our arms around each other.

"My brother, a maiden's tears washed my stern resolves away. The lure of a voice rolling quietly from between two soft lips, enticed me from re-membrance of my grandsire's wisdom. I forgot his teachings, and married the woman I loved.

"Ah! how sweetly sped the seasons! We were blessed. True, there came crossings and evils, but we withstood them all, and holding each other by the hand, forgot that such a thing as sorrow remained in the world.

"Children were born to us—brave boys and fair girls. Oh, Mark, that, *that* is a pleasure—that swelling of tenderness for our offspring, which the rigorous doctrines of your course of life have withheld from you!

"Like you, I engaged in trade. Various fortune followed my path. I will not deny but that some in whom I thought virtue was strong, proved

13. "defection"   14. "chalked out"

cunning hypocrites, and worthy no man's trust. Yet are there many I have known, spotless as far as humanity may be spotless.

"Thus, to me, life has been alternately dark and fair. Have I lived happy? No, not completely; it is never for mortals to be so. But I can lay my hand upon my heart, and thank the Great Master, that the sunshine has been far oftener than the darkness of the clouds.

"Dear brother, the world has misery—but it is a pleasant world still, and affords much joy to the dwellers!"

As Nathan ceased, his brother looked up in his face, like a man unto whom a simple truth had been for the first time revealed.

The Angel of Tears[1]

HIGH, high in space floated the angel Alza. Of the spirits who minister in heaven he[2] is not the chief; neither is he employed in deeds of great import, or in the destinies of worlds and generations. Yet if it were possible for envy to enter among the Creatures Beautiful, many would have pined for the station of Alza. There are a million million invisible eyes which keep constant watch over the earth—each Child of Light having his separate duty. Alza is one of the Angels of Tears.

Why waited he, as for commands from above?

There was a man upon whose brow rested the stamp of the guilt of Cain. The man had slain his brother. Now he lay in chains awaiting the terrible day when the doom he himself had inflicted should be meted to his own person.

People of the black souls![3]—beings whom the world shrinks from, and whose abode, through the needed severity of law, is in the dark cell and massy prison—it may not be but that ye have, at times, thoughts of the beauty of virtue, and the blessing of a spotless mind. For if we look abroad in the world, and examine what is to be seen there, we will know, that in every human heart resides a mysterious prompting which leads it to love the right[4] for its own sake. All that is rational has this prompting. It can never be entirely stifled.[5] It may be darkened by the storm of guilt,[6] but ever and anon the clouds roll away, and it shines out again. Murderers and thieves, and the most abandoned criminals, have been unable to deaden such involuntary homage to goodness.[7]

It came to be, that an hour arrived when the heart of the imprisoned fratricide held strange imagining. Old lessons and long forgotten hints, about heaven, and purity, and love, and gentle kindness, floated into his memory—vacillating, as it were, like delicate sea-flowers on the bosom of the turgid ocean. He remembered him of his brother as a boy—how they played together of the summer afternoons—and how, wearied out at evening, they slept pleasantly in each other's arms. O, Master of the Great

1. The text followed here is that printed in Colonel Alden Spooner's *Brooklyn Evening Star*, February 28, 1846, at which time Whitman was a member of the *Star*'s staff. Much earlier, from the fall of 1832 to the spring of 1835, Whitman had worked as a compositor for Spooner's *Long Island Star*. The story originally appeared in the *Democratic Review*, September 1842. Whitman's efforts to sell this tale to the *Boston Miscellany* are recorded in two letters in *Correspondence*, I, 25–26. Miller, quoting in a footnote the last sentence of the story, transcribes "sigh" as "sight," following an error in the reprint of the original version (*UPP*, I, 86). Whitman's revisions in the *Star* version are entirely verbal and one of them removes the

Laws! couldst thou but roll back the years, and place that guilty creature a child again by the side of that brother! Such were the futile wishes of the criminal. And as repentance and prayer worked forth from his soul, he sunk[7.1] on the floor drowsily, and a tear stood beneath his eyelids.

Repentance and prayer from *him!* What hope could there be for aspirations having birth in a source so polluted? Yet the Sense which is never sleepless heard that tainted soul's desire, and willed that an answering mission should be sent straightway.

When Alza felt the mind of the Almighty in his heart—for it was rendered conscious to him in the moment—he cleaved the air with his swift pinions, and made haste to perform the cheerful duty. Along and earthward he flew—seeing far, far below him, mountains, and towns, and seas, and stretching forests. At distance, in the immeasurable field wherein he travelled, was the eternal glitter of countless worlds—wheeling and whirling, and motionless never. After a brief while the spirit beheld the city of his destination; and, drawing nigh, he hovered over it—that great city, shrouded in the depths of night, and its many thousands slumbering.

Just as his presence, obedient to his desire, was transferring itself to the place where the murderer lay, he met one of his own kindred spreading his wings to rise from the ground.

"O Spirit," said Alza, "what a sad scene is here!"

"I grow faint," the other answered, "at looking abroad through these guilty places. Behold that street to the right."

He pointed, and Alza, turning, saw rooms of people, some with their minds maddened by intoxication, some uttering horrid blasphemies—sensual creatures,[7.2] and mockers of all holiness.

"O, brother," said the Tear-Angel, "let us not darken our eyes with the sight. Let us on to our appointed missions. What is yours, my brother?"

"Behold!" answered the Spirit.

And then Alza knew for the first time that there was a third existence[8] near by. With meek and abashed features[8.1] the soul of a dead girl[9] stood forth before them. Alza, without asking his companion, saw that the Spirit had been sent and accompany[9.1] the stranger through the Dark Windings.

So he kissed the brow of the re-born, and said—

illogical context in which "sigh" was originally placed. The variants of the *Democratic Review* text are given in the footnotes that follow.

    2. Alza   3. People of the Black Souls!   4. goodness
    5. It never dies. It can never be entirely stifled.
    6. by the tempests and storms of guilt
    7. to deaden this faculty.
    7.1. sank   7.2. sensual creatures, and wicked,
    8. living thing   8.1. gesture   9. a girl just dead
    9.1. to guide and accompany

"Be of good heart! Farewell, both!"

And the soul and its monitor departed upward, and Alza went into the dungeon.

Then, like a swinging vapor, the form of the Tear-Angel was by and over the body of the sleeping man. To his vision, night was as day, and day as night.

At first, something like a shudder went through him, for when one from the Pure Country approaches the wickedness of evil, the presence thereof is made known to him by an instinctive pain. Yet a moment, and the gentle Spirit cast glances of pity on the unconscious fratricide. In the great Mystery of Life, Alza remembered, though even *he* understood it not, it had been settled by the Unfathomable that Sin and Wrong *should be*. And the Angel knew, too, that Man, with all the darkness and the clouds about him, might not be contemned, even by the archangels of the Nighest Circle to God.[10]

He slept. His hair, coarse and tangly through neglect, lay in masses about his head, and clustered over his neck. One arm was doubled under his cheek, and the other stretched straight forward. Long steady breaths, with a kind of hissing sound came from his lips.

So he slumbered calmly. So the fires of a furnace, at night, though not extinguished, slumber calmly, when its swarthy ministers impel it not. Haply, he dreamed some innocent dream. Sleep on, dream on, outcast! There will soon be for you a reality harsh enough to make you wish those visions had continued alway, and you never awakened.

Oh, it is not well to look coldly and mercilessly on the bad done by our fellows. That convict—that being of the bloody hand—who could know what palliations there were for his guilt? Who might say there was no premature seducing aside from the walks of honesty—no seed of evil planted by others in his soul during the early years? Who should tell he was not so bred, that had he at manhood possessed aught but propensities for evil it would have been miraculous indeed? Who might dare cast the first stone?

The heart of man is a glorious structure;[11] yet its Builder has seen fit to let it become, to a degree, like the Jewish temple[12] of old, a mart for gross traffic, and the presence of unchaste things. In the Shrouded Volume, doubtless, it might be perceived how this is a part of the mighty and beautiful Harmony; but our eyes are mortal, and the film is over them.

The Angel of Tears bent him by the side of the prisoner's head. An

10. even by the princes of the Nighest Circle to the White Throne.
11. temple   12. structure   13. his hair

instant more, and he rose, and seemed about to depart, as one whose desire had been attained. Wherefore does that pleasant look spread like a smile over the features of the slumberer?

In the darkness overhead yet linger the soft wings of Alza. Swaying above the prostrate mortal, the Spirit bends his white neck, and his face is shaded by the curls of hair,[13] which hang about him like a golden cloud. Shaking the beautiful tresses back, he stretches forth his hands, and raises his large eyes upward, and speaks murmuringly in the language used among the Creatures Beautiful:

"I come. Spirits of Pity and Love, favored children of the Loftiest—whose pleasant task it is to make record of those things[14] which, when computed together at the Day of the End, are to outcancel the weight of the sum of evil—your chambers I seek!"

And the Angel of Tears glided away.

While a thousand air-forms, far and near responded in the same tongue wherewith Alza had spoken:

"Beautiful, to the Ear of God,[15] is the sigh which ushers repentance!"

14. "with your pens of adamant to make record upon the Silver Leaves of those things"
15. "to the Eye of the Centre"

FRANKLIN EVANS

OR

The Inebriate

A TALE OF THE TIMES[1]

1. The text is that of the original version published in the *New World*, II (No. 10, Extra Series, November 1842), 1–31, where it was described as an "Original Temperance Novel." The issue, completely given over to this novel, was an octavo pamphlet selling for 12½¢—a common medium among New York newspapers in the 1840s for the dissemination of both local pot-boilers and such superior pirated English fiction as the installments of Dickens's *Dombey and Son*. J. Winchester, publisher of the *New World*, and Park Benjamin, editor, probably hoped for the patronage of the Washingtonians and other temperance groups when they announced in the *New World* for November 5, 1842, that *Franklin Evans* would appear on November 23, and reminded their readers that orders for copies of the Extra Series would be taken at ten for $1 or one hundred for $8. Park Benjamin may have decided to forget Whitman's attacks in the *Aurora* a few months before (see Rubin and Brown, pp. 110–111). The *New World* announcement of November 5— after hailing "Friends of Temperance, Ahoy!" and revealing that *Franklin Evans* had been composed "By a Popular American Author" (who was not identified; however, "by Walter Whitman" appeared under the title of the novel in the Extra Series issue) —continued: "THIS NOVEL, which is dedicated to the Temperance Societies and the friends of the Temperance Cause throughout the Union, will create a sensation, both for the ability with which it is written, as well as the interest of the subject, and will be universally read and admired. It was written expressly for the NEW WORLD, by one of the best Novelists of this country, with a view to aid the great work of Reform, and rescue Young Men from the demon of Intemperance. The incidents of the plot are wrought out with great effect, and the excellence of its moral, and the beneficial influence it will have, should interest the friends of Temperance Reformation in giving this Tale the widest possible circulation" (*UPP*, I, Note One, 103– 104). Apparently the tale did sell well (possibly 20,000 copies: see Binns, p. 35), for it was advertised again in the *New World*, August 19, 1843, with a slightly altered title: "Franklin Evans; or the Merchant's Clerk: A Tale of the Times" (*UPP*, I, Note One, 104).

The circumstances under which Whitman composed *Franklin Evans* are not entirely clear—except that he probably needed the money and that he was, editorially and personally, a friend of temperance, though not of teetotalism. It would appear that he was embarrassed in his later years (and probably much earlier) by having produced the novel. It is not clear what Whitman drank while he composed *Franklin Evans*, as he claimed, in three days; and the onus for this ambiguity is either Whitman's or his reporters'.

The earliest of Whitman's comments on *Franklin Evans* is recorded in Traubel, I, 93—dated in the spring of 1888: "W. said about Franklin Evans 'I doubt if there is a copy in existence: I have none and have not had one for years; it was a pamphlet. Parke Godwin and another somebody . . . came to see me about writing it. Their offer of cash payment was so tempting—I was hard up at the time—that I set to work at once ardently on it (with the help of a bottle of port or what not). In three days of constant work I finished the book. Finished the book? Finished myself. It was damned rot—rot of the worst sort—not insincere perhaps, but rot, nevertheless: it was not the business for me to be up to. I stopped right there: I never cut a chip off that kind of timber again.' " Perhaps Whitman had forgotten that he had begun the publication of another temperance novel—*The Madman*—about two months after the appearance of *Franklin Evans*.

On a September afternoon in 1888, Horace Traubel and Thomas Harned arrived at Mickle Street to find Whitman sitting before two bottles of home-made wine brought him that day by some country friends. The ensuing conversation is reported in Traubel, II, 322–323; Whitman is speaking: " 'Let's open one—shall we? Will you take a glass?' Took up the bottle. 'You won't do like a fellow I had here a little while ago: he sat across from me, as you do—saw me open the bottle for him—then said he was a temperance man, or something—never drank at all.' W. took a corkscrew out of his pocket and handed it with the bottle to me. 'Open it, Horace.' I laughed. 'Do you carry the corkscrew about with you, Walt?' 'Yes.' Harned said: 'That's bad, Walt—they'll throw you out of the temperance society.' 'They can't—I never was in.' I asked: 'But didn't you write a temperance novel once?' 'Yes, so I did—for seventy-five dollars cash down. And, by the way, that seventy-five dollars was not the end of it, for the book sold so well they sent me fifty dollars more in two or three weeks.' . . . Tom drank. W. did not touch the wine. Tom remarked, 'It's sour, Walt.' 'Yes, Ingram knows what I like.' "

A taste for sour home-made wine does not rule out port as the Muse which inspired Whitman for three days in 1842. But a new inspirational drink was introduced into the picture by J. G. Schumaker, an old journalistic friend of Whitman, in the New York *Tribune*, April 4, 1892. Whitman had told him, said Schumaker, that he had written *Franklin Evans* "mostly in the reading room of Tammany Hall, which was a sort of Bohemian resort, and he afterward told me that he frequently indulged in gin cocktails while writing it, at the 'Pewter Mug,' another resort for Bohemians around the corner in Spruce Street" (Perry, p. 28). Schumaker perhaps was being facetious in his use of "Bohemian": the Pewter Mug catered to Tammany Democrats.

A third nontemperance drink applied for the position of the Muse in a letter from Charles W. Eldridge (Thayer & Eldridge had published the third edition of *Leaves of Grass*) to John Burroughs, written March 7, 1896. "Think," wrote Eldridge, "of the man who wrote 'Franklin Williams, or the Inebriate's Doom,' under the stimulus, as he once told me, of relays of strong whiskey cocktails, in order to keep the printer's devil, who was waiting, supplied with copy, afterward writing the sublime passage beginning, 'I am an acme of things accomplished, and I am the encloser of things to be!'—equal to anything in the Book of Genesis, or Revelation, for that matter" (Barrus, p. 322). Eldridge's memory of what Whitman said he drank as he wrote *Franklin Evans* may have been as faulty as his recollection of the title of that novel; but it is difficult to disagree with Eldridge that it is almost incredible that the man who wrote *Leaves of Grass* also wrote *Franklin Evans*. That Whitman wrote a 60,000-word tale, even so badly written as this one, in three days, is debatable. That he wrote it with the aid of alcohol seems debatable too. But his insistence that he so did has all the appearance of a perfectly understandable defense mechanism.

Whitman, while editor of the *Brooklyn Eagle*, reprinted *Franklin Evans* in his newspaper on November 16–30, 1846, with considerable revision and deletion, as "A Tale of Long Island" with a new title which omitted any reference to Franklin Evans (though he remained the hero of the tale) and with a new author whose cryptic initials were not those of Walter Whitman: *Fortunes of a Country-Boy; Incidents in Town—and his Adventures at the South*, "By J. R. S. . . . . ." Why Whitman disguised the title and the authorship of *Franklin Evans* in the *Eagle* is not known. His name was signed to all the fiction he reprinted in the *Eagle* except to the reprints of three "Fact-Romances" and to the reprint of "Arrow-Tip." In the case of the reprint of "Arrow-Tip" we have a parallel to Whitman's handling of *Franklin Evans*. In the *Eagle*, "Arrow-Tip" is renamed "The Half-Breed: A Tale of the Western Frontier," and the author is identified simply as "a Brooklynite." The variants in the *Eagle* version of *Franklin Evans*, which tend generally to soften the blatancy of

INTRODUCTORY[2]

THE story I am going to tell you, reader, will be somewhat aside from the ordinary track of the novelist. It will not abound, either with profound reflections, or sentimental remarks. Yet its moral—for I flatter myself it has one, and one which it were well to engrave on the heart of each person who scans its pages—will be taught by its own incidents, and the current of the narrative.

Whatever of romance there may be—I leave it to any who have, in the course of their every-day walks, heard the histories of intemperate men, whether the events of the tale, strange as some of them may appear, have not had their counterpart in real life. If you who live in the city should go out among your neighbors and investigate what is being transacted there, you might come to behold things far more improbable. In fact, the following chapters contain but the account of a young man, thrown by circumstances amid the vortex of dissipation—a country youth, who came to our great emporium to seek his fortune—and what befell him there. So it is a plain story; yet as the grandest truths are sometimes plain enough to enter into the minds of children—it may be that the delineation I shall give will do benefit, and that educated men and women may not find the hour they spend in its perusal, altogether wasted.

And I would ask your belief when I assert that, what you are going to read is not a work of fiction, as the term is used.[3] I narrate occurrences that have had a far more substantial existence, than in my fancy. There will be those who, as their eyes turn past line after line, will have their memories carried to matters which they have heard of before, or taken a part in themselves, and which, they know, are *real*.[4]

Can I hope, that my story will do good? I entertain that hope. Issued in the cheap and popular form you see, and wafted by every mail to all parts

the original version's reformist purpose, are identified in the following notes by "FC." Two imbedded stories in the novel, omitted in the *Eagle*, were reprinted separately: "The Death of Wind-Foot" in the *American Review*, June 1845, and again without change from the *American* text, as "The Death of Wind-Foot. An Indian Story" in the *Crystal Fount and Rechabite Recorder* (New York), V (October 18, 1845) 81–84; "Little Jane" in the *Eagle*, December 7, 1846, and in *Collect*. The variants of these two stories are indicated in the footnotes that follow by the following abbreviations: "DW," "LJE," and "LJC." Variants in paragraphing and punctuation, generally minor in nature, are not noted.

2. The "Introductory" is omitted in FC.

3. In conformity with current convention, writers of popular tales suggested by such subtitles as "A Tale of Real Life" or by discussion that their fiction was the reporting of actuality and was not the unwholesome and unsettling fancies of the imagination.

of this vast republic; the facilities which its publisher possesses, giving him the power of diffusing it more widely than any other establishment in the United States; the mighty and deep public opinion which, as a tide bears a ship upon its bosom, ever welcomes anything favorable to the Temperance Reform; its being written *for the mass*, though the writer hopes, not without some claim upon the approval of the more fastidious; and, as much as anything else, the fact that it is as a pioneer in this department of literature[5]—all these will give "THE INEBRIATE," I feel confident, a more than ordinary share of patronage.

For youth, what can be more invaluable? It teaches sobriety, that virtue which every mother and father prays nightly, may be resident in the characters of their sons. It wars against Intemperance, that evil spirit which has levelled so many fair human forms before its horrible advances. Without being presumptuous, I would remind those who believe in the wholesome doctrines of abstinence, how the earlier teachers of piety used parables and fables, as the fit instruments whereby they might convey to men the beauty of the system they professed. In the resemblance, how reasonable it is to suppose that you can impress a lesson upon him you would influence to sobriety, in no better way than letting him read such a story as this.

It is usual for writers, upon presenting their works to the public; to bespeak indulgence for faults and deficiences. I am but too well aware that the critical eye will see some such in the following pages; yet my book is not written for the critics, but for THE PEOPLE; and while I think it best to leave it to the reader's own decision whether I have succeeded, I cannot help remarking, that I have the fullest confidence in the verdict's being favorable.

And, to conclude, may I hope that he who purchases this volume, will give to its author, and to its publisher also, the credit of being influenced not altogether by views of the profit to come from it? Whatever of

4. Earlier parts of *Franklin Evans* may reflect the "reality" of Whitman's editorials a few months earlier in the *Aurora*, dealing with Manhattan boarding houses and the temptations of the metropolis for guileless youth. See Rubin and Brown, pp. 17–27.

5. Whitman's tale was not the first temperance novel, as he implied, but also not even a pioneer in that "department of literature." Among temperance novels then quite popular were Lucius Manley Sargent's *My Mother's Gold Ring* (1833), Cyrus Mann's *The Clinton Family* (1833), and the anonymous *The Price of a Glass of Brandy* (1841). Mrs. J. Thayer had just published *The Drunkard's Daughter* and T. S. Arthur had taken his first step toward immortality by publishing *Temperance Tales; or, Six Nights with the Washingtonians*. Fiedler suggests a unique niche for *Franklin Evans* (p. 459), in "the main line of American city novels from Whitman's *Franklin Evans*, through Crane's *Maggie*, up to the fiction of Dreiser and the 'muckrakers.'"

those views may enter into our minds, we are not without a strong desire that the principles here inculcated will strike deep, and grow again, and bring forth good fruit. A prudent, sober, and temperate course of life cannot be too strongly taught to old and young; to the young, because the future years are before them—to the old, because it is their business to prepare for death. And though, as before remarked, the writer has abstained from thrusting the moral upon the reader, by dry and abstract disquisitions—preferring the more pleasant and quite as profitable method of letting the reader draw it himself from the occurrences—it is hoped that the New and Popular Reform now in the course of progress over the land, will find no trifling help from a "TALE OF THE TIMES."

CHAPTER I.

> The tree-tops now are glittering in the sun;
> Away! 'tis time my journey was begun.
>   R. H. DANA.[6]

ONE bright cool morning in the autumn of 183–, a country market-wagon, which also performed the office of stage-coach for those whose means or dispositions were humble enough to be satisfied with its rude accommodations, was standing, with the horses harnessed before it, in front of a village inn, on the Long Island turnpike. As the geography of the reader[7] may be at fault to tell the exact whereabouts of this locality, I may as well say, that Long Island is a part of the State of New York, and stretches out into the Atlantic, just south-eastward of the city which is the great emporium of our western world. The most eastern county of the island has many pretty towns and hamlets; the soil is fertile, and the people, though not refined or versed in city life, are very intelligent and hospitable. It was in that eastern county, on the side nearest the sea, that the road ran on which the market-wagon just mentioned was going to traverse. The driver was in the bar-room, taking a glass of liquor.

As the landlord, a sickly-looking, red-nosed man, was just counting out the change for the one dollar bill out of which the price of the brandy was to be taken, a stranger entered upon the scene. He was a robust youth, of about twenty years; and he carried an old black leather valise in his

---

6. The chapter mottoes are omitted in FC. The source of certain mottoes is indicated in UPP, II, where *Franklin Evans* was first reprinted in its original form. Thomas O. Mabbott—in "Notes on Walt Whitman's 'Franklin Evans,'" *Notes and Queries*, CLXXXIX (December 1925) 419–420—showed that Whitman could have found certain mottoes in Rev. George B. Cheever's *The Commonplace Book of American Poetry* (1831, but often reprinted), a standard anthology of the time. I

hand, and a coarse overcoat hanging on his arm. The proprietor of the vehicle standing outside, knew, with the tact of his trade, the moment this young man hove in sight, that he probably wished to take passage with him. The stranger walked along the narrow path that bordered the road, with a light and springy step; and as he came toward the tavern, the personages who noticed him, thought they saw him brushing something from his eyes—the traces of tears, as it were. Upon the valise which he carried in his hand, was tacked a small card, on which was written, "*Franklin Evans.*"

Reader, I was that youth; and the words just quoted, are the name of the hero of the tale you have now begun to peruse. Flattered shall I feel, if it be interesting enough to lead you on to the conclusion!

"What, Frank, is it you?" said the landlord's wife to me, coming in from an adjoining room at this moment. "Surely you cannot be going from the village? How are all your uncle's folks this morning? Baggage with you, too! Then it must be that you leave us, indeed."

"I am bound for New York," was my brief answer to the somewhat garrulous dame, as I opened the old-fashioned half-door, and entered the house. I threw my valise upon a bench, and my overcoat upon it.

The good landlady's further inquisitiveness was cut short, by my taking the driver out to his wagon, for the purpose of making arrangements and settling the price of my passage. This was soon concluded, and my rather limited stock of travelling gear was safely deposited on the top of some baskets of mutton in the rear of the vehicle.[7.1]

"Come, youngster," said he who owned the mutton; "come in with me, and take a drop before we start. The weather is chill, and we need somewhat to keep us warm."

I felt no particular wish either to drink or refuse: so I walked in, and each of us drank off a portion of that fluid, which has brought more wo into society than all the other causes of evil combined together.

The landlord and his family were old acquaintances of mine, from the fact that we had for several years resided in the same village. It was not, therefore, without some little feeling of displeasure with myself, that I repulsed all the good-natured inquiries and endeavors of him and his wife, to discover the object of my journey. I had known him as a worthy man in times past, previous to his keeping the tavern. Young as I was, I

am indebted to both Holloway and Mabbott for the identifications of the mottoes in *Franklin Evans.* The motto for Chapter I, from "The Changes of Home," by R. H. Dana, Sr., appears in Cheever.

7. of some reader FC

7.1. FC omits the following five paragraphs and the first two sentences of the sixth.

could well remember the time, when his eyes were not bleared, and his face flushed with unnatural redness, and his whole appearance that of a man enfeebled by disease: all of which characterized him now. Ten years before, he had been a hale and hearty farmer; and with his children growing up around him, all promised a life of enjoyment, and a competency for the period of his own existence, and for starting his sons respectably in life. Unfortunately, he fell into habits of intemperance. Season after season passed away; and each one, as it came, found him a poorer man than that just before it. Everything seemed to go wrong. He attributed it to ill luck, and to the crops being injured by unfavorable weather. But his neighbors found no more harm from these causes than in the years previous, when the tippler was as fortunate as any of them. The truth is, that habits of drunkeness in the head of a family, are like an evil influence— a great dark cloud, overhanging all, and spreading its gloom around every department of the business of that family, and poisoning their peace, at the same time that it debars them from any chance of rising in the world.

So, as matters grew worse, my hapless friend narrowed down the operations of his farm, and opened his dwelling as a country inn. Poor fellow! he was his own best customer. He made out to glean a scanty subsistence from the profits of his new business; but all the old domestic enjoyment and content, seemed fled for ever. The light laugh, and the cheerful chuckle with which he used to toss his infant child in his arms, when returned at evening from his labor, were heard no more. And the cozy and comfortable winter fireside—the great wide hearth, around which they used to cluster when the hail pattered against the small windows from without—where was its comfort now? Alas! while the hearth itself remained in its old place, the happy gatherings were passed away! Many a time, when a young boy, I had stolen from my own home of an evening, to enjoy the vivacity and the mirth of that cheerful fireside. But now, like an altar whose gods and emblems were cast down and forgotten, it was no more the scene of joy, or the spot for the pleasantness of young hearts. The fumes of tobacco, and the strong smell of brandy and gin, defiled its atmosphere; while its huge logs, as they blazed upward, lighted the faces of pallid or bloated inebriates!

The farmer's sons, too, had left him, and gone to seek their living in a more congenial sphere. Intemperance is the parent of peevishness and quarrels, and all uncharitableness. Every day brought new causes of grievance and of dissention. Sometimes, the father was unreasonable, and demanded of his children far more than was consistent with justice. Sometimes, they forgot the respect due from son to parent; for whatever may be the faults of those who give us birth, there is little excuse for thankless ones, whose disobedience to the parental will, is indeed sharper than the serpent's tooth. And so the grown up children went away from the family residence, and were thenceforward almost as strangers.

I have been led into an episode. Let me return to the matter more immediately in point to the plot of my narrative. Upon getting into the vehicle, I found that it already had four occupants, whom I had not seen before; as the canvas top had concealed and sheltered them, and they had remained silent during my conversation with the driver and the people of the tavern. Some part of what I learned about these personages in the course of our journey, I may as well state here.

There was a young man about four or five years older than myself. His name was John Colby. He was a book-keeper in a mercantile establishment in the city, and from his lively, good-tempered face, one might easily judge that fun and frolic were the elements he delighted in. Colby sat on the same seat with myself, and not many minutes passed away before we were on quite sociable terms with one another.

Back of us sat an elderly country woman, who was going to visit a daughter. Her daughter, she took occasion to inform us, had married a very respectable citizen about three months previous, and they now lived in good style in the upper part of a two-story house in Broome-street. The woman was evidently somewhat deficient in perception of the ridiculous —as she herself was concerned; but still, as she *was* a woman, and a mother, and her conversation was quite harmless—no one thought of evincing any sign of amusement or annoyance at her rather lengthy disquisitions upon what, to us, were totally uninteresting topics.

At her side was a middle-aged gentleman, named Demaine. He was dressed with such exceeding neatness, that I could not but wonder how he came to ride in so homely a conveyance. Of his character, more will be learned in the subsequent pages.

On the back seat of all, and crowded among a heterogenous mass of 'market truck,' sat a gentleman, the last of my four companions. I could occasionally hear him humming a tune to himself, which was proof that he did not feel in any other than a pleasant mood. He was dressed plainly, though I thought richly; and I understood by my friend, the driver, at one of the stopping places, that his rear passenger had come with him from an obscure village, whence there was no other conveyance, and where he had been for sporting purposes.

CHAPTER II.

There stood the Indian hamlet, there the lake
Spread its blue sheet that flashed with many an oar,
Where the brown otter plunged him from the brake,
And the deer drank; as the light gale flew o'er,
The twinkling maize-field rustled on the shore;
And while that spot, so wild, and lone, and fair,
A look of glad and innocent beauty wore,
And peace was on the earth, and in the air,
The warrior lit the pile, and bound his captive there.

Not, unavenged—the foeman from the wood
Beheld the deed.
                                        BRYANT.[8]

THE journey on which we were all bound, (each of us was going to New-York,) might have been rather monotonous, were it not that after a few miles we most of us allowed the reserve of strangers to melt away, and began to treat one another as familiar acquaintances. My neighbor by the side of the country woman, was the only exception to this. He preserved a stiff pragmatical demeanor, and evidently thought it beneath him to be amused, and quite indecorous to join in the laugh at our little witticisms. Colby and I, however, chatted away, occasionally interchanging a remark with the gentleman on the back seat, whom we found to be quite a fine fellow, according to our notions. Though there was a species of dignity about him which forbade too near an approach of familiarity, there was nothing of that distant haughtiness which characterized our other male passenger.

With the disposition of cheerful hearts, we found a source of pleasure in almost everything. The very slowness and sleepiness of the pace with which our horses jogged along, was the text for many a merry gibe and humorous observation. Entering into the spirit of our gayety, the sportsman in the further seat entertained us with numerous little anecdotes, many of them having reference to scenes and places along the road we were passing. He had, he told us, a fondness for prying into the olden history of this, his native island; a sort of antiquarian taste for the stories and incidents connected with the early settlers, and with the several tribes of Indians who lived in it before the whites came.[9]

---

8. "The Ages," stanzas xxx–xxxi; appears in Cheever.
9. FC omits all that follows, ending Chapter I here, until the second paragraph of the *New World* Chapter III, which commences FC Chapter II.

I could see, indeed, that the gentleman was quite an enthusiast on the subject, from the manner in which he spoke upon it. He dwelt with much eloquence upon the treatment the hapless red men had received from those who, after dispossessing them of land and home, now occupied their territory, and were still crowding them from the face of their old hunting-grounds.

"The greatest curse," said he, growing warm with his subject—"the greatest curse ever introduced among them, has been the curse of *rum!* I can conceive of no more awful and horrible, and at the same time more effective lesson, than that which may be learned from the consequences of the burning fire-water upon the habits and happiness of the poor Indians. A whole people—the inhabitants of a mighty continent—are crushed by it, and debased into a condition lower than the beasts of the field. Is it not a pitiful thought? The bravest warriors—the wise old chiefs—even the very women and children—tempted by our people to drink this fatal poison, until, as year and year passed away, they found themselves deprived not only of their lands and what property they hitherto owned, but of everything that made them noble and grand as a nation! Rum has done great evil in the world, but hardly ever more by wholesale than in the case of the American savage."

We could not but feel the justice of his remarks. Even our driver, whose red nose spoke him no hater of a glass of brandy, evidently joined in the sentiment.

As we crossed a small creek over which a bridge was thrown, he who had spoken so fervently in behalf of the Indians, pointed us to over the fields in the distance, where we could see quite a large inland sheet of water. He told us it was a lake about two miles broad, and gave us a long and unpronounceable word, which he said was the Indian name for it.

"There is an old tradition," said he—and we could perceive that he was now upon a favorite hobby—"there is a very old tradition connected with this lake, which may perhaps diversify our journey, by the relation."

We all professed our pleasure at the idea of hearing it, and without further preliminary the antiquarian began:[10]

Among the tribes of red men that inhabited this part of the world three hundred years ago, there was a small brave nation, whose hunting-grounds lay adjacent to the eastern shore of that lake. The nation I speak

10. The antiquarian's story, which follows, was printed in 1845 (see Note One) as "The Death of Wind-Foot" in the *American Review*. The *American* variants, identified by "DW," are recorded in the next seventy-nine footnotes.

of, like most of its neighbors, was frequently engaged in war. It had many enemies, who sought every means to weaken it, both by stratagem and declared hostility. But the red warriors who fought its battles were very brave; and they had a chief, whose courage and wonderful skill in all the savage arts of warfare, made him renowned through the island, and even on no small portion of the continent itself. He was called by a name which, in our language, signifies "Unrelenting." There were only two dwellers in his lodge—himself and his youthful son; for twenty moons had filled and waned since the chieftain's wife was placed in the burial-ground of her people.[11]

As the Unrelenting sat alone one evening in his rude hut, one of his people came to inform him that a traveller from a distant tribe had entered the village, and desired food and repose. Such a petition was never slighted by the red man; and the messenger was sent back with an invitation for the stranger to abide in the lodge of the chief himself. Among these simple people, no duties were considered more honorable than arranging the household comforts of a guest. These duties were now performed by the chief's own hand, his son having not yet returned from the hunt on which he had started, with a few young companions, at early dawn. In a little while the wayfarer was led into the dwelling by him who had given the first notice of his arrival.

"You are welcome, my brother," said the Unrelenting.

The one to whom this kind salute was addressed was an athletic Indian, apparently of middle age, and habited in the scant attire of his race. He had the war-tuft on his forehead, under which flashed a pair of brilliant eyes. His rejoinder to his host was friendly, yet very brief.

"The chief's tent is lonesome. His people are away?" said the stranger, after a pause, casting a glance of inquiry around.

"My brother says true, that it is lonesome," answered the other. "Twelve seasons ago the Unrelenting was a happy ruler of his people. He had brave sons, and their mother was dear to him.[12] He was strong, like a

---

11. The first paragraph of DW reads as follows:
     Three hundred years ago—so heard I the tale, not long since, from the mouth of one educated like a white man, but born of the race of whom Logan and Tecumseh sprang,—three hundred years ago, there lived on lands now forming an eastern county of the most powerful of the American states, a petty Indian tribe governed by a brave and wise chieftan. This chieftan was called by a name which in our langage signifies Unrelenting. His deeds of courage and subtlety made him renowned through no small portion of the northern continent. There were only two dwellers in his lodge—himself and his youthful son; for twenty moons had filled and waned since his wife, following four of her offspring, was placed in the burial ground.

12. "Twelve seasons ago, the Unrelenting saw five children in the shadow of his wigwam, and their mother was dear to him." DW

cord of many fibres. Then the Spirit Chief snapped the fibres, one by one, asunder. He looked with a pleasant eye on my sons and daughters, and wished them for himself. Behold all that is left to gladden my heart!"

The Unrelenting turned as he spoke, and pointed to an object just inside the opening of the tent.

A moment or two before, the figure of a boy had glided noiselessly in, and taken his station back of the chief. The new-comer seemed of the age of fourteen or fifteen years. He was a noble youth! His limbs never had been distorted by the ligatures of fashion; his figure was graceful as the slender ash, and symmetrical and springy as the bounding stag. It was the chief's son—the last and loveliest of his offspring—the soft-lipped nimble Wind-Foot.[13]

With the assistance of the child,[14] the preparations for their simple supper[15] were soon completed. After finishing it, as the stranger appeared to be weary, a heap of skins was arranged for him in one corner of the lodge, and he laid himself down to sleep.

It was a lovely summer evening. The moon shone, and the stars twinkled, and the million voices[16] of a forest night sounded in the distance.[17] The chief and his son reclined at the opening of the tent, enjoying the cool breeze that blew fresh upon them, and idly flapped the piece of deerskin that served for their door—sometimes swinging[18] it down so as to darken the apartment, and then again floating suddenly up, and letting in the bright moonbeams.[19] Wind-Foot spoke of his hunt that day. He had met with poor luck,[20] and in a boy's impatient spirit, he peevishly wondered why it was that other people's arrows should hit the mark, and not his.[21] The chief heard him with a sad smile, as he remembered his own youthful traits: he soothed the child with gentle words, telling him that even brave warriors sometimes went whole days with the same ill success as had befallen him.[22]

"Many years since," said the chief, "when my cheek was soft, and my limbs[23] had felt the numbness of but few winters, I myself vainly trav-

13. Hardly twelve years seemed the age of the new-comer. He was a noble child! His limbs, never distorted with the ligatures of civilized life, were graceful as the ash, and symmetrical and springy as the bounding stag's. It was the last and loveliest of the chieftan's sons—the soft-lipped, nimble Wind-Foot. DW
  14. With the youth's assistance DW
  15. For their frugal meal DW   16. the thousand voices DW
  17. in every direction DW   18. flinging DW
  19. then raising it suddenly up again, as if to let in the bright moonbeams. DW
  20. with no success DW
  21. wondered why it was that others' arrows should hit the mark, and failure be reserved for him alone. DW
  22. with the same perverse fortune. DW
  23. "my arms" DW

ersed our hunting-grounds, as you have done to-day. The Dark Influence was around me, and not a single shaft would do my bidding."

"And my father brought home nothing to his lodge?" asked the boy.

"The Unrelenting came back without any game," the other answered; "but he brought what was dearer to him and his people than the fattest deer or the sweetest bird-meat. His hand clutched the scalp of an accursed Kansi!"

The voice of the chief was deep and sharp in its tone of hatred.

"Will my father," said Wind-Foot, "tell—"

The child started, and paused. A sudden guttural noise came from behind them. It seemed between a prolonged grunt and a dismal groan, and proceeded from that part of the tent where the stranger was lying.[24] The dry skins which formed the bed rustled as if he who lay there was changing his position, and then all continued silent. The Unrelenting turned to his son, and proceeded in a lower tone, fearful that their talk had almost broken the sleep of their guest.[25]

"Listen!" said he, "You know a part, but not all of the cause of hatred there is between our nation and the abhorred enemies whose name I mentioned. Longer back than I can remember, they did mortal wrong to your fathers, and your fathers' people. The scalps of two of your own brothers hang in Kansi tents; and I have sworn, boy, to bear for them a never-sleeping hatred.[26]

"On the morning I spoke of,[27] I started with fresh limbs and a light heart to search for game. Hour after hour I roamed the forest with no success; and at the setting of the sun I found myself weary and many miles from my father's lodge. I lay[28] down at the foot of a tree and sleep came over me. In the depth of the night, a voice seemed whispering in my ears —it called me to rise quickly—to look around. I started to my feet, and found no one there but myself; then I knew that the Dream Spirit had been with me. As I cast my eyes about in the gloom, I saw a distant brightness. Treading softly, I approached. The light, I found, was that of a fire,

---

24. An exclamation, a sudden guttural noise, came from that part of the tent where the stranger was sleeping. DW

25. The Unrelenting proceeded in a lower tone, fearful that they had almost broken the slumber of their guest. DW

26. "The scalps of two of your near kindred hang in Kansi lodges, and I have sworn, my son, to bear them a never-ending hatred." DW

27. "of which I spoke" DW   28. "I laid" DW

29. "two sleeping figures" DW

30. "as I saw who they were—a Kansi warrior, and a child, like you, my son, in age." DW

31. "the edge of my tomahawk" DW

32. "I raised my weapon to strike" DW

and by the fire lay two figures.[29] Oh, my son, I laughed the quiet laugh of a deathly mind, as I saw who they were. Two of our hated foes—I knew them well—lay sleeping there; a Kansi warrior, and a child, like you, my son, in age.[30] I felt of my hatchet's edge[31]—it was keen as my hate. I crept toward them as the snake crawls through the grass—I bent over the slumbering boy—I raised my tomahawk to strike[32]—but I thought that, were they both slain, no one would carry to the Kansi tribe the story of my deed.[33] My vengeance would be tasteless to me if they knew it not, so I spared the child. Then I glided to the other. His face was of the same cast as the first; so my soul was gladdened more, for I knew they were of kindred blood.[34] I raised my arm—I gathered my strength—I struck, and cleft his dastard brain[35] in quivering halves!"

The chief's speech trembled with agitation. He had gradually wrought himself up to a pitch of loudness and rage; and his hoarse tones, at the last part of his narration, rang croakingly through the lodge.

At that moment the deer-skin at the door was down, and obscure darkness filled the apartment. The next, the wind buoyed the curtain aside again; the rays of the moon flowed in, and all was a halo of light. Spirits of Fear! what sight was that back there![36] The strange Indian was sitting up on his couch; his ghastly features glaring forward to the unconscious inmates in front,[37] with a look like that of Satan to his antagonist angel. His lips were parted, and his teeth clenched; his neck stretched forward—every vein of his forehead and temples bulged out as if he was suffocating—and his eyes fiery with a look of demoniac hate. His arm was raised, and his hand doubled; each nerve and sinew of them in bold relief. It was an appalling sight, though it lasted only for a moment. The Unrelenting and his son saw nothing of it, their faces being to the front of the tent: in another instant the Indian had sunk back, and was reposing with the skins wrapped round him, and motionless.[38] It was now an advanced hour of the evening.[39] Wind-Foot felt exhausted by his day's travel; so they[40] arose from their seat at the door, and retired to rest. In a few min-

33. "would carry the tale to the Kansi tribe." DW
34. "which gladdened me, for then I knew they were of close kindred." DW
35. "the warrior's brain" DW
36. At that moment, the deer-hide curtain kept all within in darkness; the next, it was lifted up, and a flood of the moonlight filled the apartment. A startling sight was back there, then! DW
37. his distorted features glaring toward the unconscious ones in front DW
38. His lips were parted, his teeth clenched, his arm raised, and his hand doubled—every nerve and sinew in bold relief. This spectacle of fear lasted only for a moment; the Indian at once sank noiselessly back, and lay with the skins wrapped round him as before. DW
39. night DW   40. the father and son DW

utes the father and son were fast asleep;[41] but from the darkness which surrounded the couch[42] of the stranger, there flashed two fiery orbs, rolling about incessantly, like the eyes of a wild beast in anger.[43] The lids of those orbs closed not in slumber during that night.

Among the primitive inhabitants who formerly occupied this continent, it was considered very rude to pester a traveller or a guest[44] with questions about himself, his last abode or his future destination. He was made welcome to stay, until he saw fit to go—whether for a long period or a short one. Thus, the next day, when the strange Indian showed no signs of departing, the chief entertained little surprise, but made his guest quite as welcome; and indeed felt the better pleased at the indirect compliment paid to his powers of giving satisfaction.[45] So the Indian passed a second night in the chieftain's tent.

The succeeding morn,[46] the Unrelenting called his son to him, while the stranger was standing at the tent door. He told Wind-Foot that he was going on a short journey, to perform which and return would probably take him till night-fall. He enjoined the boy to remit no duties of hospitality toward his guest, and bade him be ready there at evening with a welcome for his father. As the Unrelenting passed from the door of his tent, he was surprised to witness a wildness in the stranger's bright black eyes. His attention, however, was given to it but for a moment; he took his simple equipments, and started on his journey.[47]

It was some public business for his tribe that the Unrelenting went to transact. He travelled with an elastic step, and soon arrived at his destined place. Finishing there what he had to do, sooner than he expected, he partook of a slight refreshment and started for home. When he arrived in sight of his people's settlement, it was about the middle of the afternoon. The day, though pleasant, was rather warm; and making his way to his own dwelling the Unrelenting threw himself on the floor. Wind-Foot

---

41. In a little while, all was silence in the tent DW
42. bed DW   43. of an angry wild beast. DW
44. Among the former inhabitants of this continent, it was considered rudeness, of the highest degree, to annoy a traveler or guest DW
45. Until he saw fit to go, he was made welcome to stay, whether for a short time or a long one. Thus, on the morrow, when the strange Indian showed no signs of departing, the chief expressed not the least surprise, but felt indeed a compliment indirectly paid to his powers of entertainment.
   The sentence which concludes this paragraph in the original version is deleted. DW
46. Early the succeeding day DW
47. The two final sentences of this paragraph do not appear in DW.
48. This paragraph reads as follows in DW:
   The sun had marked the middle of the afternoon—when the chief, finishing what he had to do sooner than he expected, came back to his own dwell-

was not there; and after a little while, the chief rose and stepped to the nearest lodge to make inquiry after him. A woman appeared to answer his questions:[48]

"The young brave," said she,[49] "went away with the chief's strange guest many hours since."

The Unrelenting turned to go back to his tent.

"I cannot tell the meaning of it," added the woman, "but he of the fiery eye bade me, should the father of Wind-Foot ask about him, say to the chief these words: *'Unless your foe sees you drink his blood, that blood is not sweet, but very bitter.'* "[50]

The Unrelenting started, as if a snake[51] had stung him. His lip quivered,[52] and his hand involuntarily moved to the handle of his tomahawk. Did his ears perform their office truly? Those sounds were not new to him. Like a floating mist, the gloom of past years rolled away in his memory, and he recollected that the words the woman had just spoken,[53] were the very ones himself[54] uttered to the Kansi child, whom he had spared in the forest, long, long ago—and sent back to his tribe to tell how and by whom his companion was killed.[55] And this stranger? Ah, now he saw it all! He remembered the dark looks, the mystery and abruptness that marked his guest; and carrying his mind back again, he traced the same features in his face and that of the Kansi boy. Wind-Foot then was in the hands of this man, and the chief felt too conscious for what terrible purpose. Every minute lost might be fatal! He sallied from his lodge, gathered together a dozen of his warriors, and started in search of the child.[56]

All the chief's suspicions were too true.[57] About the same hour that he returned to his village,[58] Wind-Foot, several miles from home, was just coming up to his companion, who had gone on a few rods ahead of him, and was at that moment seated on the body of a fallen tree, a mighty giant of the woods, that some whirlwind had tumbled to the earth. The child

ing, and threw himself on the floor to obtain rest,—for the day though pleasant, had been a warm one. Wind-Foot was not there, and after a little interval the chief stepped to a lodge near by to make inquiry after him.

49. said a woman, who appeared to answer his questions DW
50. *"that blood loses more than half its sweetness!"* DW
51. a scorpion DW 52. trembled DW
53. the woman spake DW 54. he himself DW
55. the Kansi child whose father he slew long, long ago, in the forest! DW
56. He remembered the dark looks of his guest—and carrying his mind back again, traced the features of the Kansi in their matured counterpart. And the chief felt too conscious for what terrible purpose Wind-Foot was in the hands of this man. He sallied forth, gathered together a few of his warriors, and started swiftly to seek his child. DW
57. Deleted in DW.
58. About the same hour that the Unrelenting returned from his journey DW

had roamed about with his new acquaintance through one path after another, with the heedlessness of his age; and now, while the Indian[59] sat in perfect silence for many minutes, the boy[60] idly sported near him. It was a solemn place: in every direction around, were the towering fathers of the wilderness—aged patriarchs, that grew up and withered in those solitudes, and shaded underneath them the leaves of untold seasons.[61] At length the stranger spoke:

"Wind-Foot!"

The child, who was but a few yards off, approached at the call. As he came near, he started, and stopped in alarm; for his companion's features were wild, and bent toward him like a panther, about to make the fatal spring. Those dreadfully bright eyes were rolling, and burning with a horrid glitter; and he had the same fearful appearance that has been spoken of as occurring on the first night he spent in the chief's tent. During the moment that passed while they were thus looking at each other, terrible forebodings arose in the child's mind.[62]

"Young warrior," said the Indian,[63] "you must die!"

"The brave stranger is in play," said the other,[64] "Wind-Foot is a little boy."

"Serpents are small at first," the savage replied, "but in a few moons they have fangs and deadly poison. Hearken! branch from an evil root. I am a Kansi! The boy whom your parent spared in the forest, is now become a man. Young warriors of his tribe point to him and say, 'his father's scalp crackles in the dwelling of the Unrelenting, and the tent of the Kansi is bare.' Offspring of my deadliest foe! Ere another sun has travelled over our heads, your blood must fatten the grave of a murdered father."[65]

The boy's heart beat quickly, but the courage of his race did not forsake him.[66]

"Wind-Foot is not a girl," he said. "The son of a chief can die without wetting his cheek by tears."[67]

---

59. the latter DW   60. Wind-Foot DW

61. It was a solemn spot; in every direction around were towering patriarchs of the wilderness, growing and decaying in solitude. DW

62. As he came near, he stopped in alarm; his companion's eyes had that dreadfully bright glitter again—and while they looked at each other, terrible forebodings arose in the boy's soul. DW

63. "Young chieftain," said the stranger DW

64. "The brave is in play," was the response DW

65. "The youth your parent spared in the forest has now become a man. Warriors of his tribe point to him and say, 'His father's scalp adorns the lodge of the Unrelenting, but the wigwam of the Kansi is bare!'—Wind-Foot! it must be bare no longer!" DW

66. but beat true to the stern courage of his ancestors. DW

67. "I am the son of a chief," he answered, "my cheeks cannot be wet with

The savage looked on him for a few seconds with a malignant scowl. Then producing from an inner part of his dress, a withe of some tough bark, he stepped to the youth, to bind his hands behind him.[68] It was useless to attempt anything like resistance, for besides the disparity of their strength, the boy was unarmed; while the Indian had at his waist a hatchet, and a rude stone weapon, resembling a poniard. Having his arms thus fastened, the savage, with a significant touch at his girdle, pointed to Wind-Foot the direction he was to travel—himself following close behind.[69]

When the Unrelenting and his people started to seek for the child, and that fearful stranger whom they dreaded to think about as his companion, they were lucky enough to find the trail which the absent ones had made. None except an Indian's eye would[70] have tracked them by so slight and round-a-bout[71] a guide. But the chief's vision seemed sharp with paternal love, and they followed on, winding and on again—at length coming to the fallen tree on which the Kansi had sat.[72] Passing by this, the trail was less devious,[73] and they traversed it with greater rapidity. Its direction seemed to be to the shores of a long narrow lake, which lay between the grounds of their tribe and a neighboring one.[74] So onward they went, swiftly but silently; and just as the sun's red ball sank in the west, they saw its last flitting gleams dancing in the bosom of the lake. The grounds in this place were almost clear of trees—a few scattered ones only being interspersed here and there. As they came out from the thick woods, the Unrelenting and his warriors swept the range with their keen eyes.[75]

Was it so, indeed? Were those objects they beheld on the grass some twenty rods from the shore, the persons they sought? And fastened by that shore was a canoe. They saw from his posture, that the captive boy was bound; and they saw, too, from the situation of things, that if the Kansi should once get him in the boat, and start for the opposite side of the wa-

---

tears" DW

68. The Kansi looked at him a few seconds with admiration, which soon gave way to malignant scowls. Then producing from an inner part of his dress a withe of some tough bark, he stepped to Wind-Foot, and began binding his hands. DW

69. He pointed to Wind-Foot the direction he must take, gave a significant touch at his girdle, and followed close on behind. DW

70. could DW   71. and devious DW

72. "on which the Kansi had sat" deleted in DW.

73. This sentence opens in DW with "The trail was now less irregular."

74. a long narrow lake which lay adjacent to their territory. DW

75. Onward went they, and as the sun sank in the west, they saw his last flitting gleams reflected from the waters of the lake. The grounds here were almost clear of trees; and as they came out, the Unrelenting and his warriors swept the range with their keen eyes. DW

ters, where very possibly some of his tribe were waiting for him, the chances for a release would be hopelessly faint. For a moment only they paused; then the Unrelenting sprang off like a wolf deprived of her cubs, uttering loud and clear the shrill battle-cry of his nation.

The rest joined in the terrible chorus, and followed him.[76] As the sudden sound was swept along by the breeze to the Kansi's ear, he jumped to his feet, and with that wonderful self-possession which distinguishes his species, was aware at once of the position of the whole affair, and the course he had best pursue.[77] He seized his captive[78] by the shoulder, and ran toward the boat, holding the person of Wind-Foot between himself and those who pursued, as a shield from any weapons they might attempt to launch after him. He possessed still the advantage. They, to be sure, being unencumbered, could run more swiftly; but he had many rods the start of them.[79] It was a fearful race; and the Unrelenting felt his heart grow very sick, as the Indian, dragging his child, approached nearer to the water's edge.

"Turn, whelp of a Kansi!" the chief madly cried. "Turn! thou whose coward arm warrest with women and children![80] Turn, if thou darest, and meet the eye of a full-grown brave!"

A loud taunting laugh of scorn[81] was borne back from his flying enemy, to the ear of the furious father. The savage did not look around, but twisted his left arm, and pointed with his finger to Wind-Foot's throat. At that moment, he was within twice his length of the canoe. The boy whom he dragged after him, heard his father's voice,[82] and gathered his energies, faint and bruised as he was, for a last struggle. Ah! vainly he strove: the only result was, to loosen himself for a moment from the deathly grip of the Kansi; and his body fell to the ground—though it was useless, for his limbs were bandaged, and he could not rescue himself

---

76. This sentence and the paragraph which precedes it are combined in this fashion in DW:

> Was it so indeed?—There, on the grass not twenty rods from the shore, were the persons they sought—and fastened near by was a canoe. They saw from his posture that the captive was bound; they saw, too, that if the Kansi should once get him in the boat, and gain a start for the opposite side, where very likely some of his tribe were waiting for him, release would be almost impossible. For a moment only they paused. Then the Unrelenting sprang off, uttering the battle cry of his tribe, and the rest joined in the terrible chorus and followed him.

77. his species, determined at once what was safest and surest for him to do. DW

78. Wind-Foot DW

79. holding the boy's person as a shield from any weapons the pursuers might attempt to launch after him. He possessed still the advantage. DW

80. "warrest against children!" DW

81. "of scorn" deleted in DW

from his doom.[83] That moment, however, was a fatal one for the Kansi. With the speed of lightning, the chief's bow was up to his shoulder—the cord twanged sharply—a poison-tipped arrow sped through the air—and, faithful to its mission, cleft the Indian's side, just as he was stooping to lift Wind-Foot in the boat. He gave a wild shriek—his life-blood spouted from the wound—and he staggered and fell on the sand.[84] His strength, however, was not yet gone. Hate and measureless revenge—the stronger, that they were baffled—raged within him, and appeared in his glaring countenance. Fiend-like glances shot from his eyes, glassy as they were beginning to be with the death damps; and his hand felt to his waist-band, and clutched the poniard handle. Twisting his body like a bruised snake, he worked himself close up to the bandaged Wind-Foot. He raised the weapon in the air—he shouted aloud—he laughed a laugh of horrid triumph—and as the death-rattle shook in his throat,[85] the instrument (the shuddering eyes of the child saw it, and shut their lids in intense agony) came down, driven too surely to the heart of the hapless Wind-Foot.[86]

When the Unrelenting came up to his son, the last signs of life were quivering in the boy's countenance.[87] His eyes opened, and turned to the chief; his beautiful lips parted in a smile, the last effort of innocent fondness.[88] On his features flitted a transient lovely look, like a passing ripple of the wave—a slight tremor shook him—and the next moment, Wind-Foot was dead![89]

82. The boy heard his father's voice DW
83. Vain his efforts! for a moment only he loosened himself from the grip of his foe, and fell upon the ground. DW
84. his blood spouted from the wound, and he staggered down upon the sand. DW
85. raged within him, and shot through his eyes, glassy as they were beginning to be with death-damps. Twisting his body like a bruised snake, he worked himself close up to the bandaged Wind-Foot. He felt to his waistband, and drew forth the weapon of stone. He laughed a laugh of horrid triumph—he shouted aloud—he raised the weapon in the air—and just as the death-rattle sounded in his throat DW
86. the hapless boy. DW
87. were fading in the boy's countenance DW
88. of expiring fondness. DW
89. On his features flitted a lovely look, transient as the ripple athwart the wave, a slight tremor shook him, and the next minute Wind-Foot was dead. DW

CHAPTER III.

> Thine is the spring of life, dear boy,
>   And thine should be its flowers;
> Thine, too, should be the voice of joy,
>   To hasten on the hours:
> And thou, with cheek of rosiest hue,
>   With winged feet, should'st still
> Thy sometime frolic course pursue,
>   O'er lawn and breezy hill.   19
> Not so! what means this foolish heart,
>   And verse as idly vain?
> Each has his own allotted part
>   Of pleasure and of pain!
>   HENRY PICKERING.[90]

WE were so interested in the legend of the antiquary, that we did not notice how time passed away while it was being related. For some minutes after its conclusion, there was silence among us; for the luckless death of the poor Indian boy, seemed to cast a gloom over our spirits, and indispose us for conversation.

As it was now past noon, we began to feel as though we should be none the worse for our dinner. Accordingly, in good time, our driver drew up at a low-roofed public house, and proceeded with great deliberation to ungear his horses, for the purpose of giving them a temporary respite from their labors.[91]

Glad of being able to get out in the open air, and upon our legs once more, myself and Colby (for we had become quite cronies) sprang lightly from the vehicle, and bouncing along the little dooryard, felt quite refreshed at stretching our cramped limbs on the low porch which ran along in front of the house. Demaine got out very leisurely, and with a cool disdainful look, stood by the front wheels of the wagon, eyeing the house and the people of the place, some of whom now made their appearance. The country woman also made a movement forward. She was a fat and somewhat clumsy dame; and we thought the least Demaine could do, would be to offer her some assistance in getting down upon the ground. He stood in such a position himself, that he effectually precluded any one else from offering that assistance. But he continued his contemptuous stare, and paid, apparently, not the least attention to what was going on around him.

90. The first stanza of Pickering's "To a Young Invalid"; in Cheever.

Turning around a moment to look at Colby, who called my attention in the room, the next minute my hearing was assailed by a quick cry; and upon looking toward the wagon, I saw that the woman had entangled her dress, and was on the point of falling. A little longer, and she might have been down upon that part of the vehicle just behind the horses, or even under their feet; and yet Demaine, with his arrogant look, offered her no assistance! I sprang toward her; but before I could reach the place, the antiquary had rapidly jumped out upon the ground, and was safely landing her beside him. The incident was a trifling one; but I don't know that I ever, merely from one item of conduct, took such a dislike to any man as I did to Demaine, from that occurrence.

I thought I noticed during our dinner, that the antiquary regarded Demaine with peculiarly cool and distant demeanor. To us, he was affable and pleasant, and polite in his attentions to the old lady; but though not rude, I am sure the same feelings which took root in my own mind, started in his also.

Upon resuming our journey, the same vivacity and fund of anecdote, which had so agreeably entertained us, from our companion in the back seat, was again in requisition. I don't know how it was, but I felt confident that the antiquary was more than he seemed. His manners were so simple, and at the same time so free from anything like coarseness, that I said to myself, if I should aspire to be a *gentleman*, here would be my model. There was nothing in his conduct from which it might be inferred that he wished to demand your respect; on the contrary, he was quite friendly, and talked about plain things in plain language. Yet he had the stamp of superior station, and an indescribable air of something which told us that he would have been quite as much at home, and quite as unassuming, in the parlors of the richest people of the land. In the course of conversation, it came to be mentioned by me, that I was going to the city for the first time since I was a little child, and that I intended making it my future residence. Whether the antiquary was interested in my remarks, or whether he merely spoke from his natural good-will, I do not know; but he addressed me somewhat after this fashion:

"You are taking a dangerous step, young man. The place in which you are about to fix your abode, is very wicked, and as deceitful as it is wicked. There will be a thousand vicious temptations besetting you on every side, which the simple method of your country life has led you to know nothing of. Young men, in our cities, think much more of dress than they do of decent behavior. You will find, when you go among them, that

91. This paragraph commences Chapter II of FC, the preceding paragraph naturally having been deleted because of the omission of Wind-Foot's tale.

whatever remains of integrity you have, will be laughed and ridiculed out of you. It is considered 'green' not to be up to all kinds of dissipation, and familiar with debauchery and intemperance. And it is the latter which will assail you on every side, and which, if you yield to it, will send you back from the city, a bloated and weak creature, to die among your country friends, and be laid in a drunkard's grave; or which will too soon end your days in some miserable street in the city itself. It is indeed a dangerous step!"

The kindness of the motives of the speaker, prevented any displeasure I might have felt at being thus addressed by a perfect stranger. Colby whispered to me, that the antiquary was undoubtedly a good fellow, but somewhat too sour in his judgments; which may have been the case, in truth. The subsequent pages,[92] however, will prove the wisdom of his warning upon the subject of intemperance.[93]

As the afternoon waned, and the sun sank in the west, we drew nigher and nigher to our destination. The increasing number of carriages, the houses closer to one another, and the frequent sight of persons evidently just out from the city for a ride, admonished us that we were on the point of entering the great emporium of our western world.

When at last we came upon the paved streets, I was astonished at the mighty signs of life and business everywhere around. It was yet sometime ere sunset, and as the day was fine, numbers of people were out, some of them upon business, and many enjoying an afternoon saunter.

The place at which our conveyance stopped was in Brooklyn, near one of the ferries that led over to the opposite side of the river. We dismounted; glad enough to be at the end of our journey, and quite tired with its wearisomeness. Our passengers now prepared to go to their several destinations. The antiquary took a little carpet-bag in his hand, and politely bidding us adieu, made his way for the boat near by. Demaine was more lengthy in his arrangements. He had not much more to carry than the antiquary, but he called a porter, and engaged him to take it down to the landing. The country woman, also, hurried away; eager, no doubt, with parental fondness, to see her child.

Before Colby left me, we spoke for several minutes together. Though we had never seen each other until the morning of that day, a kind of friendship had grown up between us; and as I was in a strange place, with hardly an acquaintance in all its wide limits, it may be imagined I felt in no disposition to dissolve the bands of that friendship. Colby gave me

92. The subsequent narration FC
93. "upon the subject of intemperance" deleted in FC.

the street and number where I could find him. The place of his business was in Pearl-street; his boarding-house further up town.

"I shall always be glad to see you," said he, "and as you seem to be unused to the town, perhaps you may find me of some advantage. Call and see me to-morrow."

"You may expect me," I answered, and we parted.

And now I was in the city. Here I had come to seek my fortune. What numbers had failed[94] in the same attempt!

It may not be amiss to let the reader into the few simple incidents of my former history. My father had been a mechanic, a carpenter;[95] and died when I was some three or four years old only. My poor mother struggled on for a time—what few relations we had being too poor to assist us—and at the age of eleven, she had me apprenticed to a farmer on Long Island, my uncle. It may be imagined with what agony I heard, hardly twenty months after I went to live with my uncle, that the remaining parent had sickened and died also. The cold indifference of the strangers among whom she lived, allowed her to pass even the grim portals of death before they informed me of her illness. She died without the fond pressure of her son's hand, or the soothing of a look from one she loved.

I continued to labor hard, and fare so too; for my uncle was a poor man and his family was large. In the winters, as is customary in that part of the island, I attended school, and thus picked up a scanty kind of education. The teachers were, however, by no means overburthened with learning themselves; and my acquirements were not such as might make any one envious.

As I approached my nineteenth year, my uncle, who was an honest and worthy man, evidently felt that he was hardly justifiable in keeping me at work in an obscure country town, to the detriment of my future prospects in life. With a liberality therefore, of which many a richer person might be glad to be able to boast, he gave up the two last years of my apprenticeship—and the very two, which perhaps, would have been of more value to him than all the others. He called me to him one day, and addressing me in the kindest terms, informed me, what he felt he ought to do for his brother's child—but which his poverty prevented him from doing. He gave me my choice—whether to go to New York, and see what I could do there for a living, or to remain a while longer with him; not to labor, but to attend school, and perfect myself in some more valuable parts of education. Probably, it would have been far better had I chosen

94. had fallen FC
95. "a carpenter" is omitted in FC

the latter of the two alternatives. But with the anxious and ambitious heart of youth, I immediately determined upon the former.

The matter thus settled, arrangements were soon made—my little stock of clothes packed up in the old valise already introduced to the reader—and receiving with thankfulness from my uncle a small sum of money, which I felt sure he must have cramped himself to bestow on me, I made my adieus to my aunt and my sorrowful cousins, and went my way. The first day of my leaving home, found me at evening, as the reader knows, on the borders of that great city, where I was to take up my abode.

Yes, here I had come to seek my fortune! A mere boy, friendless, unprotected, innocent of the ways of the world—without wealth, favor, or wisdom—here I stood at the entrance of the mighty labyrinth, and with hardly any consciousness of the temptations, doubts, and dangers that awaited me there. Thousands had gone on before me, and thousands were coming still. Some had attained the envied honors—had reaped distinction—and won princely estate; but how few were they, compared with the numbers of failures! How many had entered on the race, as now I was entering, and in the course of years, faint, tired, and sick at heart, had drawn themselves out aside from the track, seeking no further bliss than to die. To die! The word is too hard a one for the lip of youth and hope. Let us rather think of those who, bravely stemming the tide, and bearing up nobly against all opposition, have proudly come off victorious—waving in their hands at last, the symbol of triumph and glory.

What should be *my* fate? Should I be one of the fortunate few? Were not the chances much more against me than they had been against a thousand others, who were the most laggard in the contest? What probability was there, that amid the countless multitude, all striving for the few prizes which Fortune has to bestow, *my* inexperienced arm should get the better of a million others?

Oh, how good a thing it is that the great God who has placed us in this world—where amid so much that is beautiful, there still exists vast bestowal among men of grief, disappointment, and agony—has planted in our bosoms the great sheet-anchor, Hope![96] In the olden years, as we look back to our former life, we feel indeed how vain would have been our strife without the support of this benignant spirit.

To be sure, thousands had gone before me, in the struggle for the envied things of existence, and *failed*. But many others had met with *success*. A stout heart, and an active arm, were the great levers that might raise up fortune, even for the poor and unfriended Franklin Evans. In our

96. the great impression, Hope! FC

glorious republic, the road was open to all; and, my chance, at least, was as good as that of some of those who had began with no better prospects.

CHAPTER IV.

> Stay, mortal, stay! nor heedless thus,
>   Thy sure destruction seal:
> Within that cup there lurks a curse
>   Which all who drink shall feel.
> Disease and death, for ever nigh,
>   Stand ready at the door;
> And eager wait to hear the cry,
>   Of "Give me one glass more!"
>   WASHINGTONIAN MINSTREL.[97]

WHEN I arose the next morning, and thought over in my mind what it would be better for me to do first, I saw that it was necessary to provide myself with a boarding-house. After breakfast, I crossed the ferry, and purchasing a paper of one of the news-boys, for a penny, I looked over to the column containing advertisements of the places similar to what I wished. I was somewhat surprised to find that every one had the most "airy, delightful location," the very "best accommodations," with "pleasant rooms," and "all the comforts of a home." Some of them informed the reader that there were "no children in the house." These I passed over, determining not to go there; for I loved the lively prattle of children, and was not annoyed as some people pretend to be, by their little frailties.

Noting down upon a memorandum several that I thought might suit me, I started on my voyage of discovery. The first place that I called at was in Cliff-street. A lean and vinegar-faced spinster came to the door, and upon my inquiring for the landlady, ushered me into the parlor, where in a minute or two I was accosted by that personage. She was as solemn and sour as the spinster, and upon my mentioning my business, gave me to understand that she would be happy to conclude a bargain with me, but upon several conditions. I was not to stay out later than ten o'clock at night—I was to be down at prayers in the morning—I was never to come into the parlor except upon Sundays—and I was always to appear at table with a clean shirt and wristbands. I took my hat, and politely in-

---

97. From the anonymous "One Glass More," which may be found complete in A. B. Grosh's *Temperance Pocket Companion*, 1852.

formed the lady, that if I thought I should like her terms, I would call again.

I next made a descent upon a house, which in the advertisement, was described as offering good conveniences on "very reasonable terms." This I supposed meant that it was a cheap boarding-house. The mistress took me up into an open attic, where were arranged beds of all sorts and sizes. She pointed me to a very suspicious looking one, in a corner, which she said was not occupied. She told me I could have that, and my meals, for three dollars a week, payable punctually on every Saturday night. I did not like the look of the woman, or the house. There was too little cleanliness in both; so I made the same remark at parting, as before.

A third and fourth trial were alike unsuccessful. The fifth, I liked the house very well, but upon being informed that all the boarders were men, I determined upon making another trial. I desired to obtain quarters where the society was enlivened with ladies.

Quite tired at length with my repeated disappointments, and more than half suspicious that I was myself somewhat too fastidious, I determined that my next attempt should bring matters to a conclusion. Fortunately, the place I called at, had very few of the objections I found with the others. The landlady seemed an intelligent, rather well-bred woman, and the appearance of the furniture and floors quite cleanly. And here it will perhaps be worth while for me to state, that this item of cleanliness was one which I could not forego, from the effects of my country life. I had been used to see, amid much poverty, the utmost freedom from anything like dirt, dust, or household impurity. And without it, I could not be comfortable in any situation.

I concluded an arrangement with the woman, and told her I should come that very day. I was to have a snug little room in the attic, exclusively for my own use, and was to pay three dollars and a half per week.

Soon after leaving this place, which I gave a good look at when I got outside, lest I might forget it, I went down in Pearl-street to call upon Colby. He was glad to see me, but as it was now the business part of the day, and I saw he had plenty to do, I did not stay but a few minutes. I gave him the street and number of my new residence, and he engaged to call and see me in the evening, when his employments were over.

Who should I meet, as I was coming up from the ferry after having been over to Brooklyn for my valise, but my friend of the day before, the antiquary. He expressed his pleasure at seeing me by a smile, and a few kind words.

"And how do you like the city?" said he.

"I have hardly had an opportunity of finding out much about it yet, sir. But I dare say I shall know more by-and-by."

"Too much," he rejoined, shaking his head—"too much, perhaps. There are a thousand things here, my young friend, which no man is the better for knowing."

He paused, and I knew not exactly what reply to make.

"May I ask what you intend doing in New-York," said he, at length.

"I hardly know myself, sir," I answered; "I have come here with the intention of getting employment. What that may be, will depend a good deal upon my luck. I shall not mind much what I turn my hand to, so that I gain an honest living by it, and a fair chance of bettering myself as I grow older."

"That is a strange way," said my companion, evidently with some interest. "People are not apt to get any employment worth having in this city, if they come here in the way I understand you to say you come."

"I am determined to do my best. Perhaps," I added, for I thought the antiquary showed quite a friendly disposition—"perhaps, sir, you could suggest something to me in the way of getting a situation?"

My friend looked down upon the ground awhile, and smiling good-humoredly as he raised his face, replied,

"Well, Evans, I possibly may do something for you. Look you: I do not wish to conceal that I am somewhat interested in your case. When but a little older than you, I came to this city, in pretty much the same way that you come now. I was not poor, but was without acquaintances or friends, as you say you are. And though I had money, I received, God knows, but little friendliness from those who might have shown at least some kindness to me: but whose dispositions were not as large as their means, for they were rich. I have, however, lived long enough to do without their friendship, and I don't know what reason there is that I should not give you a helping hand. Perhaps what I may do for you may not be much, and may not cost me anything. So much the more scope for your own exertions, and honor to you if you hew out your fortune for yourself. Here is my card," and he handed it to me: "come to me to-morrow morning at eleven. I am punctual, and shall expect you to be the same; and perhaps you will not regret the chance acquaintance you made in the market-wagon. Good day."

I could hardly return the salutation, so pleased was I at the turn events were taking. To be sure, I did not know the nature of the business my friend would employ me in, but it *was* employment, and that was the first stepping-stone to the heights that lay above. I looked at the card; upon it was written, "*Stephen Lee,*—, Exchange Place." I carefully deposited it in my breast pocket, and with a lighter step wended on to my new boarding-house.

Whether it was that I had gained confidence since my interview with Mr. Lee, or from some other cause, I felt myself very little abashed at sitting down, for the first time in my life, at dinner with some twenty[98] well-bred ladies and gentlemen. Though many of the observances were somewhat new to me, and one or two of my nearest neighbors, plainly saw, and felt amused, at my unsophisticated conduct in some respects; I believe I came off, upon the whole, with tolerable credit.

I had an opportunity, too, of seeing who were the really well-bred people of the house. For those possessed of the truest politeness will never deign to wound the feelings of one in their company, by showing that they notice his deficiencies, and are entertained at his ignorance and awkwardness. On the contrary, they would rather do like that greatest of rakes, and of gentlemen, George IV.; who, when some court ladies, at tea, simpered at a couple of unfashionable companions for pouring their tea in their saucers, instead of drinking it from their cups; poured his also into the saucer, and thus commended it to his royal lips, that they might not be mortified by the mirth of the rude ones.

At night, Colby, according to his promise, paid me a visit. He was much pleased when I told him of my encounter with Lee, and of his promise to me. He told me, when I showed him the card, that he had frequently heard of that personage, who was a merchant of much reputation and no small wealth. Colby congratulated me on my luck, and jokingly told me, he should not be surprised to see me one day the owner of warehouses and the head of great business.

"But come," said he, "this is dull fun here. Let us go out and cruise a little, and see what there is going on."

"Agreed," said I. "I shall like it of all things."

So we took our hats and sallied forth from the house.

After strolling up and down one of the most busy streets several times, I became a little more used to the glare of the lamps in the windows, and the clatter and bustle which was going on around me. How bright and happy everything seemed! The shops were filled with the most beautiful and costly wares, and the large, clear glass of the show-windows flashed in the brilliancy of the gas, which displayed their treasures to the passers-by. And the pave was filled with an eager and laughing crowd, jostling along, and each intent on some scheme of pleasure for the evening. I felt confused for a long time with the universal whirl, until at

---

98. "twenty" is omitted in FC.

length, as I said, the scene grew a little more accustomed, and I had leisure to think more calmly upon what I saw.

In a little while, Colby asked me if I did not wish to hear some fine music and drink a glass of wine. I assented, and we entered a beautifully furnished room, around which little tables were placed, where parties were seated drinking and amusing themselves with various games. We took our station at the first vacant seats, and called for our drinks. How delicious everything seemed! Those beautiful women—warbling melodies sweeter than ever I had heard before, and the effect of the liquor upon my brain, seemed to have me in happiness, as it were, from head to foot!

Oh, fatal pleasure! There and then was my first false step after coming in the borders of the city—and *so soon* after, too! Colby thought not, perhaps, what he was doing—but still he was very much to blame. He knew I was young, fond of society, and inexperienced; and it would have been better for me had he ushered me amid a pest-house, where some deadly contagion was raging in all its fury.

I tremble now as I look back upon the results which have sprung from the conduct of that single night, as from one seed of evil. Over the lapse of ten years I gaze, and the scene comes back to me again in the most vivid reality. I can remember even the colors of the chequer-board, and the appearance of the little table, and the very words of some of the songs that were sung. We drank—not once only, but again and again.

Yes, with a singular distinctness, the whole appearance of the room, and of the men with their hats on and cigars in their mouths, that sat all about, are as plain before my eyes as though they were painted in a picture there. It was all new to me then. A hundred more exciting scenes have passed over my head since, and have left no impression, while this is marked as with a steel pencil upon the tablets of my memory.

I remember being struck with the appearance of one poor fellow in a corner. He probably was not much older than myself; yet his face was bloated, his eyes inflamed, and he leaned back in that state of drowsy drunkeness which it is so disgusting to behold. I presume his companions—those who had made merry with him until he was brought to this stage of degradation—had left him in scorn; and there he sat, or rather supported himself in the corner, not half awake, and the subject of many a gibe and light laugh. Was it not a warning to me? And yet I was not warned.

After a time, some of the white-aproned subordinates of the place came to him, roughly broke his slumbers, and put him forth from the place. Miserable man! Without doubt, he now sleeps the sleep which no jostle can awaken, and which no curl of the lip, or gibe of the scoffer, can start from its dark repose. He must have died the death of the drunkard![99]

Colby saw at length that he had been too heedless with me. Used as he was to the dissipation of city life, he forgot that I was from the country, and never in my life before engaged in such a scene of *pleasure*.

With some difficulty preserving the steadiness of my pace, as we left the room, I took his arm, and he walked with me toward my residence. Indeed, if he had not done so, I question whether I should have reached it; for my head swam, and the way in the night was somewhat difficult to find. Leaving me at the door, my companion bade me good night, and departed.

I entered, took a light from a number which were left upon a table in the hall for the use of the boarders, and slowly ascended the stairs to my room. My slumbers were deep and unbroken. So were those of the preceding evening, and yet the nature of the two was widely different. The former was the repose of health and innocence—the latter, the dull lethargy of *drunkeness*.

CHAPTER V.

All is not gold that glitters.—OLD PROVERB.

THE reflections which operated in my mind the next morning, are not a sufficiently tempting theme for me to dwell upon. I can hardly say that shame and remorse possessed me to such a degree, as to counterbalance the physical discomfort which weighed painfully upon every part of my frame.

In the course of the forenoon, I visited my antiquarian merchant friend, Mr. Lee. He had not forgotten me, but was as good as his word. His own establishment, he said, already employed a sufficiency of clerks and attendants whom he could not turn out without doing them injustice. He had made inquiries, and informed me that a Mr. Andrews, a gentleman doing business in Wall-street, with whom he was slightly acquainted, might be able to give me a situation.

My patron wrote a note, addressed to Andrews, which I carried to that personage. I found him in a handsome granite edifice, in a back room furnished sumptuously, out of which opened another, fronting on the

99. This sentence is omitted in FC.
1. (Second Series). In FC, Evans does not go again this night to the "musical drinking-house," and the paragraph continues at this point as follows:
I had always (like most young country fellows,) felt a desire to go to the

street. It was a bank. Numerous people were constantly coming and going, upon business; everything was transacted with a quiet easy air, and without much bustle, though I could see that the matters which were discussed involved the value of thousands.

What conceivable situation Mr. Lee could have had in view for me there, I could not imagine; but I was soon undeceived. Mr. Andrews looked over the note, and called me to him. He was a thin, black-eyed, rather delicate-looking man, and had a completely professional appearance. He told me he was a lawyer, and that his connection with the institution in which I now saw him did not prevent him from attending to his other avocations. He wanted some one as a kind of clerk, porter, and errand boy— three in one—to take care of his office while he was absent. The office was in an upper part of the same street.

I readily agreed to accept the terms which Andrews proposed, and he desired me to commence my duties on the morrow. As I took my departure from the place, who should I see in front, with a quill behind his ear, but my market-wagon acquaintance, Demaine. I accosted him with the salutation of the day, but he made a very slight and cool answer; and as I did not care much about his good-will, I went forth without further parley.

Somewhat at a loss what to do with myself, I walked down to Colby's place of business, and made him promise to call upon me again that evening, as he had the preceding one.

"And how have you felt to-day?" said he, smiling mischievously; "you country boys cannot hold up under a few glasses, like us of the city."

I blushed, as I brought to mind the folly I had committed, and internally thought I could never be guilty of it again.

"I know," answered I, "that there are many things in which you will find me rather awkward. But my very visit here, to ask you again to-night, proves that I am willing to get knowledge."

Knowledge! Better would it have been for me had I remained in ignorance through the whole course of my life, than attained to *such* knowledge.

When Colby came in the evening, and we started out to walk as before, I felt determined not to go in the musical drinking-house again.[1] But I don't know how it was, the very first proposition my companion made to that effect, found me a willing listener. We entered, and called for our drinks.

theatre. And as Colby was willing, we bent our steps to that place of amusement now. On our way we were joined by a third person named Mitchell, a friend of my friend's. I tried to appear as much at ease as possible—though every thing was stranger to me, even than before.
The paragraph immediately following this one in FC is indicated in the next note.

It was indeed a seductive scene. Most of the inmates were young men; and I noticed no small number quite on the verge of boyhood. They played the same as the rest, and tossed off glasses of liquor, without apparently feeling any evil effects from it. Little as I knew of the world, I felt that there was something wrong here. The keeper of the house was not an American. He made his appearance now and then among the company, smiling and bowing, and highly pleased, no doubt, that shillings were pouring into his pockets with such profitable rapidity.

And the music again! How sweet it sounded out, combined with the fascinating looks of the females who sang. I was completely enthralled, and drank deeper even than the night before.

In the course of the evening some little incidents happened, which served as a proof of the truth of the old proverb, which declares that glittering things may not be of the value they seem. It happened thus. Colby and myself, accompanied by a friend of my friend's, whom we met at the drinking-room, determined to go to the theatre that evening, and accordingly did so. The house was crowded.[2] Beautiful women and elegant men—moustached dandies and lively youth—brilliant fashionables of all varieties, combined to render the scene exhilarating and splendid. And the music from the orchestra, now soft and subdued, now bursting out with notes of thunder—how delicious it glided into the ear! The curtain drew up and the play began. It was one of those flippant affairs, that pretend to give a picture of society and manners among the exclusive. The plot worse than meagre—the truthfulness of the scene a gag, which ought not to have excited aught but ridicule—the most nauseous kind of mock aristocracy tinging the dialogue from beginning to end—yet it was received with applause, and at the conclusion, with vociferous and repeated cheers! The manager had printed upon his bills that London was pleased with it, and that one of the scenes represented life as in the private parlor of an English Duke—with the curtains, carpets, and drapery of the parlor, as good as real! I blushed for the good sense of my countrymen.

In the farce which followed, one of the characters was a wild hoyden of a girl. It was done very agreeably by one of the actresses, whose beauty excited my admiration to no small degree. So much indeed was I fascinated with her, that I expressed my opinion in terms which the liquor I had drank just before by no means contributed to render less strong.[3] I vowed that if I could see her, side by side, and speak to her, I would give the world. Mitchell, the one who made the third of our party, listened to me for some time with a kind of sober surprise; and then, giving a wink to

---

2. FC takes up the narrative of the original with this sentence.

Colby, told me he was acquainted with the actress who had pleased me so much, and would introduce me to her that very evening, if I desired. I thanked him a thousand times.

In the interval between the acts, my eyes were attracted by the figure of a young gentleman in the stage-box, (we sat in the pit,) who seemed to me a perfect pattern of perfection in his dress and manners—in fact, a gentleman of the highest order. I saw Mitchell looking at him also.

"Do you know him?" said I.

"Yes," he answered.

"A fine looking fellow," said I.

He assented.

When the play was over, we went out. Along by the theatre, there were the glaring gas lights of several fashionable refectories.

"Gentlemen," said our companion, "suppose we go down here, and get some oysters."

We agreed, and down we went.

While waiting in our little box, Mitchell called one of the men in attendance:

"John, bring us a bottle of Port."

The wine was brought.

"Mr. Evans," said Mitchell to me, "do you know I have a fancy always to be served by a particular individual in this refectory? Just notice the man's face, now, and tell me what you think of my taste."

When the waiter came again, in obedience to our companion's call, he held him in talk several minutes about some trivial details respecting the cooking of the articles we had ordered. When he went out, I looked up in Mitchell's face—

"Why," said I, "that—that—that man is the very fellow!"

"What very fellow?"

"He is the picture of the gentleman we saw in the boxes at the theatre!"

"I dare say he is the person; in fact, I know he is."

I changed the subject, and we finished our oysters.

"And now," said Mitchell to me, "if your friend Colby will wait here five minutes, I will introduce you to the actress."

My mistake in regard to the *fashionable gentleman*, had taught me a lesson, and my country life had taught me also to keep better hours. So I would have excused myself, but Mitchell seemed anxious that I should go with him.

3. that I expressed my opinion in prodigious terms. FC

"It's but a step," said he.

So we walked round the block, into a dirty alley leading to the rear of the theatre. Mitchell told me he had the *entree* there (to the theatre, I mean, not the alley) and in we walked.

I pass over my stares of wonder, and my running aslant dungeon walls, castles, and canvas palaces. We reached an open space, on one side, where there were quite a number of persons idling. At a little table sat a woman, eating some cheese and thick bread, and drinking at intervals from a dingy pewter mug, filled with beer. She was coarse—her eyes had that sickly bleared appearance, which results from the constant glitter of strong light upon them; her complexion was an oily brown, now quite mottled with paint, and her feet and ancles were encased in thick ill-blacked shoes.

Mitchell went up to the table, (I leaning on his arm,) and engaged in chit chat with the delectable creature. He introduced me. I was thunderstruck! *She* was my charmer, of the hoyden in the farce! Her voice was coarse and masculine, and her manners on a par with her voice.

After ten minutes conversation, we bade the lady good night, and wended our way back to Colby, whom we found waiting for us. Neither myself nor Mitchell alluded to the subject, and Colby, no doubt understanding how matters stood, did not mention it either.

The occurrences of the night, I may as well confess, taught me to question the reality of many things I afterward saw; and reflect that, though to appearance they were showy, they might prove, upon trial, as coarse as the eating-house waiter, or the blear-eyed actress. I lost also, some of that reverence, and that awkward sense of inferiority, which most country folk, when they take up their abode in this brick-and-pine Babel, so frequently show—and which, by the way, is as amusing to the observers, as it is unfair to themselves.

CHAPTER VI.

> "Strange that such difference there should be
> 'Twixt tweedle-dum and tweedle-de."[4]

In the course of a few weeks I became quite at home in my new situation, in the office of Andrews. He treated me very civilly always, though of course he never made any approach to friendliness. I could not expect it, in the situation I occupied.

4. The closing lines of John Byrom's epigram "On the Feuds Between Handel and Bononcini."

Under the auspices of my friend Colby, I became pretty well used to city life; and before the winter passed away, I could drink off nearly as much strong liquor as himself, and feel no inconvenience from it. My employer, Mr. Andrews, had become so well satisfied with my performance of my duties, that he advanced me somewhat above my original situation. I had now none of the more menial services to perform. An Irishman, named Dennis, was engaged to act as porter, and to make the fires, open and shut the office, and so on. Andrews occasionally employed him to do business also for the financial institution of which he was an officer.

There is hardly much need that I should detain the reader with a minute account of this part of my career. Though I knew it not at the time, it was the downward career of a drunkard![5] I concealed from Andrews, as a matter of course, my habits of intemperance, and attended with tolerable carefulness to my duties during the day. Through Colby's means, I soon obtained a wide circle of acquaintance, mostly young men in the same walk of life with ourselves, and having the same habits. We used frequently to go round of nights from place to place, stopping every now and then at some bar-room, and taking a drink all round. This we used to call a 'red circle.' How appropriate a name that was, the reader can judge for himself.

And about this time (I had lived nearly six months in my situation with Andrews) an incident occurred, which had an important bearing upon my future course of life. Though I saw my good benefactor, Mr. Lee, but seldom, I was not ungrateful for the kindness he had shown me, and often wished that there might be some way of repaying it. One evening, when I had finished my supper, and was going up to my room to prepare for a visit to the theatre, which I had engaged to attend that night with Colby and a party of friends, the landlady handed me a note, which had been left for me during the day. Quite curious to know who could have written to me, and what about, I opened it hastily, and read the following:

"—Exchange Place, tuesday morning,

"Dear young friend,

"The interest I have taken in your welfare, has by no means grown cold, though of late I have not seen you, or had any opportunity of showing my good will. The particular reason of my writing is, that one of my clerks has lately left me; his situation, I think would be an agreeable one for you, and if you choose to accept it, it is at your service. The salary is $800 per year.

5. of dissipation! FC

"Give your present employer a couple week's notice, before you leave him, in order that he may have an opportunity of getting some one in your place. At the end of that time come to me, and I will induct you in your new duties. If this proposition meets your approval, write me to that effect as soon as convenient.

"STEPHEN LEE."

I was quite overjoyed! Not only was the stipend offered me by my old friend more than twice as much as that I received from Andrews, but then I should be in the service of a man I loved, instead of one whom, at best, I could look upon with no stronger feeling than indifference. I sat down immediately, and indited a grateful acceptance of Mr. Lee's offer.

My duties at Andrews', of late, had not been, to tell the truth, of the most pleasant description. We found out, after Dennis had been with us awhile, that he had an unfortunate habit of tippling, which sadly interfered with his efficiency at work. For my own part, I could not conscientiously find fault with him, and therefore concealed his mistakes as much as possible. But they became so glaring at length, that they could not be hidden, and Andrews discharged him. Dennis frequented a little drinking-shop, which was in one of the streets on my way home, and there I often saw him afterward. So that my own labors were now as heavy as when I first commenced them.

Besides, I occasionally saw things which looked very suspicious, in connection with Andrews' business arrangements. I heard rumors too, in my intercourse with the neighboring clerks, which by no means increased my opinion for my employer's honesty. Those who were supposed to be at home in such affairs, more than hinted that he would before long be summarily removed from his station in the moneyed establishment, before alluded to in these pages.[6] It was asserted also, that Andrews had lately used immense sums of money, the origin of which no one could tell. So I felt not at all grieved at the idea of finding another master, and gave the notice premonitory which Mr. Lee desired, with but ill-concealed gratification.

Some days after, as I was passing down to the office from my breakfast, I saw Dennis, the discharged porter, come out of the little groggery I have mentioned. He stepped forward, and stood upon the curb-stone, looking down upon the ground, very miserable to all appearance. Dennis had gone from bad to worse, until he was now at the very lowest stage of degradation. Though I saluted him, I could hardly conceal my disgust at his filthy and bloated looks. How little did I think, that one day might find

6. in these columns. FC

me so little removed from his present condition![7] Perhaps it will not be without a wholesome moral, if I finish this chapter with the relation of poor Dennis's subsequent conduct that day, and an off-set of the doings of another personage, who has figured somewhat in my narrative—as those occurrences subsequently came to my knowledge.

At the early hour I saw him, Dennis was passing through the agonies which mark the period immediately after a fit of intoxication. Pain and hunger racked him in the corporeal frame; despair, mortification and disgust with himself burnt in his heart. He felt that he was a degraded man. With an unwonted bitterness, thoughts of many chances neglected—of weeks spent in riot—of the scorn of the world—and the superciliousness of those called respectable—cut at his heart with a sharp grief. Heaving an inward groan, he started off, and passed down a by-street, to walk away, if possible, such fearful reflections.

Nearly an hour, he rapidly traversed, at hap-hazard, the narrowest and darkest ways he could pick; for he did not wish to be seen. Then his appetite became acute, and he wished for food. Wishing, merely, was vain; and he had not a single cent. Poor creature! In the preceding two days, he had not eaten a single meal. Should he beg? Should he ask for work? His suspicious appearance might subject him to denial; besides, the emergency was one not to be postponed. In an evil moment Dennis yielded to the tempter. He saw, in a small grocery, some bread piled upon a barrel top. He entered, and while the owner was busy at a back shelf, the ravenous man purloined a loaf and made off with it. The keeper of the grocery saw him as he went out, discovered the theft, and pursued the criminal. He was brought back, a police officer called, and the bread found upon him.

So the thief was taken off to prison, and being arraigned a few hours afterward, was summarily convicted, and sentenced to the customary place, just out of the city; there to remain for several days, at hard labor and confinement.

During the same hour wherein these things were being transacted, in another and distant part of the town, sat a gentleman in a parlor. The carpet was very rich, the curtains glossy silk, and the chairs heavy mahogany. The person who sat there was Andrews, my master. On a table before him lay some written papers. By the opposite side of the table, and just about to depart, stood a second gentleman, elegantly attired, and with a lofty look, which spoke of pride within.

"The time is as favorable now," said Andrews, in reply to something

7. This sentence is omitted in FC, since it refers to episodes not included in FC.

his companion had spoken, "as it ever was. Besides, we must make hay while the sun shines. Who knows whether we shall have the chance, five days from this?"

"And yet you are not willing to take the bold steps," rejoined the other; "the transfer ought to have been made a week ago."

"Are you sure it can be made without the others knowing it?" said Andrews.

"As easy as speak," was the answer; "they never examine."

"But they *might* examine."

"I tell you, only pay them a handsome dividend, and they'll rest easy any length of time."

Andrews, put his finger under his chin, and looked down a moment abstractedly.

"Have you not determined yet?" asked the person standing.

"Long ago, sir—long ago," was Andrews' reply. "But it is a dangerous game, and should be played cautiously."

"Well; shall we take this step, or no?"

Andrews raised up his head; his dark eye twinkled as it met the glance of his companion, and the two looked at each other a minute. There was evil fraternity in that look. Then Andrews bent his head two or three times without speaking. The other understood him. He smiled, and turning, left the apartment.

A person looking on as they parted, would hardly have thought them to be aught else than two respectable citizens—yet were they two most consummate scoundrels. It was indeed too true—the host of rumors I had heard about my employer's honesty. The situation he occupied, he turned to account, by schemes which were nothing more or less than swindling; and his well-dressed companion was of kindred spirit with himself. He had now come to have a private conference with Andrews, and the subject of that conference was a scheme for making a splendid fortune jointly, by means of the peculiar facilities for cheating possessed by both. A long time ago, the plan had been marked out; and now the hour was nigh, to strike the finishing stroke.

It would be painful to describe, as it would also be to read, all the villainy, the deceit, the underhand swindling, and the imposition which these two wicked men had followed, and were on the eve of closing. In all their rascality, however, they acted warily—with the wisdom of the serpent. They knew that whatever might be the execrations of people, the *law* could not touch them. Opinions, too, might be bought: defence and character might be bought. And what, that it was possible to buy, might they not purchase?

In the course of the succeeding week, the conspiracy worked its way out. The bubble burst! The master hands had arranged things well, and they triumphed.

Yet was the tempest a terrible one. Widows, left with a narrow competence; young children; sick people, whose cases were hopeless, but who might languish on for many years; sailors, away upon the ocean; fishermen, whose earnings were scant and dearly bought; mechanics; young men just commencing business; economical doctors and clergymen in their novitiate; all these, and hundreds more, had either deposited sums of money in the institution, or were sufferers by its bankruptcy in other ways. Many lost their all. There was one woman, a widow, an energetic country trader, the mother of a large family, which she supported by her business habits, who had come to the city with what was for her quite a large sum—all she was worth, and some borrowed funds besides. Her intent was to purchase a heavy stock of goods, for sale the subsequent season. For security, she had her money placed in the vaults of the institution —and lost every cent!

It would be almost an endless effort to tell who was injured. All classes, all ranks, all occupations, felt more or less of the withering blight.

But the tempest blew over at last. The two men who had provoked it, went out still among their fellow-men, with forms erect, and with smooth smiles. He of the dark eye was just finishing, a few miles from the city, a palace-like residence, of great size and beauty. Now he had it furnished with the most sumptuous luxury. Cost and pains were not spared, until Desire had no further room for wishing. Here this rich man settled himself; and here, when he had become a little used to his grandeur, so that it did not sit awkwardly upon him, he determined to give a superb entertainment. Preparations were accordingly made; scientific cooks were engaged; foreign delicacies purchased, and the most exquisite dishes prepared.

The hour and the company arrived; and the master of the feast looked around with a smile, as each one seated himself at his appointed place. They ate, and drank, and made merry. Delight, and Friendliness, and Content, seemed the presiding spirits of the banquet.

After awhile, when their glasses were filled with rich wine, it was proposed that they should have a toast. So a benevolent-looking elderly gentleman rose, and after speaking a few minutes, to the purport that he felt sure those present would all cordially join him, he raised his glass aloft—his example being followed by the others, and said—

"*Even-handed laws*—which, in our glorious republic, dispense to all impartially their due."

Where the revellers heard this sentiment, they clinked their glasses together, and raised a peal which made the lofty ceiling ring again. Then a second, and then a third—which was a louder and a gladder peal than either of the others.

And at the same moment that the echoes died away, there was, about a mile off, a human soul writhing in its final struggle. It was that of the poor drunkard Dennis, who stole the loaf in his hunger, and had been sent to expiate his crime in toil and imprisonment. The dissipation of years had made him weak; and he could not bear up against the exposure, joined with the hard work. But his task-master was merciless; and as long as the wretched man could stand, he was kept laboring. At last, he fell very ill. Who would medicine a rascally jail-bird? He went on from bad to worse, and was soon in a dying condition.

Before the splendid dinner party returned to their homes that night, the corpse of the *convicted* thief lay cold and clayey upon the prison floors.

CHAPTER VII.

"Look not upon the wine when it is red!"[8]

AFTER I had been a while in my situation at Mr. Lee's store, I thought I might safely indulge myself in adding a little to my expenses. I made improvements both in my style of living, and in my dress. The new boarding-house in which I took up my quarters, was in the upper part of the town. Colby came to see me quite often, as usual. The reader probably, by this time, has gained no small insight into the character of my friend. He was by no means a bad man; and yet his early habits, and giving way to temptation, had brought him to be anything else but a fit companion for a country youth, just beginning life in the city.

One morning, while I was attending to my usual duties in the counting-room, a stranger, with a dark and swarthy complexion, came in and asked for Mr. Lee. He was not in at the time; and thinking that the business of the dark-faced personage was very likely some trifling affair, I told

---

8. Proverbs xxiii:31.

9. In FC, because of the altered plot, the following paragraph was inserted between this and the next paragraph:

> The stranger told his name as Bourne. I knew that my employer had had large dealings with him, and frequently sent letters to him, and once or twice had despatched his most confidential clerks on personal missions to him. One of these had been described to me by a fellow clerk—who represented Mr.

him that my employer was away, but would probably return in a half-hour, or less. The stranger paused a moment, with a troubled expression upon his countenance; then drew from his breast-pocket a couple of sealed documents, and handed them to me.

"Give these papers," said he, "to your master, the moment he arrives. They are of more consequence than you know, and I would that I could have delivered them to his own hands."

"I will do as you desire," said I, laying the papers up in a little partition on the desk.[9]

A few minutes afterward, I learned from one of my fellow-clerks, that Mr. Lee had gone out that morning, leaving word that he would not be back till the close of the day. I thought of the stranger's parting injunction; but he was gone some time, and could not be informed how the fact really was. After all, perhaps, the documents might be of no weighty moment, and I reflected no more upon the subject.

On my way down from dinner, Colby met me in the street.

"This is lucky," he exclaimed, seizing me by the hand. "We have made up a fine party for the play to-night, and you must promise to be one of us."

"With pleasure," was my reply; "nothing could delight[10] me more."

So it was arranged, that when the hour arrived, they should call upon me, and we would all go together.

We did not close our store as early as usual that evening, in consequence of our master's absence. Though doing an extensive business, he was a man very careful of the details, and was in the practice of being in his counting-room until the last moment. We waited therefore until the very evening, and the neighbors all around had shut up, and left us quite solitary. As the porter was making the usual arrangements of closing, Mr. Lee returned. He looked around him a moment, remarked that he did not know his presence there was necessary, and was on the point of departing. So selfish was I, that though at that moment the remembrance of the swarthy stranger, and his letters, came to my mind, I debated a moment whether I should give them to Mr. Lee, as that would detain us some minutes longer. I was in haste to get home, that I might be ready in time for our visit to the theatre. Happily, however, duty triumphed.

Bourne's residence as filled with comfort and hospitality. And Mr. Lee had partly engaged that on the next occasion, which demanded such an agency, I should be sent on it.

This paragraph makes it possible for the hero of FC to appear "at the South" without going through the most harrowing experiences of the more intemperate *New World* hero.

10. "please" FC

"I had nearly forgot, sir," said I, "these papers were left here this morning, by a man who desired that you might get them as soon as possible."

Mr. Lee took them, and opened them. The very moment he began to read, I could see that he was deeply interested. After finishing one, he perused the other with the same eagerness. And thus a second time, with a slower and more careful manner, he read over both the letters again, from beginning to end.

"It's a lucky thing, Evans," said he, "that you did not miss giving me these. Not for half my fortune would I have been without them this very evening."

He then explained to me, that he had of late been engaged in some mercantile speculations at the south, which proved a failure. Some traders with whom he had intercourse there, were becoming alarmed, and demanded certain moneys, or their value, which Mr. Lee was bound to pay; but which, it had been the understanding, were to remain uncalled for, for several months yet. A statement of this sudden demand was forwarded by Mr. Lee's agent, with a sorrowful acknowledgment that he had not the wherewithal to meet it, and asking directions for his conduct. The swarthy southerner, who was a planter, come to the north on business, was going to leave the city the next morning, at an early hour, and prompt action was therefore necessary.

Mr. Lee immediately sat down and wrote to his agent, directing where and how he could obtain the needed funds. He enjoined him to pay the liabilities the moment they were called for, as he would rather be at the expense of them, twice over, than have his reputation and fair name as a merchant put in danger. Having made up and endorsed his reply, he gave it into my hands, with the address of the planter, who was to take it on, telling me to call at his hotel in the course of the evening, and place it in his hands. I promised to do so, of course, and went home to my supper.

As it was now quite in the evening, I had hardly finished my meal before my companions came, according to arrangement, to take me with them to the play. I debated a little while whether I had not better postpone my evening's enjoyment, as I had the planter's letter to carry. But I feared they would suspect that I did not like their companionship; and determined, in my own mind, to go out between some of the earlier acts of the piece, and convey my message.

I went to the theatre. We enjoyed ourselves highly, for the performances were creditable, and each of us naturally fond of that species of amusement, and moreover, in great spirits. As the first piece was one I had long wished to see acted, I concluded not to go until that was finished.

Then there was to come a dance, which one of my companions praised so highly that I was determined to stay and see that also. And then the intermission was so very short that, before I knew it, the curtain was up, and the actors on in the after-piece. Feeling that I was not doing right, I made a bold push, and bade my companions good night, if I should not see them again, telling them that I had some business to transact for my employer. They laughed at me, stating the improbability of such a thing, at that time of night. If ever there was anything that annoyed me, it was to be suspected of trying to sneak out from the truth by a kind of back-door, as it were. Accordingly, when they promised that if I would wait until the end of the first act, they would all go with me, I sat down again by them. I knew I was culpable, and yet I had not resolution of mind enough to break away.

We went from the theatre. On our way to the hotel, we were to pass one of our favorite drinking-places, where, as we came off against the entrance, we heard the inmates stamping and applauding at a great rate. There was evidently something more than usual going on, so one of our party insisted that we should step in and have a look.

"Only one moment," said he, "and then we will walk on with Evans."

But the moment stretched on to minutes, and the minutes to almost half an hour; at the end of which time we were snugly seated round a table, imbibing fragrant liquors through long glass tubes. And with the contents of the first glass, came a total disregard of anything but the pleasure of drink. Forgetful of my own duty—of my master's honor, and the crisis which would turn against him, if I continued sitting there a little while longer, I drank, and drank, and drank; until, as the night advanced, lost to the slightest vestige of remembrance with regard to the pacquet, I was the wildest and most exhilarated of the party.

What fire burnt in my brain! I laughed, and with garrulous tongue, entertained those about me with silly stories, which the quantity of liquor they had taken, alone prevented them from being nauseated with. All around us were the scenes which belonged to such a place, and which I have partly described before. The music went on, but we heard it no longer. The people talked, and the dice rattled, but we heeded them not. The Demon of Intemperance had taken possession of all our faculties, and we were his alone.[11]

A wretched scene! Half-a-dozen men, just entering the busy scenes of life, not one of us over twenty-five years, and there we were, benumbing our faculties, and confirming ourselves in practices which ever too surely

---

11. This sentence is omitted in FC.

bring the scorn of the world, and deserved disgrace to their miserable victims! It is a terrible sight, I have often thought since, to see *young men* beginning their walk upon this fatal journey![12] To reflect that those faculties which have been given us by God, for our own enjoyment, and the benefit of our fellows, are, at the very outset rendered useless, and of not so much avail as the instinct of the very beasts. To know that the blood is poisoned, and that the strength is to be broken down, and the bloom banished from the cheek, and the lustre of the eye dimmed, and all for a few hours' sensual gratification, now and then—is it not terrible! If there were no other drawback, the mere physical prostration which follows a fit of drunkenness were enough. But to the young, it saps the foundations, not only of the body's health, but places a stigma for the future on their worldly course, which can never be wiped out, or concealed from the knowledge of those about them.

CHAPTER VIII.

> Yet sense and passion held them slaves,
>   And lashed them to the oar,
> Till they were wrecked upon their graves,
>   And then they rose no more.
> Oh! God of mercy, make me know
>   The gift which thou hast given;
> Nor let me idly spend it so,
>   But make me fit for Heaven!
>   CHRISTIAN EXAMINER.[13]

READER, I am coming to the dark and cloudy part of my fortunes. I would that I had not to tell what you will see in the following pages—but a sentiment of good-will for my fellows, prompts the relation. I think that by laying before them a candid relation of the dangers which have involved me, and the temptations which have seduced me aside, the narrative may act as a beacon light, guiding their feet from the same fearful hazards.[14]

There is no need that I should pause here to dwell on my meeting with my benefactor Lee, and the shame with which I acknowledge my guilt, and gave him back his letter. But great as was my fault, I was hardly pre-

12. The remainder of the paragraph after this sentence is omitted in FC.
13. The fourth and fifth stanzas of an anonymous poem "Man Giveth Up the Ghost and Where Is He?"; appears in Cheever, where it is said to have been taken from the *Christian Examiner*.
14. This paragraph is omitted in FC, where the hero escapes the darkest and

pared for his storm of anger. I did not know how much he worshipped his good name among the mercantile world, or I might have been better prepared for it. He had jealously guarded his professional honor, as the apple of his eye; and now there was no escape. The mails to the distant place were very irregular; and besides, a letter to that town where his agent resided, would not reach it in time, now, if there were no impediment.

Though conscious of my remissness, the irritability, which is one of the results of intemperate habits, caused me in the course of our interview, to attempt an excuse for my conduct. High words arose—in the end I was insolent, and Mr. Lee bade me leave the place and never enter it again! I departed, telling him he should be obeyed.

Dearly, during that day, and many subsequent ones, did I repent my folly. How often did I curse that miserable weakness of my mind, which led me to yield to the slightest opening of temptation!

And what was to be done now, for a living? Some employment must be had—I could not starve. Though my salary had been quite liberal, I had spent every cent, and with the exception of a small sum, due me on a back account, I owned not a dollar in the world. Will it be believed, that, in this strait, I was besotted enough to run into the very jaws of the lion?[15] I accidentally learned that the proprietor of a second-rate hotel, where I had in times past been in the habit of going, was in want of a bar-keeper. I made application for the place, and, after some demur, was accepted. But the scenes which I witnessed there, and the duties my situation obliged me to perform, were too repulsive, even for my callous heart: and at the end of a fortnight I left my place.[16]

During my avocations there, I saw many an occurrence, which, had I possessed true judgment, might have served as a sufficent warning to me, of the curses of intemperance. There was one of the customers at our bar, quite a small boy, who came almost every evening with a little jug, which he had filled[17] with brandy. I never asked the child—but I knew the principal part of his story from his actions. He had a drunken parent![18] Their dwelling was nigh the tavern. I had occasion, two or three times, to show some little kindness to the boy, when he was rudely treated by the inmates of our place; who exhibited, at times, all those various phases of temper which brandy can produce.[19]

One evening, I had a respite from my employment, and amused my-

cloudiest parts of his fortunes.
15. FC substitutes the following for this sentence: "I took the first chance that offered."
16. were not pleasant: and at the end of a fortnight I left my place. FC
17. got filled FC   18. He had an intemperate parent! FC
19. The part of this sentence following the semicolon is omitted in FC.

self[20] by my favorite recreation, the theatre. As I was returning quite late, and was passing through a narrow, dirty street, a boy asked me for some[21] pennies, in a piteous tone. He said he wanted them to buy bread. I thought the voice was familiar—and scanning the lad's features, discovered my little acquaintance who had so often brought the jug. Of late, however, I had missed his accustomed visits to the bar. I spoke kindly to him—and the poor fellow, no doubt unaccustomed to such treatment, burst into tears. More and more interested, I inquired of him what distress had sent him forth at that hour; and he acknowledged that, instead of wanting the pennies to buy bread, he wished to purchase liquor—and for his *mother!*

"I don't know what ails her," said the little wretch, "but she acts more strange to-night, than I ever saw her before."

"Where does she live?" said I.

"Not a block off," answered the boy. "Wouldn't you just step and see her, sir? She has been ill for a long time."[22]

I thought it no wonder, when, as the child turned to go on before,[23] and show me the way, I caught sight of the little red jug, under his jacket. He led me up a dirty rickety stoop, into a dark entry of the same description; and it was not without considerable risk of my personal safety, that I arrived at last at the door of a room in the attic, where, he said, his mother was lying. He opened the door, and we entered. Never before had I been in so miserable a place. The furniture of the apartment, what there was of it, would have been scouted from a negro hovel. The bed on which the woman herself lay in one corner, was a filthy thing of feathers and soiled rags. Another corner was tenanted by a little girl, the sister of the boy who had conducted me: she was asleep. There was no fire—hardly any light; for the flickering of a half-burned tallow candle on the hearth-stone, only served to cast strange, shadowy hues[24] around, making the place drearier and still more desolate. I stood and looked upon the scene—then, approaching the woman, I gazed down upon her, and the very first glance I gave in her face, saw that she was dying! Horror-struck, I stepped away from the bed, and for several minutes was silent and motionless with awe.

Every little while, the woman would turn uneasily, and raise herself somewhat from the bed, and look about—oftenest looking at the spot where her girl slumbered. My little guide crouched down close by my feet —it may be that the knowledge of the presence of death was upon him. Again the woman raised herself—then sank wearily back again, her faint groans sounding through the apartment. Poor creature! She was very

20. when I had a respite from employment, I amused myself FC
21. for a few FC
22. "Would'nt [*sic*] you just come and see her, sir? She has been sick for a

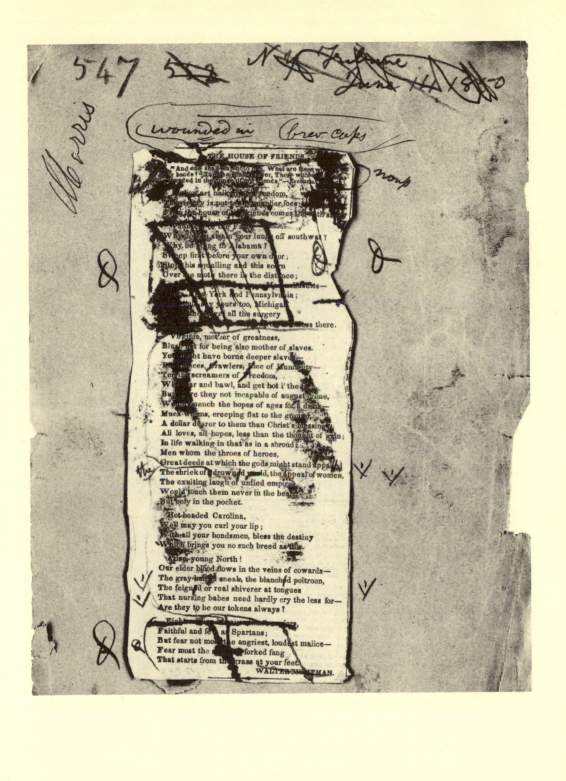

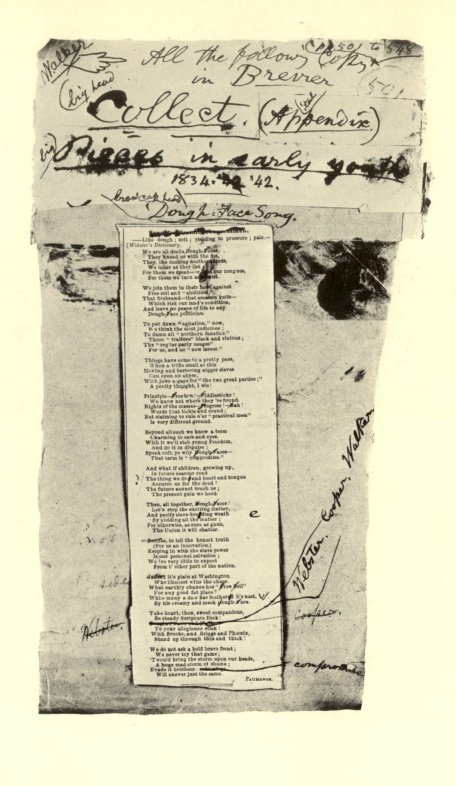

Walker
(big head)
All the follow Copy p. 501 to 548
in Brevier

Collect. (Appendix)

Pieces in early youth
1834 '42.

brevcap head

Dough-Face Song.

—Like dough; soft; yielding to pressure; pale.—
[*Webster's Dictionary.*]

We are all docile Dough-Faces,
  They knead us with the fist,
They, the dashing southern lords,
  We labor as they list;
For them we speak—or hold our tongues,
  For them we turn and twist.

We join them in their howl against
  Free soil and "abolition,"
That firebrand—that assassin knife—
  Which risk our land's condition,
And leave no peace of life to any
  Dough-Face politician.

To put down "agitation," now,
  We think the most judicious;
To damn all "northern fanatics,"
  Those "traitors" black and vicious;
The "reg'lar party usages"
  For us, and no "new issues."

Things have come to a pretty pass,
  When a trifle small as this
Moving and bartering nigger slaves
  Can open an abyss,
With jaws a-gape for "the two great parties;"
  A pretty thought, I wis!

Principle—Freedom!—Fiddlesticks!
  We know not where they're found.
Rights of the masses—Progress!—Bah!
  Words that tickle and sound;
But claiming to rule o'er "practical men"
  Is very different ground.

Beyond all such we know a term
  Charming to ears and eyes,
With it we'll stab young Freedom,
  And do it in disguise;
Speak soft, ye wily Dough-Faces—
  That term is "compromise."

And what if children, growing up,
  In future seasons read
The thing we do—and heart and tongue
  Accurse us for the deed?
The future cannot touch us;
  The present gain we heed.

Then, all together, Dough-Faces!
  Let's stop the exciting clatter,
And pacify slave-breeding wrath
  By yielding all the matter;
For otherwise, as sure as guns,
  The Union it will shatter.

Besides, to tell the honest truth
  (For us an innovation,)
Keeping in with the slave power
  Is our personal salvation;
We 've very little to expect
  From t' other part of the nation.

Indeed it's plain at Washington
  Who likeliest wins the chase,
What earthly chance has "Free Soil"
  For any good fat place?
While many a daw has feathered his nest,
  By his creamy and meek Dough-Face.

Take heart, then, sweet companions,
  Be steady Scripture Dick!
To your allegiance stick!
With Brooks, and Briggs and Phoenix,
  Stand up through thin and thick!

We do not ask a bold brave front,
  We never try that game;
'Twould bring the storm upon our heads,
  A huge mad storm of shame;
Evade it brothers
  Will answer just the same.

          PAUMANOK.

Webster. Cooper. Walker
Webster.
Cooper.
compromise

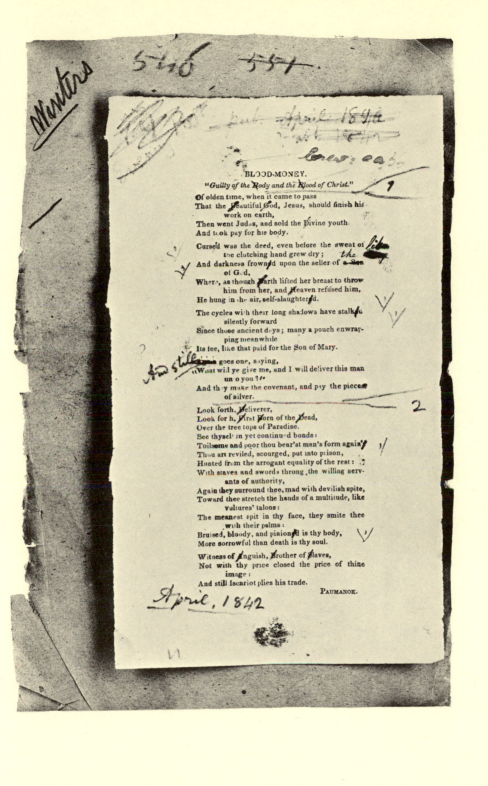

BLOOD-MONEY.

"Guilty of the Body and the Blood of Christ."

Of olden time, when it came to pass
That the Beautiful God, Jesus, should finish his
    work on earth,
Then went Judas, and sold the Divine youth.
And took pay for his body.

Cursed was the deed, even before the sweat of
    the clutching hand grew dry;
And darkness frowned upon the seller of
    of God,
Where, as though Earth lifted her breast to throw
    him from her, and Heaven refused him,
He hung in the air, self-slaughtered.

The cycles with their long shadows have stalked
    silently forward
Since those ancient days; many a pouch enwrap-
    ping meanwhile
Its fee, like that paid for the Son of Mary.

And still goes one, saying,
    "What will ye give me, and I will deliver this man
    unto you?"
And they make the covenant, and pay the pieces
    of silver.

Look forth, Deliverer,
Look forth, First Born of the Dead,
Over the tree tops of Paradise.
See thyself in yet continued bonds:
Toilsome and poor thou bear'st man's form again,
Thou art reviled, scourged, put into prison,
Hunted from the arrogant equality of the rest;
With staves and swords throng the willing serv-
    ants of authority,
Again they surround thee, mad with devilish spite,
Toward thee stretch the hands of a multitude, like
    vultures' talons:
The meanest spit in thy face, they smite thee
    with their palms:
Bruised, bloody, and pinioned is thy body,
More sorrowful than death is thy soul.

Witness of Anguish, Brother of Slaves,
Not with thy price closed the price of thine
    image:
And still Iscariot plies his trade.

                                PAUMANOK.

brev. caps 5-14

The Last Loyalist,

"She came to me last night,
The floor gave back no tread."

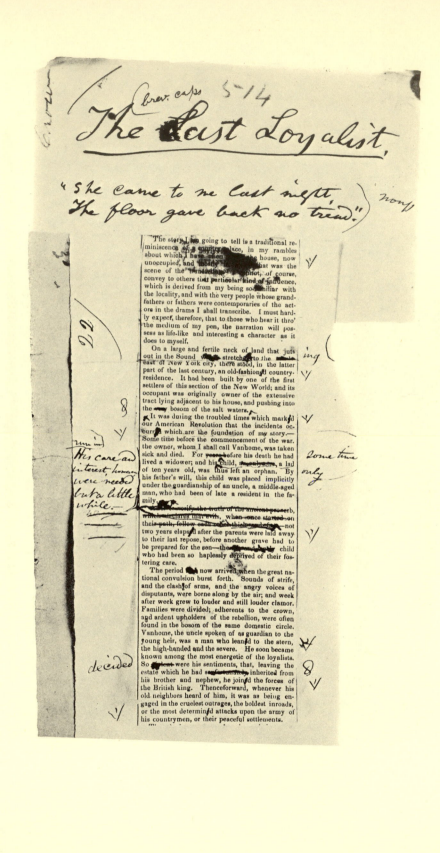

The story I am going to tell is a traditional reminiscence of a country place, in my rambles about which I have often ⸺ house, now unoccupied, and ⸺ hat was the scene of the transactions ⸺ not, of course, convey to others that particular kind of influence, which is derived from my being so familiar with the locality, and with the very people whose grandfathers or fathers were contemporaries of the actors in the drama I shall transcribe. I must hardly expect, therefore, that to those who hear it thro' the medium of my pen, the narration will possess as life-like and interesting a character as it does to myself.

On a large and fertile neck of land that juts out in the Sound which stretches to the ⸺ east of New York city, there stood, in the latter part of the last century, an old-fashioned country-residence. It had been built by one of the first settlers of this section of the New World; and its occupant was originally owner of the extensive tract lying adjacent to his house, and pushing into the very bosom of the salt waters.

It was during the troubled times which marked our American Revolution that the incidents occurred which are the foundation of my story.—Some time before the commencement of the war, the owner, whom I shall call Vanhome, was taken sick and died. For years before his death he had lived a widower; and his child, an only son, a lad of ten years old, was thus left an orphan. By his father's will, this child was placed implicitly under the guardianship of an uncle, a middle-aged man, who had been of late a resident in the family.

⸺ verify the truth of the ancient proverb, which declares that evils, when once started on their path, follow each other thick and fast—not two years elapsed after the parents were laid away to their last repose, before another grave had to be prepared for the son—the ⸺ child who had been so haplessly deprived of their fostering care.

The period had now arrived when the great national convulsion burst forth. Sounds of strife, and the clash of arms, and the angry voices of disputants, were borne along by the air; and week after week grew to louder and still louder clamor. Families were divided; adherents to the crown, and ardent upholders of the rebellion, were often found in the bosom of the same domestic circle. Vanhome, the uncle spoken of as guardian to the young heir, was a man who leaned to the stern, the high-handed and the severe. He soon became known among the most energetic of the loyalists. So ⸺ were his sentiments, that, leaving the estate which he had unfortunately inherited from his brother and nephew, he joined the forces of the British king. Thenceforward, whenever his old neighbors heard of him, it was as being engaged in the cruelest outrages, the boldest inroads, or the most determined attacks upon the army of his countrymen, or their peaceful settlements.

[Marginal annotations in manuscript:] 22 · 8 · His care and interest however were needed but a little while.— · decided · Some time only · non · ing · decided

Eight years brought the rebel States and their leaders to that glorious epoch when the last remnant of a monarch's rule was to leave their shores — when the last waving of the royal standard was to flutter as it should be hauled down from the staff, and its place filled by the proud testimonial of our warriors' success.

Pleasantly over the autumn fields shone the November sun, when a horseman, of somewhat military look, plodded slowly along the road that led to the old Vanhome farm-house. There was nothing peculiar in his attire, unless it might be a red scarf which he wore tied round his waist.— He was a dark-featured, sullen-eyed man; and as his glance was thrown restlessly to the right and left, his whole manner appeared to be that of a person moving amid familiar and accustomed scenes. Occasionally he stopped, and looking long and steadily at some object that attracted his attention, muttered to himself, like one in whose breast busy thoughts were moving. His course was evidently to the homestead itself, at which in due time he arrived. He dismounted, led his horse to the stables, and then, without knocking, though there were evident signs of occupancy around the building, the traveller made his entrance as composedly and boldly as though he were master of the whole establishment.

Now it so happened that the house being in a measure deserted for many years, and the successful termination of the strife rendering it probable that the Vanhome estate would be confiscated to the new government,—an aged, poverty-stricken couple had been encouraged by the neighbors to take possession as tenants of the place. Their name was Gills; and these people the traveller found upon his entrance were likely to be his host and hostess. Holding their right as they did, by so slight a tenure, they ventured to offer no opposition when the stranger signified his intention of passing several hours there.

The day wore on, and the sun went down in the west. Still the interloper made no signs of departing. But as the twilight (whether the darkness was congenial to his sombre thoughts, or whether it merely chanced so), he seemed to grow more affable and communicative.

'Tell me,' said he to his aged host, when they were all sitting round the ample hearth, at the conclusion of their evening meal, 'tell me something to while away the hours.'

'Ah! sir,' answered Gills, 'this is no place for new or interesting events. We live here from year to year, and at the end of one, we find ourselves at about the same place which we filled in the beginning.'

'Can you relate nothing, then,' rejoined the guest—and a singular smile passed over his features; 'can you say nothing about your own place? this house or its former inhabitants, or its former history?'

The old man glanced across to his wife, and a look expressive of sympathetic feeling started in the face of each.

'It is an unfortunate story, sir,' said Gills, 'and may cast a chill upon you, instead of the pleasant feeling which it would be best to foster when in strange walls.'

'Strange walls!' echoed he of the red scarf; and for the first time since his arrival, he half laughed, but it was not the laugh which comes from a man's heart.

'You must know, sir,' continued Gills, 'I am

21/

THE LITTLE SLEIGHERS.

A SKETCH OF A WINTER MORNING ON THE BATTERY.

suggest

flat on his belly.

JUST before noon, one day last winter, when the pavements were crusted plentifully with ice-patches, and the sun, though shining out ~~~~ brightly by fits and starts, seemed incapable of conveying any warmth, I took my thick overcoat, and prepared to sally forth on a walk. The wind whistled as I shut the door behind me, and when I turned the corner it made the most ferocious demonstrations toward my hat, which I was able to keep on my head not without considerable effort. My flesh quivered with the bitter coldness of the air. My breath appeared steam. Qu-foo-o! how the gust swept along!

Coming out into Broadway, I wended along by the Park, St. Paul's church, and the icicle-tipped trees in Trinity grave-yard. Having by this time warmed myself into a nice glow, I grew more comfortable, and felt ready to do any deed of daring that might ~~~~~~~ itself—even to the defiance of the elements which were growling so snappishly around me.

When I arrived at Battery-place—at the crossing which leads from that antique, two story, corner house, to the massive iron gates on the opposite side—I must confess that I was for a moment in doubt whether I had not better, after all, turn and retrace my steps. The wind absolutely roared. I could hear the piteous creaking of the trees on the Battery as the branches grated against one another, and could see how they were bent down by the power of the blast. Out in the bay the waves were rolling and rising, and over the thick rails which line the shore-walk dashed showers of spray, which fell upon the flag stones and froze there.

But it was a glorious and inspiriting scene, with all its wildness. I gave an extra pull of my hat over my brows—a closer adjustment of my collar around my shoulders, and boldly ventured onward. I stepped over the crossing, and passed through the gate.

Ha! ha! Let the elements run riot! There is an exhilarating sensation—a most excellent and enviable fun—in steadily pushing forward against the stout winds!

The whole surface of the Battery was spread with snow. It seemed one mighty bride's couch, and was very brilliant, too, as though varnished with a clear and glassy wash. This huge, white sheet, glancing back a kind of impudent defiance to the sun, which shone sharply the while, was not, it seemed, to be left in its repose, or without an application to use and jollity. Many dozens of boys were there, with skates and small sleds—very busy. Oh, what a noisy and merry band!

The principal and choicest of the play tracks was in that avenue, the third from the water, known to summer idlers there as "Lovers' Walk." For nearly its whole length it was a continued expanse of polished ice, made so partly by the evenness of the surface and partly by the labor of the boys. This fact I found out to my cost; for, turning in it before being aware that it was so fully preoccupied and so slippery, I found it necessary to use the utmost caution or run the certainty of a fall.

"Pawny-guttah!" Gentle lady, (I must here remark,) or worthy gentleman, as the case may be, whose countenance bends over this page, and whose opportunities have never led you to know the use, meaning and import, conveyed in the term just quoted—call to your side some bright-eyed boy—a brother or a son, or a neighbor's son, and ask *him*.

"Pawny-guttah!" I stepped aside instinctively, and, with the speed of an arrow there came gliding along, lying ~~~~~~~~~~~~ one of the boyish troop. The polished steel runners of his little vehicle sped over the ice with a slightly grating noise, and he directed his course by touching the toe of either boot, behind him, upon the ice, as he wished to swerve to the right or left.

Who can help loving a wild, thoughtless, heedless, joyous boy? Oh, let us do what we can—we who are past the time—let us do what we may to aid their pleasures and their little delights, and heal up their petty griefs. Wise is he who is himself a child at times. A man may keep his heart fresh and his nature youthful, by mixing much with that which is fresh and youthful. Why should we, in our riper years, despise these little people, and allow ourselves to think them of no higher consequence than trifles and unimportant toys?

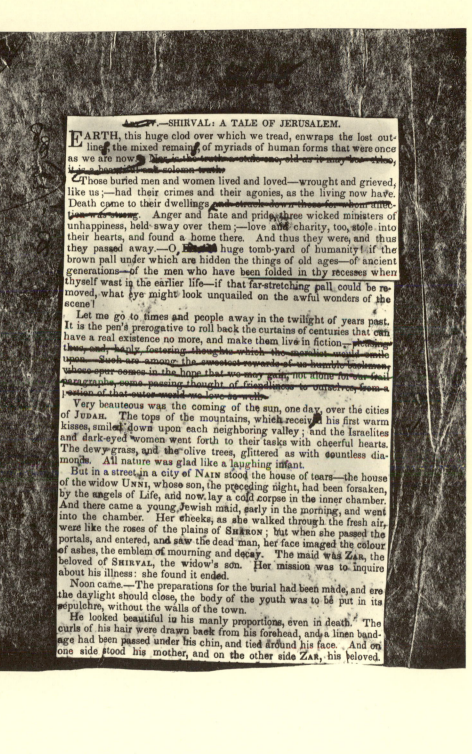

EARTH, this huge clod over which we tread, enwraps the lost outlines, the mixed remains, of myriads of human forms that were once as we are now. ~~Nor is the truth a stale one, old as it may but true, it is a beautiful and solemn truth.~~

Those buried men and women lived and loved—wrought and grieved, like us;—had their crimes and their agonies, as the living now have. Death came to their dwellings ~~and struck down those for whom affection was strong.~~ Anger and hate and pride, three wicked ministers of unhappiness, held sway over them;—love and charity, too, stole into their hearts, and found a home there. And thus they were, and thus they passed away.—O, ~~thou this~~ huge tomb-yard of humanity! if the brown pall under which are hidden the things of old ages—of ancient generations—of the men who have been folded in thy recesses when thyself wast in the earlier life—if that far-stretching pall could be removed, what eye might look unquailed on the awful wonders of the scene!

Let me go to times and people away in the twilight of years past. It is the pen's prerogative to roll back the curtains of centuries that can have a real existence no more, and make them live in fiction ~~pleasing thus, and, haply, fostering thoughts which the moralist would smile upon. Such are among the sweetest rewards of us humble bookmen, whose spur comes in the hope that we may gain, not alone for our frail paragraphs, some passing thought of friendliness to ourselves, from a portion of that outer world we love so well.~~

Very beauteous was the coming of the sun, one day, over the cities of JUDAH. The tops of the mountains, which received his first warm kisses, smiled down upon each neighboring valley; and the Israelites and dark-eyed women went forth to their tasks with cheerful hearts. The dewy grass, and the olive trees, glittered as with countless diamonds. All nature was glad like a laughing infant.

But in a street in a city of NAIN stood the house of tears—the house of the widow UNNI, whose son, the preceding night, had been forsaken, by the angels of Life, and now lay a cold corpse in the inner chamber. And there came a young Jewish maid, early in the morning, and went into the chamber. Her cheeks, as she walked through the fresh air, were like the roses of the plains of SHARON; but when she passed the portals, and entered, and saw the dead man, her face imaged the colour of ashes, the emblem of mourning and decay. The maid was ZAR, the beloved of SHIRVAL, the widow's son. Her mission was to inquire about his illness: she found it ended.

Noon came.—The preparations for the burial had been made, and ere the daylight should close, the body of the youth was to be put in its sepulchre, without the walls of the town.

He looked beautiful in his manly proportions, even in death. The curls of his hair were drawn back from his forehead, and a linen bandage had been passed under his chin, and tied around his face. And on one side stood his mother, and on the other side ZAR, his beloved.

Graham 507

all this (pp 501 to 548) in Brewer remember

Brev. Caps

From the Democratic Review.

One Wicked Impulse!

(Incidents of a Murderer tempted.)

That section of Nassau street which runs into the great mart in New York brokers and stock-jobbing, has for a long time been much occupied by practitioners of the law. Tolerably well known amid this class some years since, was Adam Covert, a middle-aged man of rather limited means, who, to tell the truth, got more by trickery than he did in the legitimate and honorable exercise of his profession. He was a tall, bilious-faced widower; the father of two children; and had lately been seeking to better his fortunes by a rich marriage. But somehow or other his wooing did not seem to thrive well, and, with perhaps one exception, the lawyer's prospects in the matrimonial way were hopelessly gloomy.

Among the early clients of Mr. Covert had been a distant relative named Marsh, who, dying somewhat suddenly, left his son and daughter, and some little property, to the care of Covert, under a will drawn out by that gentleman himself. At no time caught without his eyes open, the cunning lawyer, aided by much sad confusion in the emergency which had caused his services to be called for, and disguising his object under a cloud of technicalities, inserted provisions in the will, giving himself an almost arbitrary control over the property and over those for whom it was designed. This control was even made to extend beyond the time when the children would arrive at mature age. The son, Philip, a spirited and high-tempered fellow, had some time since passed that age. Esther, the girl, a plain, and somewhat devotional young woman, was in her nineteenth year.

Having such power over his wards, Covert did not scruple openly to use his advantage, in pressing his claims as a suitor for Esther's hand. Since the death of Marsh, the property he left, which had been in real estate, and was to be divided equally between the brother and sister, had risen to very considerable value; and Esther's share, was to a man in Covert's situation, a prize very well worth seeking. In all this time, while really owning a respectable income, the young orphans often felt the want of the smallest sums of money—and Esther, on Philip's account, was more than once driven to various contrivances—the pawn-shop, sales of her own little luxuries, and the like, to furnish him with means.

Though she had frequently shown her guardian unequivocal evidence of her aversion, Esther continued to suffer from his persecutions, until one day he proceeded farther and was more pressing than usual. She possessed some of her brother's mettlesome temper, and gave him an abrupt and most decided refusal. With dignity, she exposed the baseness of his conduct, and forbade him ever again mentioning marriage to her. He retorted bitterly, vaunted his hold on her and Philip, and swore an oath that unless she became his wife, they should both thence-forward become penniless. Losing his habitual self-control in his exasperation, he even added insults such as woman never receives from any one deserving the name of man, and at his own convenience left the house. That day, Philip returned to New York, after an absence of several weeks on the business of a mercantile house in whose employment he had lately engaged.

wretched—and no doubt she had been as guilty as she was wretched; and thoughts of remorse might be the cause of that restlessness which I saw depicted in her countenance. But amid all her agony—amid the dark re-memberances that came trooping up there, like fiends in the silence of midnight, to torment her—amid her doubts and fears about the Dim Beyond —amid faintness, and thirstiness, and pain—one controlling thought was mightier than all the rest—motherly love. She called in a hoarse whisper,

"Mary!"

There was no answer. A second time she called, and sank down her head, and held very still, to listen if she was heard. The quiet, regular breathing of the sleeping girl, was the only sound that broke that terrible stillness—for we were mute with dread. Again, the whisper sounded out with even a ghastlier tone than before,

"My daughter!"

The hoarse sound seemed to be re-echoed from other voices. It was as if around the room, and peering down from the upper corners of the wall, the death-stricken outcast fancied she saw faces, bodiless, and working with strange grins of mockery. She sat up in the bed—horror giving her strength—and stared wildly about. I was half petrified as her look was directed toward me, and the child at my feet. I stood as still as a statue. With a feeble hand, she drew from its place, the rag-heap used for her pillow; she tightened and bound it with her trembling fingers—I looking on in wonder the while—and then she threw it toward *me!* I half shrieked with fear.

The woman was plainly losing her senses, as the dread moment came nigh.

"Oh, Jack!" she exclaimed, as she saw her boy near me, "come to your poor mother!"

I raised the child, and bade him obey her. He was frightened at her fearful wildness, and crept toward the bed with trembling steps.

"Dear one, lean to my face!" she said.

The poor lad speechlessly obeyed the injunction. The girl slept on. And now the dying woman lay, her mouth partly open, drawing in the breath at intervals with a convulsive movement of the jaws. Her face was livid, and covered with large drops of sweat, and her eyes turned upward. It was evident, that she struggled with the Grim Messenger.

To me, the fearful novelty of the scene almost took away all power of speech or action. What I have narrated was done in the space of but few

long time." FC

23. turned on before FC

24. to cast shadowy hues FC

seconds. Indeed, I was not in the room, from first to last, more than ten or twelve minutes. The woman's arm, numb as it was getting to be, wound itself around her child, and pressed him closer. Something like a smile—a most deathly one—settled upon her features. She tried to speak—but just then her sinking powers forbade the effort. It seemed from her looks and faint gestures, that she would have had the boy rouse his sister, and bring her there also. Then she probably felt conscious how very short were her moments, and how she might die ere the drowsy child could be fully awakened. Her pallid lips moved—just moved, and that was all.

"Father in Heaven!" was the slight thin sound, "hallowed be thy name—thy will be done on earth as in heaven—forgive us our trespasses, as—"

A ghastly rattle shook the repentant sinner's neck.

"Forgive us our trespasses—"

There was a choking gush, as of wind and water in the throat.

"Forgive us—"

Her head turned slowly, and fell on its side with a kind of leaden sound; her arm relaxed its hold; and the guilty creature lay there a corpse—her last prayer smothered in its utterance, and her immortal part starting from its now useless tabernacle, to waft itself on the journey for the Strange Land.

CHAPTER IX.[25]

> Her image 'tis—to memory dear—
> That clings around my heart,
> And makes me fondly linger here
> Unwilling to depart.
> THOMAS WELLS.[26]

MORE than two years had now passed away since my leaving the country; and I am coming, reader, to tell of things which nothing but a resolution to relate *all* my adventures, could wring from me. There is a sacredness in some of our sorrows, which prevents them from being fit subjects for the rude and common gaze. Wife of my youth! of my early youth! Forgive me if I transcribe your name, and your worth, for the admiration and example of those who may hear my mention of you!

When I left my bar-keeping duties, for the reasons I have alluded to, I found it necessary to change my residence for a cheaper one. Passing

25. Chapters IX, X, XI, XII, XIII, and XIV are omitted in FC, which enables Evans to become reconciled quickly with Mr. Lee.

along an upper and quiet street of the city, one day, I noticed a plain, clean-looking house, of wood, with the sign, "Boarding," on the door. I inquired there, and finding I could be accommodated, soon took up my quarters in it. My fellow-boarders were in the humbler walks of life; but I soon found an attraction, which made up for every deficiency.

My landlady was a widow, with only one child, her daughter Mary. She was a modest, delicate, sweet girl, and before I had been in the house a week, I loved her. I do not choose to dwell upon the progress of our affection, for it was mutual. The widow knew nothing of my former intemperance—in fact, I had desisted during my residence with her, from any of my dissolute practices.

Six months passed away. I had obtained employment soon after taking up my abode there, in a factory not far from the house; where, though I was forced to labor, and my remuneration was moderate, because I did not understand the business well at first, I was in a fair train for doing better, and getting higher wages. The widow grew sick. She was of the same delicate temperament which her daughter inherited from her, and in less than a fortnight from the commencement of her illness, she left the world for ever.

Poor Mary! I have seldom seen such violent and inconsolable grief as followed the death of her mother. She leaned on me for support, and no doubt, the deprivation of any other comforter forced her to look to one, who, with all his faults, had a pure passion for her—as the only resource from utter friendliness.

As soon as it could with propriety be done, after her mother's death, Mary and I were married. And a more happy union never took place; for, possessed of a treasure which no temptation would have induced me to jeopardize, I had quite reformed, and no longer visited my former haunts; while Mary was the most industrious, prudent, and affectionate of young wives. My sweet Mary! ah, even as I write, a tear is almost falling upon the words—for, wicked as I have been, my heart is not callous enough to be unaffected by remembrance of that hapless one. My wife was a *good woman*, if ever God made one. She was not learned or accomplished in the branches that constitute what is called a fashionable education; but she possessed something a million times better than all the abstractions of philosophy, or the ornaments acquired at a genteel boarding-school. She had a gentle, kindly heart; she had good temper; she had an inherent love of truth, which no temptation could seduce aside, and which she never failed to put in practice; she had charity, a disposition to look with an eye of ex-

26. The last stanza of Thomas Wells' "At Musing Hour," which is in Cheever.

cuse on the faults of her fellow-creatures, and aid them as far she could in their poverty, and console them in their griefs.

The weeks passed on. We were doing very well for people in our humble circumstances. Debt was unknown to us, at least to any great degree. We never purchased until we saw the means of payment, and never promised, unless we had made such arrangements that we felt pretty sure we could perform. I say *we*, for though my wife was a meek woman, I never took any step without consulting over the matter with her: there was no such thing as *my* and *thy*.

But about a year after our marriage, the serpent came into our little Eden! Ambition—the poison that rankles in the hearts of men, and scorches all peace, and blights the bloom of content—ambition entered there. What is called low life, affords, perhaps, as much scope for this intoxicating passion, as that sphere which called forth the ardor of Napoleon, or which brings into play the mighty minds of statesmen. And petty as the objects among the poor may seem, they are striven for as eagerly, and the chase after them is attended with as many doubts, and as many fluctuations and fevers, as mark the gaining of generalships or cabinet offices.

One of the proprietors at the factory where I was employed, owned some vacant lots, in a rather pleasant part of the city, one of which he proposed I should purchase from him. Straightway visions of independence and a home of my own, and the station of a man of property, floated before my eyes. I accepted the offer, and as the terms were very favorable, I for a time found no inconvenience from my new purchase. Not long afterward, I thought I had a good opportunity of hiring money enough to put up a convenient house upon my lot—and I took advantage of the opportunity. As ill-luck, and partly my own ill-judgment, would have it, when the house was about half finished, my means fell out, and I could not go on with the work. We pondered, my wife and I, and we worried, and turned a great many projects in our minds—but none were able to be put in effect. At this stage my creditors grew alarmed, and demanded what was due them. Had it been to save my life, I could not raise the money. They were inexorable —and at one fell swoop all my towering dreams of happiness and a competency were crushed to the dust, by their seizing on my little property, and putting it to a forced sale. The house, unfinished as it was, did not bring one quarter what I had expended upon it. I was half crazed with mortification and disappointment.

Yet—yet we might have been happy. Yet we might have risen, and baffled our evil genius—yet we might have gained our little place back again, in time—and, wiser by experience, kept our wishes within moderate bounds, and journeyed on pleasantly until our appointed number of years had been fulfilled. But the Great Master, in his unfathomable wisdom, allowed it not to be so. For comfort in my sorrows, I frequented my old places of resort, the drinking-shops, and the bar-rooms: I bent beneath the storm, and went back to habits which, until then, my poor Mary had never even suspected as belonging to me.

How well do I remember the first night I returned home, and showed my wife that she had bound her fortunes to a *drunkard!* She had been sitting up for me, for many weary hours, until midnight passed away, and exhausted nature could stand it no longer. She sank her head on the table by her side, and slept. The noise of my shutting the street door awakened her, and she sprang to receive me, and inquire the cause of my absence. Alas! the light she carried in her hand showed her too plainly the bitter reason of that absence—the terrible truth that I was intoxicated! Steeped as my senses were in liquor, I was alarmed at her sudden paleness, and the sickly look which spread over her features. She almost fell to the ground —so agonized were her feelings.

The fatal habit once taken up again, seemed to revive with even more than its former strength and violence. I disregarded my business; and, before long, grew so heedless of my wife's comforts, that I neglected to provide even those matters which are indispensable to subsistence. Where was my former love? Where the old tenderness, and the vow I had made to love and protect? Ah, reader! intemperance destroys even the remembrance of love—and this is one of the most horrible of its consequences. To think that the affection of the early years—the kind and innocent tenderness, which was reciprocated from heart to heart, and which was as a fountain of fond joy—to think all this is given up merely for a beastly and gross appetite, is painful and fearful indeed!

I sicken as I narrate this part of my story. The recollection comes of the sufferings of my poor wife, and of my unkindness to her. I paid no attention to her comforts, and took no thought for her subsistence. I *think* I never proceeded to any act of violence—but God only knows what words I spoke in my paroxysms of drunken irritation, to that humble, uncomplaining creature. Yes; I remember well, with what agony she has often leaned over my prostrate form, and the hot tears that fell upon my bloated face. I remember the gathering degradation that fixed itself round our name. I remember how my wretched Mary's face grew paler and paler every day —the silent uncomplaining method of her long, long time of dying—for my conduct killed her at last. I remember the scorn and jeers of unfeeling neighbors—the avoidance of me by my old friends—the sinking, grade by grade, until it was at length as though there were no lower depths in which to sink—all are burnt into my mind, Oh, how ineffaceably!

Then came the closing scene of that act of the tragedy. My wife, stricken to the heart, and unable to bear up longer against the accumulating weight of shame and misery, sank into the grave—the innocent victim of another's drunkenness. Oh, that solemn—that terribly solemn hour of her death! Thank God! I was sober at the time—and received her forgiveness. I did not weep as she died, for my throat and the fountains of my eyes, were alike parched and dry. I rushed madly from the house—I knew not and cared not whither. Hell seemed raging in my breast. All my cruelty—all my former love—all my guilt—all my disregard of the sacred ties—seemed concentrated in a thought, and that thought pressing like a mountain of fire all round my heart.

It was night. I walked madly and swiftly through the streets, and though the people stared, I recked not of their notice, but kept my way. What would I have given for power to call back but one little year? One moment only, did I think of drowning my horrible agony in drink; but I cursed the very reflection, as it was formed in my soul. Now, I thought upon Mary's tenderness to me—upon her constant care, and regard, and love; and now, the idea of the repayment I had made her, filled my bosom.

As I wended thus heedlessly on with long strides, I came off against the entrance of a tavern which, in times past, I had frequently visited. In the door, talking with a party of companions, stood a form which in the imperfect light, I thought I recognized. Another moment, he turned, and his face was shone upon by the gas-lamp; I was right in my conjecture—It was Colby. With a sudden revulsion of feeling, I remembered that it was he who had tempted me, and through whose means all my follies and crimes had been committed. I sprang madly toward the place where he stood.

"Devil!" cried I furiously, seizing him by the throat, "you have brought death to one for whom I would willingly have suffered torments for ever! It is fitting that you pay the penalty with your own base life. Die! villain, even on the spot where you started me upon *my* ruin!"

I clutched him with a grasp of desperation. Those who stood near, were motionless with amazement and fright—and in two minutes more, I had added *murder* to my other crimes. Happily for both, myself and the one I would have made my victim—as he had made me his—the bystanders recovered their self-possession sufficiently soon to interfere, and prevent the accomplishment of my sanguinary purpose. They dragged me from his neck, and relieved him from the imminent danger of his situation; for as sure as there is a heaven above, I would have killed that man, had I been left to myself three minutes longer.

CHAPTER X.

Dehortations from the use of strong liquors have been the favorite topic of declaimers in all ages, and have been received with abundance of applause by water-drinking critics. But with the patient himself, the man that is to be cured, unfortunately their sound has seldom prevailed. Yet the evil is acknowledged—the remedy simple. Abstain. No force can oblige a man to raise the glass to his head against his will. 'Tis as easy as not to steal—not to tell lies.

CHARLES LAMB.[27]

DURING the days that followed, one thought alone—apart from my engrossing grief and remorse—possessed my mind. It was a desire to leave the city, where I had come merely to go astray from the path of honor and happiness, and find relief for my sorrow in a new place, and amid the faces of strangers. It may easily be supposed, that after what I have described in the last chapter, I felt no desire to continue in my course of dissipation. Whether my good resolves held out for any length of time, will be seen in the sequel. I had my household effects sold, and gathering in several debts that were due me, I found I had quite a respectable sum of cash. Careless where I should cast my fortune, so that I got away from New York, I took passage in a steamboat, and journeyed to a small town some thirty miles distant. Here I staid for a few weeks; but getting tired at length of its monotony, I started and went inland, continuing my travel for a day and a night, and stopping then to rest. I was pleased when I awoke in the morning, with the aspect of the place, and determined to fix my abode there.

I informed the landlord of the hotel of my intentions, and asked him if there was any kind of business upon which I could enter—telling him of the small sum of cash which I had at my disposal. With an appearance of great friendliness, he told me, that he was himself just entering upon some speculations, which were very safe and profitable, and which required the assistance of a partner. He told me if I would join with him, I could more than double my money, and that my labors would be very light. The man spoke fair, and his projects seemed plausible. So in the evening, over a bottle of wine, in his own parlor, we sealed our agreement. I found, in truth, that I had but little call upon my services. My leisure I employed in roaming about the surrounding country, and in various country sports.

Though I did not drink to anything like my former excess, I was by no means abstemious. During the afternoon, and frequently when at evening the place was filled with visitors, I indulged myself with wine, and with

27. The first paragraph of Lamb's "Confessions of a Drunkard," *The Last Essays of Elia.*

those drinks, originally derived from our thirsty south—drinks that are very pleasant to the taste, but which have led thousands down the path to the lower stages of intemperance, and at last to ruin. As I did not pay for them, when they were used, (the landlord and myself having accounts together) I felt no thought of the expense.

Among my amusements, I have said, were walks about the place. In one of these an incident occurred, where I was the instrument of performing an action that served as some small offset to the much evil I have ever brought, through my weakness of mind, to those about me. Through the village of my residence passed a railroad, and the cars generally stopped there some ten or fifteen minutes. Not far from the depot was a mill supplied with water from a large pond, along the dam of which, as is usual, were several short sluices, covered with bridges. It was a pleasant place, and the miller, an intelligent countryman, was frequently favored with my visits at his place of labor.

One day, on the arrival of the cars, several of the passengers, being informed that they were to stop a little longer than ordinary, determined to get out, and stroll a few steps for recreation. Among the number was a lady, elegantly dressed, and leading by the hand a little girl, a child of six or seven years. The lady appeared to be very much pleased with the scenery of the pond, and creek; she strolled along the dam, and occassionally stopped to admire some fine prospect, or cull the beautiful pond-flowers which grew upon the banks in great profusion. While she was resting upon one of the narrow bridges I have mentioned, the child scrambled down the banks to pluck a gaudy blossom that had caught her eyes. I was at that moment standing, leaning on the door of the mill, and gazing listlessly at the bustle around the stopping-place of the cars. All of a sudden, there came a loud shriek! The lady was standing upon the dam, the very picture of distraction, and uttering loud and shrill cries for help.

"She will be drowned! For the love of God, come and rescue her!" she cried to me as, alarmed by her cries, I ran hastily toward the place.

I saw at once what was the matter; the little girl, reaching over after the flower, had lost her balance and fallen into the pond. With promptness, I divested myself of my shoes and coat, and plunged into the pond. Fortunately I was an excellent swimmer. The current was running in from the other side very strongly, and I knew the child must have been carried some distance. I dashed rapidly out, and catching a glimpse of the end of a ribbon, made toward it, and seized the girl, just as she was sinking, probably for the last time. I brought her safely to the shore, and restored her to the arms of her half delirious protector.

Ding-dong! ding-dong! went the bell of the cars, calling the passengers together, and sounding the signal for starting. The lady, carrying the child, hurried toward the depôt, uttering incoherent blessings on my head; and beseeching, if ever I came to New-York, the place of her residence, to call at her house. As she seated herself in the vehicle, she threw me, from the window, a card, with her name, and the street and number of her dwelling, which I placed in my pocket-book. In the very midst of her flood of gratitude, the train rattled away. As I walked away slowly toward the public house where I lived, it may be supposed that my reflections were of a quite complacent nature, for the deed of kindness which I had been performing.

In the course of the ensuing weeks, my want of active employment led me to the glass, as my resource from low spirits. Two or three times I was more than half drunk; and it came to be so, at length, that I could not spend the day as I thought comfortably, without drinking five or six times before dinner, and as many more between that and bedtime. What will the reader think of my resolution of mind? I had made a compact with myself, after my poor Mary's death, that I would drink nothing but wine; and though I stuck to that for a while, I soon caught myself indulging in the stronger kinds of liquor. Perhaps, if I had filled up my time with active employment, I might have kept to my resolution, and even in the end totally reformed. But of what mischief is idleness a parent! That time which hung heavy on my hands, I drowned in the forgetfulness of the oblivion-causing cup.

Reader! perhaps you despise me. Perhaps, if I were by you at this moment, I should behold the curled lip of scorn, and the look of deep contempt. Oh, pause stern reverencer of duty, and have pity for a fellow-creature's weakness! I would ask, with the gentle Elia, that thou shouldst mingle compassion and human allowance with thy disapprobation. With him, too, I say, trample not on the ruins of a man. Thou sayest, perhaps—Begin a reformation, and custom will make it easy. But what if the beginning be dreadful? The first steps, not like climbing a mountain, but going through fire? What if the whole system must undergo a change, violent as that which we conceive of the mutation of form in some insects? What if a process comparable to flaying alive, have to be endured? Is the weakness which sinks under such struggles, to be compared with the pertinacity which clings to vice, for itself and its gross appetites? I have known one (relates the same pleasant moralist I quote above) in that state, when he has tried to abstain but for one evening, though the poisonous potion had long ceased to bring back its first enchantments; though he was sure it would rather deepen his gloom than brighten it, in the violence of the struggle, and the necessity he has felt of getting rid of the present sensation at any rate—I have known him to scream out, to cry aloud, for the anguish and pain of the strife within him. Many, perhaps, on whom liquor never produced powerful results, will here laugh at a weak brother, who, trying his strength and coming off foiled in the contest, would fain persuade them that such agonistic exercises are dangerous. On them my remarks are wasted. It is to a very different description of persons I speak. It is to the weak—the nervous; to those who feel the want of some artificial aid to raise their spirits in society to what is no more than the ordinary pitch of those around them. Such must fly the convivial class in the first instance, if they do not wish to sell themselves, for their term of life, to misery.

A man once, whom I knew well, and whose name was honored over all New-York for his many virtues, was seen by me to take a glass in an obscure drinking-shop. I afterward found that he *had* to drink, or engage in the fearful contest described above. He was of irritable and weak temperament, and though he knew his habits were secretly hurrying him to the grave, he quailed before the agony of the trial. He had commenced it more than once, but was never able to complete his own conquest. Now, though I have an abiding faith in the ability to reform, through the GLORIOUS TEMPERANCE PLEDGE, and the strength which Providence gives to those who honestly set about a good work—yet I know the awful horrors which such men as the one I speak of, must go through. Reader, if you are not one of that sort yourself, you can conceive not of those trials. Not only has habit made liquor necessary to their enjoyment, but to the very action of the vital powers; and at the very time it quickens and brightens their faculties into a dim kind of action, it warns them how it is wafting them onward to the verge of decay with a horrible rapidity!

The pure and virtuous cast scorn upon such as I have been, and as thousands now are. But oh, could they look into the innermost recesses of our hearts, and see what spasms of pain—what impotent attempts to make issue with what appears to be our destiny—what fearful dreams—what ghastly phantoms of worse than hellish imagination—what of all this resides, time and again, in our miserable bosoms—then, I know, that scorn would be changed to pity. It is not well to condemn men for their frailties. Let us rather own our common bond of weakness, and endeavor to fortify each other in good conduct and in true righteousness, which is charity for the errors of our kind. The drunkard, low as he is, is a *man*. The fine capacities, the noble marks which belong to our race, those glorious qualities which the Great Builder stamped upon his masterpiece of works, are with him still. They are not destroyed, but hidden in darkness, as precious gems cast down in the mire. And the object of the truly wise and good will be, to raise him up again; to reform and brighten those capacities, and to set in operation a train of causes, which will afford him a chance of attaining once more a respectable station in society. Once *thoroughly regenerated*, the remembrance of his old defamation will stand before his eyes like a pillar of fire, and warn him back from any further indulgence in his vicious courses.

I am the more particular in my remarks upon this matter, because I have seen so many cases of hopeless and confirmed intemperance, made thus by the injudicious severity of the neighbors and relatives of the unhappy victim. Little aware of the strength of the chains which bind him, and the horrors which surround a man in those moments when he is without that stimulus which custom has rendered necessary to him, they cast every slight upon the drunkard, and are unguarded in their expressions of anger and contempt. A little moderation perhaps, a little friendliness and sympathy, bestowed at the proper moment, would work a complete revolution in his character. But it is not bestowed, and the wretched one goes on from bad to worse, until there is no hope left. I remember a case in point.

While living with my uncle in the country, one of our most esteemed neighbors was a young farmer, lately married, and come with his wife to settle in the town. He had bought a fine little farm, and occasionally when work was pressing, he employed me to assist him, my uncle consenting. During the time I spent in that way, I became acquainted with the circumstances I am going to relate. The name of our neighbor was Fanning.

As was customary in those parts, in the hot days when we were getting in the harvest of hay, and the early grain, a couple of jugs of ardent spirits were brought into the field for the use of the work-people. It has since been a wonder to me that all of the villagers were so tacitly agreed as to the benefit of this custom. Now, medical men, and not only medical men, but all men of common sense know that intoxicating drinks are highly detrimental to the strength, and improper for use during laborious employment. They sap the very essence of energy, and prostrate the arm of the strong man. A feverish impulse may be given for a moment; but it reacts in a tenfold deficiency of power for twenty times as long a time. Be that as true as it undoubtedly is, however, among Fanning and his fellow-townsmen it was the common custom.

Fanning had a brother, a middle-aged, gentlemanly man, who possessed a small estate, invested in stocks, from whence he drew a moderate stipend. A portion of the year he was employed in a village near by as school-teacher.

I knew the man, and loved him well. He was a quiet, good natured person, and wherever he went, he made friends. I recollect his looks, too, and some little peculiarities he had. He was small in figure, with bright black eyes and very long fine glossy hair, which used to fall quite down upon his shoulders. Notwithstanding the modest disposition of 'the little teacher,' as the people used to call him, his laugh and his voice was loud among the loudest, at the merry-makings in the neighborhood, which he invariably attended. He wore a round jacket always, which was one of his peculiarities. His size and his juvenile method of apparel, made him look like anything but a pedagogue.

The teacher, when he was not employed in his profession, would frequently aid his brother, in the work of the farm. He used to come into the field, in hay time, and give his assistance there. We always welcomed him, for his pleasant mirth cast a charm on all around.

"Mr. Fanning," said one of the men, one day, "if you work with us, you should do as we do. The jug has passed round, and every person drinks but yourself."

"Is it needful, then," said the teacher, laughing, "that I partake of the liquor, in order to be on even-footing with the rest?"

"Of course," was the general rejoinder; "of course."

"Well, then," said Fanning, "here goes."

And he took down a moderate draught.

The whole conversation was intended as a mere joke, of course—such light talk as work-people amuse themselves with during the intermission between their morning and afternoon labors. But it proved in the end, a fatal joke to the poor teacher.

The next day, the same bantering was passed, and Fanning drank again. It is hardly necessary that I should narrate the particulars, of the method by which he became a lover of the liquid that at first he regarded with such apathy. It was all, however, plainly to be traced to the accidental invitation given him in the harvest-field. Before the end of the summer, he could drink his two or three glasses with great satisfaction, and even became an habitual visitor at the bar-room.

I have noted down thus minutely the incident which led to the teacher's intemperance, because I think it by no means an isolated case. There are many, no doubt, who will get this book, who may be the witnesses, and even practisers, of a habit of having liquor in the fields during the hot farm-work of the summer. For this lamentable habit, contrary as it is to the dictates of prudence and common sense, is not an altogether exploded one.

The teacher, as I have said, grew to the desire for drink. He conducted his school that winter, as usual, though before the end of the session, he had more than one fit of intoxication.

Summer came again. The pernicious jugs were brought into the field, and the elder Fanning was their best customer. Hardly a week passed without his being completely steeped two or three times in drunkenness. I have myself seen him lying beside the hay-cocks, divested of sense and rationality, more like a brute than a human being. He had always been attached to me, and would frequently obey my persuasions to go home, or to desist from any further indulgence in liquor, when, to any one else, he was abusive and obstinate.

"Frank!" said he to me one day, when he was just sobered from a spree, "I am a very wicked and foolish man—if things go on in this way, what is to become of me?"

I made no answer, though I was highly pleased at hearing him talk thus.

"Yes," he continued, "it certainly will not do. I cannot—I *will not* allow myself to become a common drunkard. The thought is horrible!"

A good resolution, once formed, may be broken, it is true; but the very process of reflection which leads to the forming of the resolution, is favorable to improvement. If brought back often to such reflections, it is twenty to one but the improvement will be effectual at last.

We had been sitting together, the teacher and I, in his apartment, as he made the remarks I have quoted above. We rose and went down to the common sitting-room, where Mrs. Fanning was engaged in some domestic employments.

"Is my brother home?" asked the teacher.

The woman made no reply, and Fanning repeated the question.

"If he is," was the answer, with a sneer, "it's not likely he cares about seeing a drunken sot!"

The teacher said nothing, but sat down upon a chair near the window. Soon after the farmer came in, but took no notice of the now sobered inebriate. He brushed through the room with a haughty glance, as much as to say, I feel no wish to be familiar with such as thou.

I was standing in the door, just about to depart, and my feelings could not help sympathizing with my poor friend, thus scorned by those who were nearest and dearest to him. True, he had acted wrongly, but they need not have thus wounded him in so unprovoked a manner. He rose from his chair, and we walked forth together. I could see that he felt very much agitated. As I diverged from the road to go on my own way, I prayed Heaven to continue in his soul the sentiments he had a few moments before expressed to me.

Without doubt, had he not been treated thus scornfully by his brother and sister-in-law, the reflections of the teacher would have led to his becoming a temperate man. But in his lonesomeness and weariness of heart, he retreated to the bar-room. He drank deeply, and that night saw him in a more severe intoxication than ever before. Provoked very much at his conduct, the farmer and his young wife would hardly use him with ordinary decency. It was only the odium of having him taken up as a common vagrant, that prevented their turning him entirely out of doors.

"Oh!" he has many a time said to me, "if there were only some little fastening of good-will among my family, where I could cast anchor, I feel assured I might be saved yet. But I am maddened by the coldness and contempt of my brother and his wife, when I am in a fit state to feel it. It is more poignant than even the pangs which are a result of my drinking!"

Twenty times, in his lucid intervals, did he express this opinion to me. I have no doubt it came from his very heart.

And now, all his friends dropped off from him. He was considered by them, I suppose, as a disgrace to their name. They would cross the street to avoid meeting him; they would forbid his entrance to their houses; and every contumely was heaped upon him. Of course, he could obtain his old employment of teacher no more; and the children, who formerly loved and respected him, now looked upon him with disgust. This, he told me, was one of the bitterest of his punishments.

I solemnly believe that even yet, degraded as he was, he might have been reformed, by his friends seizing a lucky moment, and by their treating him as a fellow-creature, instead of a beast. But they did not so. His frailities were visited by their virulence; and they forgot entirely that common bond of fellowship, which, as we all sin more or less, should have caused them to be lenient. Which of those friends or relatives can say—I have, on my conscience, none of the responsibility of that man's intemperance and death?

The teacher was of naturally delicate constitution, and he could not long hold up under the results of his conduct. Each successive indulgence left him a weaker and a weaker man.

Three years had not passed away, after his taking that draught from the jug in the harvest-field, before he was upon his dying bed—the dying bed of a drunkard. With his last breath he proclaimed that his wretched fate might have been prevented, had not the thoughts of reformation, whenever they arose in his mind, been stifled by the proud and contemptuous treatment he received from his relatives and friends.

CHAPTER XI.

> Whene'er thou meet'st a human form
> Less favor'd than thine own,
> Remember; 'tis thy neighbor worm,
> Thy brother, or thy son.
>   ANONYMOUS.[28]

WHEN I had been some five months in this village, I thought one morning that it would not be amiss for me to have a settlement with the landlord. Since the time I had confided my funds to him, I had heard very little of our joint speculations; and I supposed I might have quite a handsome amount of cash due me by this time.

Upon my mentioning the subject, he assented at once—stating that he had for a day or two intended suggesting the same thing to me. We therefore went into his little private parlor, and he drew out his books, and commenced reckoning. What was my amazement when he informed me, that the amount due *from me to him* was not quite one hundred dollars! I supposed at first he was in a vein of pleasantry, and laughed at him. But he gravely pushed his accounts over to me, and told me to look for myself. Considerably alarmed, I did so. I saw that one single item, that of *liquor* alone, was summed up to more than the sum I had originally put in his hands, for purposes of profit. I indignantly asked him, if he thought I was going to submit to such flagrant injustice. With an impudent coolness, he retorted, that if I chose to attempt redress, I might begin as soon as I thought fit. Had he not been liberal, he said, his demand against me would have stood much higher.

The man was a rascal—that was evident. But whether I had any chance of recovering back my money was not quite so clear. Upon consulting with a man of law, in the course of the day, I found that my prospect was gloomy indeed. I have since thought, that the landlord himself gave the lawyer his cue. Quite mad with resentment and agitation, when I returned to the house, I told the landlord plainly my opinion of his conduct. He retorted. My temper rose, and I struck him to the earth. I rushed from the house, swearing that I would not stay in so vile a place another night.

I had a small sum of money, and I immediately engaged passage to New York. In an hour I was on my way thither. The reflections that filled my mind, were anything but agreeable. To be swindled—to be the dupe of a villain, and one too whom I had looked on as a friend—was bad enough.

28. From "Thy Neighbor"; in Cheever.

Besides which, I could not but be conscious how much I was to blame for my own carelessness, and my want of sobriety, which, after all, was the foundation of the ill-luck.

The latter part of my journey was by steamboat. As the light of day dawned in the east, our craft swung alongside the wharf; and I went on shore in the city, where, four years previous, I had come an innocent and honest country youth. My unsophisticated habits had worn away, but at the expense of how much of the pure gold, which was bartered for dross!

Of course, I had no plan marked out as to any method of life, or any means to get a living. As I walked along the street, but a few rods from the landing-place, my eyes were caught by the sight of tempting bottles of liquor, arranged on a bar. What busy devil was it that tempted me then to go in and drink? Yielding to the fatal impulse, I entered and called for liquor. The ice was broken now, and I felt no more repugnance. There were some jovial-looking fellows there, and I entered into conversation with them. A little while, and we all drank again.

From that moment, I have an indistinct recollection of going through scenes which it makes my stomach now turn, to think upon—drunkenness, and the very lowest and filthiest kind of debauchery. Probably, for I never knew for certain, I spent five days upon that spree. Not at any single time was I sober, or near sober.

At last I awoke. It was a little before sunrise. I lay upon the ground, on a pier jutting out into the river. By one side of me was a high pile of wood—on the other side I heard the dashing of water against the wharf. The air, though chill, was fresh and fragrant; but the torments of the damned seemed raging in my head. Oh, that agony of pain; that thirstiness; that searing, burning dryness; that indescribable feeling of horror; that detestable nausea—never shall I forget!

I raised myself on my hands and knees, and my first thought was to throw myself over into the river, and thus put an end to my miserable existence. But, wicked as I was, I dared not rush thus blindly into the presence of an offended God. I lifted myself, and sat on the heavy piece of timber that formed the edge of the wharf.

What a miserable object! The thing I wore upon my head was crushed out of all shape of a hat; my trowsers were torn and soiled; I had no coat, and but one shoe. My face, I felt, was all dirty and brown, and my eyes bleared and swollen. What use had I for life? While, at the moment, I feared to die. And as it seemed that even now I felt the icy finger at my heart—I prayed to God that he would not crush the wounded worm.

I arose, and walked forth.

The hours rolled on. The streets filled with clatter and with busy faces;

and wherever I passed along, the crowd shrunk from me as from the pestilence.

I remember that about noon, I came out into Chatham Square. On one side were little hills of furniture of every description and quality. Many people were scanning them, apparently with the intent to become purchasers. There were also auctioneers, mounted upon tables, or barrels, and crying the goods and the prices that were bid for them. Toward the middle of the Square stood a row of coaches, and several carts, for hire. On the walks, and through the streets, hundreds of men, women, and children were constantly passing, crowd upon crowd. I stood awhile, and looked upon the scene, though vacantly.

Then I sauntered on again. All around was the deafening noise of people engaged in their thousand employments. I gazed curiously at the shops, which exhibited their merchandise in large handsome windows, many of them having a few of their best articles hung out in front, so that the passer by could not but see them. After awhile, I turned and went up a cross street. So on I wended, and across, and up and down, like a rudderless boat.

Dragging thus about, four or five hours passed away, and I began to grow foot-sore and very hungry.

Signs now appeared of the coming on of night. Lamplighters hurried past me with their ladders; the windows, one after another, began to touch up their gas; and those of the mechanics whose business was earliest through, were to be seen in groups, walking along homeward. As I came out from a narrow street, through which I had been wandering some time, I found myself in the same open place, where at noon I had seen such busy traffic. What could I do? I cast my eyes hopelessly about, and saw no sign of sunshine. I felt quite faint from want of food.

There seemed to be no better plan than to walk down the wide handsome street, leading to the east from where I stood, and knock at every house, stating my destitute situation, and asking for the remnants of a meal, and shelter or the means of shelter, until I should obtain relief. Beggary! It was a bitter pill, but I saw no medium between it and starvation; and at the best, the chances were ten to one that I should not gain what I sought.

I walked along the street. It was lined on each side with lofty brick houses. There was no flash of shop windows, and much less noise, and fewer passengers than in the thoroughfares I had hitherto seen.

As I wearily trod the flag-stones, my eyes would now and then be caught by the front rooms of the basements, some of them with family groups circling round the cheerful fire, some with the table spread for supper, and with many luxuries and comforts to tempt the appetite. Oh, how my mouth watered! Here and there I beheld through the curtains little children, all fresh and neat, and curled, frolicking about in play.

It was a long time before I could screw my courage to make application at the doors. At last I went up the stoop of one of the houses, and knocked softly with my fist. I waited several minutes, and then knocked again; no one came to open for me, and I was about retreating in despair.

"Pull the bell, my man," said a person passing, who noticed my conduct, "they'll never hear your knock."

So I applied my hand to the knob, and drew it just enough to make a slight tinkle. In a few minutes, a black man came, and swinging the door on its hinges, beheld me standing there, abashed and trembling.

"Well, what is it?" said he, after waiting a moment, and hearing me say nothing.

I began my request, but had not spoken more than four or five words, before the menial slammed the door in my face with an execration. Starting like a guilty creature, I hastily rushed down upon the walk again.

I passed several blocks before making another attempt. This time I applied at the lower entrance. A woman appeared to answer the summons.

"Come in," she answered compassionately, "wait a bit, and I'll speak to the mistress."

She went in through a side door, and I could hear talking in the apartment. After a short time the door partly opened.

"No," said some one within, "impostors are so common, and you only encourage them in idleness. Tell him to go; and be careful of the bolt, when he passes out."

The woman came from the room, and her face told the cheerless answer, she was commissioned to bear, without the necessity for words. The next minute I was in the dark street once more.

A third and fourth trial were as fruitless as the first.

At the next, the servant told me to wait awhile, as the family were at their devotions. I stood, and gazed at the circle in the inner apartment; for the door was open, and I could see all. An elderly gentleman was reading a portion of Scripture, and the rest were listening with sedate attention to all that came from his lips.

"*Inasmuch*," I heard him say, in a slow emphatic voice, his eyes fixed reverently on the book before him; "*Inasmuch as ye have refused it to the least of these my brethren, ye have refused it to me.*"

More he read of the same purport—and then closed the book and knelt, the rest following his example.

For fifteen minutes, nothing was heard there but the accents of fervent prayer. Then all arose, and after a decorous pause, the servant introduced my case. He was sufficiently bred to his station, to refrain from urging my claims in any other way than a statement of my destitute condition; yet I could not have had a more favorable advocate. When he finished,

"Richard," said the elderly gentleman, "give the poor fellow this."

The servant took the gift, and put it in my hand. It was *one cent*.

And Richard hurried me out of the light; for he felt his face suffused with a blush. And as I was leaving the door, he unclasped my finger and placed there a silver coin, just twenty-five times the value of what his master had bestowed upon me.

For my life I could not have subjected myself to any more rebuffs. I remembered a low groggery, where cheap lodgings were to let, and turned my wretched steps toward the place.

CHAPTER XII.

> What brings vice and guilt below?
> Strong drink brings!
> TEMPERANCE SONG.[29]

MONTHS swept onward in their silent course. I know not how I lived; I have never been able, to this day, to account for the method of my subsistence—but yet I did live. Sometimes, finding a chance shelter in a half finished building, left open by the workmen—sometimes, sleeping in the purlieus of the markets, or on the docks—sometimes, going for two days with hardly a morsel of food, for I was a drunkard still; and though necessity at times made me sober for awhile, I always managed to get liquor by one means or another, at last. Can it be believed that, at the very moment the eyes of the reader are scanning these pages, there are hundreds—ay thousands—roaming about the by-places of this mighty city, in the same condition, and with the same appetite, which I have described as mine during those fearful months? It seems now, as I look back to it, like a dream—a hideous phantom of a diseased mind. But there came a sudden shock after a time, and I was aroused from that mockery of a dream. Thus it came.

It was the midnight of a Sabbath in winter. Darkness spread over the great city, and the slumbering dwellers therein. The streets, the mighty veins along which currents had coursed all day, were not still and deserted. Every hour the booming of the public clocks pealed out, each stroke falling

29. From "Water *versus* Alcohol"; in Grosh, *Temperance Pocket Companion.*

distinctly and solemnly through the frosty night air. Overhead, the stars did not shine. It had been snowing, and the wind occasionally blew the drifts so as to make a perfect tempest of fine ice, dashing into the face of the late traveller. The drowsy watchman sought some sheltered nook, and drew himself close together, shivering with the rigor of the night.

Starting at one of the eastern wharves, is a street running up from the river—a narrow, dirty street, with many wooden houses, occupied as taverns for seamen and abiding places for degraded women. At one of these taverns, myself, and a party of ill-favored, gallows-looking fellows, were arranging our persons, preparatory to sallying forth in the streets. What object could we have in view, at that late hour of the night, but wickedness?

There were four of us. The leader of our gang, who was addressed by the name of Picaroon, had several weapons about his person that were evidently capable of doing dangerous work.

"Come lads," said he, "the business we are on, will be none the worse for a few glasses. Let us drink."

At the word, we helped ourselves, and tossed the liquor down our throats.

We made our egress from the place, and sticking our hands in the capacious pockets of our coats, we walked rapidly after the Picaroon, who strode ahead, as if he knew at once the road to be taken.

The wind whistled, and the fitful blasts, laden with the drift-snow, assailed our progress, and dashed in our faces as we walked along. But our leader turned neither to the right or left, and hardly deigned to bend his head to the heaviest demonstration of the tempest.

After awhile we reached a section of the city, mostly occupied by merchants for their warehouses and stores. The Picaroon now proceeded more cautiously, and turning up Wall-street, led us to a place, not far distant from the Exchange, where we stopped—partly to take breath, and partly to reconnoitre. The night was so dark, that a man at a rod's distance could not have been seen. So we listened awhile, to hear if any of the guardians of the hour were stirring.

"I believe," said the Picaroon, in a low tone, "that we are on the right track. This, I think, is the place we seek."

And he pointed to a basement immediately in front of us, which from its appearance, and the sign over the door, looked like a broker's office.

"Now boys," continued our conductor, in the same cautious voice, "let us begin. Banks, where is the key I gave you in charge?"

The person he addressed handed it to him in silence.

"Curses!" exclaimed the Picaroon, vainly trying to put it to successful use, "the thing has failed, after all. I more than suspected it would. The next time, I'll take the duplicate myself."

"Then we'll burst open the door," said one of our party.

"Of course," the Picaroon rejoined, "we have nothing else to do. Here Evans, hold this lantern!"

And coming up at his orders, I took the light, which was shaded on all sides but one, and held it as he directed.

They proceeded to their work of crime. *They?* Why should I not say *we?* For though a passive agent in the affair, I stood by with apathetic consent, and aided in it. Sunk, sunk at last, to be the companion and abettor of thieves!

"D—n the door! how firm it is!" said Banks, as his cautious blows with a sort of crow-bar, produced no effect. The Picaroon had previously used two or three saws, and was now at work with a chisel.

Our other companion was assisting actively, also, and I stood, and threw the rays from the lantern as they desired.

Crash! crash! went the instruments of our burglary, with a deadened sound, for we knew there were private watchmen in this part of the city— and though we feared little from their vigilance such a night as that, we thought our blows, if too loud, might reach their ears, and bring on a discovery.

Yielding, at last, to saw-teeth, chisel-edge, and crow-bar, the fastenings gave way. One stout thump with the latter instrument, and our entrance was clear. But it was louder than any of the preceding ones.

"Hell!" uttered the Picaroon, furiously, "I would rather have worked two hours longer than heard that blow! But it is too late now; so, Banks, come in with me, and you two keep watch here!"

He had hardly stepped out of sight, when a watchman's rattle rang on the curb-stone, not a hundred feet from where we stood. The Picaroon and his companions heard it too, and dashing from the door, threw the lantern on the ground, and fled along the street.

"Quick! quick! for your lives!" cried the Picaroon to us as he passed. "Both of you, run for your lives!"

My companion took advantage of the timely warning; but the watch were now upon our steps. I heard them close behind me, and stumbling in the darkness, fell upon the ground. They seized me, and carried me away a prisoner. The whole occurrence passed over like a whirlwind. Neither of my three companions were taken.

Was I not sunk low indeed? The very stupor, the deadened nature of my faculties—even when not under the influence of liquor which my course of life had superinduced—was not sufficient to hide from me the horrible feature of my situation. A criminal, one who had violated the laws, and was justly obnoxious to their severest punishments—where could I look for a friend, or whence hope for favor?

It were a stale homily, were I to stay here, and remark upon the easy road from intemperance to crime. Those who have investigated those matters, tell us, however, that five out of every six of the cases which our criminal courts have brought before them for adjudication, are to be traced directly or indirectly to that fearful habit. I have sometimes thought, that the laws ought not to punish those actions of evil which are committed when the senses are steeped in intoxication. But if such a principle were allowed to influence judicial decisions, how terrible an opening there would be! How great a temptation, even, to the letting loose of the worst passions! An idiot is not responsible for his actions, to be sure; but the drunkard deliberately brings his idiocy upon himself, and must not take shelter under it from the consequences thereof. And yet, that mercy and charity which should ever be present in our minds, must lead us to throw the mantle of excuse, as far as possible, over the bad done by the intemperate. None know—none can know, but they who have felt it—the burning, withering thirst for drink, which habit forms in the appetite of the wretched victim of intoxication.

CHAPTER XIII.

> Be free! not chiefly from the iron chain,
> But from the one which passion forges, be
> The master of thyself!
>
> MRS. EMBURY.[30]

WHEN I was turning over in my mind, the second day of my confinement in prison, the method I had best pursue, under all my present difficulties, the darkest and fearfullest despondency fell upon me. It seemed like a cloud stretching all around and over me, and hiding every glimpse of the cheerful light. The thought of my boyhood in the country—of a hundred different scenes in the happy life I had spent there—came to my remembrance. Then my journey to New York, and my companions of the market-waggon. The antiquary, Lee, my benefactor, to whom I had made so poor a return, and Colby, the instrument of my disgrace. I pondered upon all, and even the minutest incidents of that journey. Lee! Should I not apply to him in my tribulation? But no; I had injured him deeply, and my pride revolted

30. The only volume of Emma Catherine Embury's poems—a selected edition—was published in 1839; these lines do not appear in it.

at the idea of his knowing my present situation. And as for Colby, since the death of my poor wife, and our rencontre at the tavern, I would as soon have taken a serpent in my hand as received a favor from him.

The despondency I have mentioned, clung to me for days. I, a young man, on whom fortune had more than once smiled, whose very start of life in the city was signalized by a stroke of good luck, that might have led me on to a competence and happiness; and here I was, imprisoned for a heinous crime. More than once the fiendish resolve entered my mind, of foul self-murder! But ever the image of my sainted Mary came to me in those prison walls, and looked down, and smiled pleasantly; and I could not renounce all hope of ever seeing her again, by sealing up the sum of my wickedness beyond all power of pardon.

The time approached for my trial. So callous was I, and so resigned to my fate, that I cared little whether it went well or ill for me.

A day or two before I was to be brought up in court, one of the officers of the prison entered, stating that a gentleman without desired to see me; and he had hardly spoken the words, when the person in question was ushered into my cell. He was a middle-aged man, and what he could wish with me I could not conceive.

"Is your name Franklin Evans?" said he.

I answered in the affirmative.

"Do you know that card?"

And he handed me a dirty piece of pasteboard, with a name written upon it. The name was "*Lucy Marchion*—Bleecker-street."

Surprised at the question, and utterly unconscious of what the man's conduct could mean, I made no answer, but stared at him in surprise.

"Listen," continued he. "The lady, whose name you hold in your hand, was many months since at a distant place in the country, with a dear child. Accidentally the child fell into a dangerous stream of water, and would have been drowned, but for the kindness of a brave young stranger, who rescued it, and restored it to the lady. She was hurried away, almost on the instant, leaving in that stranger's hand, her name and residence. By some mark upon the card, the whole circumstance was brought to her mind this very morning, when a police officer called, and handed it to us, making inquiries, which it is unnecessary here to repeat."

The man ceased; and I knew the whole affair intuitively. In a preceding chapter I have mentioned the incident, where I preserved the little girl's life. The card I had placed in my pocket-book, never thinking of it since. Upon the morning after my arrest, my person had been searched, and everything taken from me—the authorities thinking, that perhaps some clue might be gained to my accomplices. The card, they fancied, could possibly afford some such clue. They went to the address upon it. Mr. Marchion, the husband of the lady, and father of the little girl I had preserved, was a lawyer, well known for his talent and respectability; and, at the solicitation of his wife, he immediately started upon a mission of benevolence to the prison where I was.

"Tell me, young man," said he, when all this was fairly understood between us, and he knew that he had indeed found the person for whom his wife had never ceased to pray down blessings—"tell me the whole story of your crime, for which you are now in durance. Keep back nothing; and I will see what can be done for you."

"Is there any prospect," inquired I, anxiously, "for acquittal, think you?"

"That question I can best answer," said he, "after your story is told."

I knew that I could place implicit reliance upon his honor, and I related the whole incidents of my folly and my crime. I told him, that for weeks my faculties had been drowned amid a sea of intemperance. I said that when I started off with the Picaroon and the others, I knew not where they were going, or for what purpose; and that, though I stood by, I had no hand in the active commission of the burglary. My defence, I could not help seeing myself, was a very weak one; but it was the best I had to offer, and the love of liberty was strong within me.

"Perhaps it would be wiser," said Mr. Marchion, when I concluded, "for me to express no opinion now; and yet I would advise you not to give up hope. The judge, whom I know well, is one that will not be apt to look upon your conduct, placed in the light you have given to it by the narrative just closed, with a too rigorous eye; and I feel assured that what you have spoken is the truth."

And as he departed, I felt new cheerfulness spring up in my breast. So pleasant is it, in time of dismay, to have one good heart, on whose friendly aid you can rest your troubles.

Before the trial, Mr. Marchion came to me two or three times again, to get the locality of the tavern whence we had started, on the night of the burglary. He also took from me the names of two or three persons, whom I had known in my better days, for witnesses that I had once borne a fair reputation. I felt some doubt, as I gave him that of Mr. Lee, among others, whether the character my old friend might give me, would prove to my advantage or no.

The crisis came at last. The prosecuting attorney proved by the officers the fact of the crime, beyond the possibility of cavil. The officers swore, also, that according to all appearance, I was one of the robbers. They had arrested me on the spot, in a vain endeavor to fly.

Mr. Marchion himself conducted my defence. He skillfully enlarged on the danger of circumstantial evidence—produced his witnesses to my former good name and honorable conduct—and then expatiated on the unhappy method of my having fallen into habits of intemperance. The keeper of the low tavern proved my evident ignorance, when the Picaroon led me away, of the business on which he was bound: and with all the dexterity for which his profession is celebrated, my fervent advocate dressed up what good points there were in my case, and closed by a pathetic appeal jointly to the jury and the court.

All was of no avail. The jury, after being out an hour or two, came in with a verdict of "*Guilty*." I could hardly support myself under the sickening sensation which followed the utterance of that word. My head swam, my ears tingled, and I heard not the foreman continue, "and recommended to the mercy of the court." Had I done so, I should have hoped for any leniency—so sure had I been, after Mr. Marchion's eloquent appeal, that I must be acquitted.

The judge consulted with those on each side of him for a few minutes, and then rose to pronounce sentence. I could hardly believe my ears, when they conveyed to me, as he went on, the intelligence that I was *not* to be sent back to prison. Amazed and overjoyed, I noted but little of the details of his discourse: how that in view of the peculiar nature of my case, sentence was to be suspended, and I discharged—or something of that sort. I only heard the word *discharged*, and could hardly remain in the box until he finished his speech. Then, as the officer in attendance came to me, and took me by the hand, and told me I was free, I rushed aside, and caught Mr. Marchion's arm, which I dampened with my tears. *Free!* Yes, after all—after being on the very verge of punishment for felony—to come off thus! Was it not, indeed, a fit cause for rejoicing?

CHAPTER XIV.

> Kneel! and the vow thou breathest there
> At that lone hour shall float on high;
> Spirits of light shall bless thy prayer,
> The dead, the crowned, shall greet thy sigh.
>   MRS. HALE'S MAGAZINE.[31]

THE kindness of Marchion and his wife did not pause, merely at saving me from an ignominious fate. I pass over the gratitude of the lady at our first meeting, the very next hour after I was liberated from bondage—simply stating, that it was fully such as a mother might be supposed to offer one who had saved her offspring from sudden and painful death.

31. From "The Dying Girl"; in Cheever.

"All that we could do," said the lady, "would not pay you, generous man, for the service you have rendered me."

And she called the little girl to her side, and bade her thank the preserver of her life. Marchion stood by, and looked on with a friendly smile.

But stop—thought I to myself, my eyes being caught by the sight of my own soiled and tattered garments—am I a fit person for the company of well-dressed and cleanly people? What excuse should I make? But Marchion already knew a large part of my history, and of my former follies; and some good spirit seemed whispering to me, no excuse but the truth. So in answer to their inquiries, I told them my whole life, without any alteration or concealment.

"Young man," said the lady, when I ended, "had you related all this to us some months ago, we should have shrunk from you, or set you down as a liar. But my observation, of late, has led both my husband and myself to the knowledge of cases, exceeding even yours in wonder and in depth of misery."

She then told me that her husband, who had in his younger days been an intemperate man, was now a member of one of the societies of the city, whose object was to aid the holy cause of Abstinence; and that at the meetings of those societies, which she occasionally attended, she had heard in the "experience," of those who addressed them, tales of wo that might harrow up a soul with sympathy.

As we sat that evening around the cheerful blaze of the parlor fire, our conversation turned upon the same topics that we had discoursed of in the morning. Mr. Marchion expressed his wonder at the strange and almost miraculous manner in which some persons, who appeared in the very deepest depth of the mire, would become reformed. A little trivial incident—an ordinary occurrence which seemed not worth the importance of a thought—would sometimes change the whole current of their wicked conduct, and present them to the world, regenerated, and disenthralled. One instance, he said, had come to his knowledge in former times, which, if I felt disposed to hear it, he would relate.

I expressed my pleasure at the suggestion, and he commenced his narrative:[32]

---

32. As was mentioned in an earlier note, the narrative that follows was twice reprinted as a separate tale with the title of "Little Jane": in the *Brooklyn Eagle* and in *Collect* (see Note One). The *Collect* version characteristically deletes the "e" in the past forms of most regular verbs. Both versions are collated below with the first edition text, which we are following. The variants that appear in the *Eagle* text of

"Lift, up!" was ejaculated as a signal—and click! went the glasses in the hands of a party of tipsy men, drinking one night at the bar of one of the middling order of taverns. And many a wild gibe was uttered, and many a terrible blasphemy, and many an impure phrase sounded out the pollution of the hearts of those[33] half-crazed creatures, as they tossed down their liquor, and made the walls echo with their uproar. The first and foremost in recklessness was a girlish-faced, fair-haired fellow of twenty-two or three years. They called him Mike. He seemed to be looked upon by the others as a sort of prompter, from whom they were to take cue. And if the brazen wickedness evinced by him in a hundred freaks and remarks to his companions, during their stay in that place, were any test of his capacity—there might hardly be one more fit to go forward as a guide on the road to destruction.

From the conversation of the party, it appeared that they had been spending the earlier part of the evening in a gambling house.[34] The incidents spoken of as having occurred, and the conduct of young Mike and his associates there, are not sufficiently tempting to be narrated.

A second, third and fourth time were the glasses filled, and the effect thereof began to be perceived in a still higher degree of noise and loquacity among the revellers. One of the serving-men came in at this moment, and whispered the bar-keeper, who went out, and in a moment returned again.

"A person," he said, "wished to speak with Mr. Michael. He waited on the walk in front."

The individual whose name was mentioned, made his excuses to the others, telling them he would be back in a moment, and left the room. He had hardly shut the door behind him,[35] and stepped into the open air, when he saw one of his brothers—his elder by eight or ten years—pacing to and fro with rapid and uneven steps. As the man turned in his walk, and the glare of the street lamp fell upon his face; the youth, half-benumbed as his senses were, was somewhat startled at its paleness and evident perturbation.

"Come with me!" said the elder brother, hurriedly, "the illness of our little Jane is worse, and I have been sent for you."

"Poh!" answered the young drunkard, very composedly, "is that all? I shall be home by-and-by."

"Little Jane" are designated in the following footnotes as "LJE"; those of *Collect* text are designated as "LJC."

33. these LJC

34. This sentence is made a part of the preceding paragraph; the sentence that follows is omitted. LJE, LJC

35. As he shut the door behind him LJE, LJC

And he turned to go back again.[36]

"But brother, she is worse than ever before. Perhaps when you arrive she may be *dead*."

The tipsy one paused in his retreat, perhaps alarmed at the utterance of that dread word, which seldom fails to shoot a chill to the hearts of mortals. But he soon calmed himself, and waving his hand to the other:

"Why, see," said he, "a score of times at least, have I been called away to the last sickness of our good little sister; and each time, it proves to be nothing worse than some whim of the nurse or the physician. Three years has the girl been able to live very heartily under her disease; and I'll be bound she'll stay on earth three years longer."

And as he concluded this wicked and most brutal reply, the speaker opened the door and went into the bar-room. But in his intoxication, during the hour that followed, Mike was far from being at ease. At the end of that hour, the words "perhaps when you arrive she may be *dead*," were not effaced from his hearing yet, and he started for home. The elder brother had wended his way back in sorrow.

Let me go before the younger one, awhile, to a room in that home. A little girl lay there dying. She was quite rational.[37] She had been ill a long time; so it was no sudden thing for her parents, and her brethren and sisters, to be called for the solemn witness of the death agony.

The girl was not what might be called beautiful. And yet, there is a solemn kind of loveliness that always surrounds a sick child. The sympathy for the weak and helpless sufferer, perhaps, increases it in our ideas.[38] The ashiness, and the moisture on the brow, and the film over the eye-balls—what man can look upon the sight, and not feel his heart awed within him? Children, I have sometimes fancied too, increase in beauty as their illness deepens. The angels, it may be, are already vesting them with the garments they shall wear in the Pleasant Land.[39]

Beside the nearest relatives of little Jane, standing round her bedside, was the family doctor. He had just laid her wrist down upon the coverlid,[40] and the look he gave the mother, was a look in which there was no hope.

"My child!" she cried, in uncontrollable agony, "my child! you die!"[41]

And the father, and the sons and daughters, were bowed down in grief, and thick tears rippled between the fingers held before their eyes.

---

36. And he turned back again. LJE
LJC follows LJE, but makes the sentence the final clause of the preceding sentence.
37. This sentence is omitted in LJC.
38. our own ideas. LJC   39. This sentence is omitted in LJC.

Then there was silence awhile. During the hour just by-gone, Jane had, in her childish way, bestowed a little gift upon each of her kindred, as a remembrancer when she should be dead and buried in the grave. And there was one of these simple tokens which had not reached its destination. She held it in her hand now. It was a very small, much-thumbed book —a religious story for infants, given her by her mother when she had first learned to read.

While they were all keeping this solemn stillness—broken only by the suppressed sobs of those who stood and watched for the passing away of the girl's soul—a confusion of some one entering rudely and speaking in a turbulent voice, was heard in the adjoining apartment. Again the voice roughly sounded out; it was the voice of the drunkard Mike, and the father bade one of his sons go and quiet the intruder.

"If nought else will do," said he sternly, "put him forth by strength. We want no tipsy brawlers here, to disturb such a scene as this!"

For what moved the sick girl thus[42] uneasily on her pillow, and raised her neck, and motioned to her mother? She would that Mike should be brought to her side. And it was enjoined on him whom the father had bade to eject the noisy one, that he should tell Mike his sister's request, and beg him to come to her.

He came. The inebriate—his mind sobered by the deep solemnity of the scene—stood there, and leaned over to catch the last accents[43] of one who, in ten minutes more,[44] was to be with the spirits of heaven.

All was the silence of deepest night. The dying child held the young man's hand in one of hers; with the other, she slowly lifted the trifling memorial she had assigned especially for him, aloft in the air. Her arm shook—her eyes, now becoming glassy with the death-damps, were cast toward her brother's face. She smiled pleasantly, and as an indistinct gurgle came from her throat, the uplifted hand fell suddenly into the open palm of her brother's, depositing the tiny volume there. Little Jane was dead.

From that night, the young man stepped no more in his wild courses, but was reformed.

When Mr. Marchion concluded his narrative, we sat some minutes in silence. I thought I noticed even more than usual interest concerning it, as he had drawn to its crisis—and I more than half suspected he was him-

40. coverlet LJC
41. "My child!" she cried, in uncontrollable agony, "O! my child!" LJE, LJC
42. "thus" is omitted in LJC.
43. last accounts LJC   44. who soon LJC

self the young man whose reform had been brought about by the child's death. I was right. He acknowledged in answer to my questioning, that he had indeed been relating a story, the hero of which was himself.

CHAPTER XV.

"The planter's house was an airy, rustic dwelling, that brought Defoe's description of such places strongly to my recollection. The day was very warm, but the blinds being all closed, a shadowy coolness rustled through the room, which was exquisitely refreshing, after the glare and heat without. Before the windows was an open piazza, where, in what they call hot weather—whatever that may be—they sling hammocks, and drink and doze luxuriously."

DICKENS'S AMERICAN NOTES.[45]

THE benevolence and good will of the Marchion family, as I have before intimated, led them to pause at nothing which might be of substantial benefit to me. It is almost needless to say that one of the first movements for my improvement, through their means, was my signing the Temperance Pledge. This was, what is in these days called the Old Pledge, which forbade only the drinking of the most ardent kind of liquors, and allowed people to get as much fuddled as they chose upon wines, and beer, and so on. At that time, those who went further, were supposed by many to be altogether too ultra in their views. It will be seen in the remaining chapters of my narrative, whether the Old Pledge was sufficient to remove the dangers which may be apprehended from habits of intemperance. For, though I had now reformed from my hitherto evil courses, and had always subsequently kept the integrity of my promise; I think it will be allowed that the fruits of temperance were not fully reaped by me in that portion of my life, which I am now going to transcribe.

The Marchions supplied me with a moderate portion of funds, and aided me with advice and recommendations in every way. Under their assistance I started myself in a respectable, lucrative, and easy business. I prospered, and the world began to look bright once more.

Some months passed away, when I took a jaunt—partly of business and partly of pleasure—to one of the southern counties of Virginia. In effecting the arrangements I had under my charge, I was now and then forced to

45. *American Notes*, 1842, p. 163.
46. FC—having omitted most of the episodes which followed, in the *New World* version, Mr. Lee's discharge of Evans (see Note 25 above)—picks up the original thread of the story with this sentence after first providing the following transition:

wait the convenience of those over whom I had no control. Accordingly, on several occasions, I was detained for days at a time, with no employment on hand except to look about and amuse myself in the best way possible. One of these waiting spells, I well recollect, was at a pleasant, old-settled village, on the banks of a fine stream. I amused the monotony of the time by getting acquainted, as far as I could, with the planters in the neighborhood, and by roaming over their settlements; and even by chatting with the slaves, from whose liveliness and cheerful good-humor, I derived no small share of mirth myself. The Virginians are proverbially hospitable, and friendly to strangers; and taking all things into consideration, the time passed quite as comfortably as I could expect.

One day, I strolled off to some distance beyond the more closely settled part of the village; sauntering lazily along, and having no more particular object in view, than a listless enjoyment of the natural scenery. My walk skirted the banks of the river. Some two miles I had gone on in this way, when I came out upon a little knoll, sloping down to the shore. Upon the highest elevation of the ground, there stood a house, which I could not help admiring for its look of comfort, and the evident good taste which had been active in adorning the grounds and walks around it.

As I walked nearer, to admire some rare plants that stood in pots, by the porch, a middle-aged gentleman came out of the entrance, and saluting me courteously, entered into conversation, and invited me to take a seat in the cool shade of the verandah. My long walk had made me somewhat weary, and I complied with his invitation. I rather thought, from his accent and manner, that he was not an American. In the course of our talk, I learned that he was a bachelor, and had inherited the estate on which he now resided from his father; and that, though somewhat lonely, he generally found sufficient amusement in taking care of the affairs of his plantation. He brought out some excellent wine, before we parted, and we finished a couple of bottles together. It was almost evening when I went away; and then my host, whose name was Bourne, only allowed me to depart under a strict promise, that I would visit him again on the morrow.

Upon my return to the village, I spoke of my entertainment by the planter at whose house I had passed the day, and inquired into his history. I found, from what I learned in the village and in my after acquaintance with the planter himself, that Bourne's father had come over from France, during the troublesome times there, in the latter part of the last century.[46]

I must not run into any thing egotistical; and therefore it will not do for me to undertake an explanation of the causes which led at this very time, to a startling but most joyful event—a reconciliation between myself and my kind mercantile employer, at the instance of the latter personage himself. He

He was among a large number of gentlemen and citizens, who left that country to obtain quiet, even at the expense of exile. The cause of his departure from his native land, however, was not a disapproval of the schemes of the revolutionizers, just then on the point of coming into power. On the contrary, he assimilated strongly to their doctrines, and afterward took every occasion to instill them into the mind of his son.

Bourne chose America as the place of his retreat, because of the liberty he might enjoy there. And here, where I found my friend of the day before,[47] he had bought himself a plantation, and placed upon it the needful requisites of slaves and material, for the purposes to which he intended applying it.

Perhaps it may hardly be the appropriate place here, to remark upon the national customs of this country; but I cannot help pausing a moment to say that Bourne, as he saw with his own eyes, and judged with his own judgment, became convinced of the fallacy of many of those assertions which are brought against slavery in the south. He beheld, it is true, a large number of men and women in bondage; but he could not shut his eyes to the fact, that they would be far more unhappy, if possessed of freedom. He saw them well taken care of—with shelter and food, and every necessary means of comfort: and he wondered in his own mind, as he remembered what misery he had seen in his travels through various countries of Europe, that the philanthropists of the Old World should wish to interfere with the systems of the New—when the merely nominal oppression of the latter is overbalanced, so many hundred times, by the stern reality of starvation and despotism in the former.[48]

The next day, and for many days after, I was constant in my visits to my new acquaintance. I found him an intelligent and very affable companion; and, as I had yet to stay some weeks in the place, it may easily be supposed I was not at all displeased that such means of amusement were

did me the favor to employ me again, (O how the succeeding days must have shown him my gratitude!) and to express a kindness, and generous intention, toward me, which affected me deeply. He gave me such advice as fathers give to beloved sons. He told me his determination to make *me* the inheritor of a handsome estate! The record I furnish of all this, here, is brief; for my heart owns a sort of sacredness in the theme, as one not lightly to be touched upon!

I pass over rapidly this era. Let it answer the reader, that in my further conduct toward Mr. Lee, I was not ungrateful for his not unremarkable friendship and liberality to me—God bless him!

Soon after the transpiring of these latter-named events, the occasion turned up, which I have before alluded to, of the necessity of a personal mission to Mr. Bourne, at the south, who was very largely connected in business with Mr. Lee. I seized the opportunity to ask the privilege of being charged with this mission; and that privilege was granted.

What I have now to relate—a train of events quite out of the method of

at my command. And the planter, too, seemed highly delighted with our companionship. He had been, as it were, buried from the world, and saw few visiters, except what chance threw in his way.

So intimate did we at length become, and so necessary to one another's comfort, that I took up my residence in his house; and forwarded to New York information, that I should probably not be home during the season. My business there was under the charge of a faithful and competent person, and I had no fear but what all would go right. The letters I had from him, from time to time, presented the most favorable accounts.

Bourne and I, during the day, were much of the time together, and night always found us over a bottle of wine. I fear that, notwithstanding my strict adherence to the pledge I had given, under the advice of the Marchions, the occasions were not a few wherein I was forced to have assistance, in order to reach my chamber.

My residence and walks about the plantation, made me familiar with all its affairs; and I even took upon myself, at times, the direction of things, as though I were upon my own property. I cannot look back upon this period of my life without some satisfaction; though, take it altogether, it was sadly to my detriment that I ever went to Virginia, as will be seen in the sequel. My evil genius was in the ascendant, and worked me harm in a method as singular, as it has ever since been disagreeable to my reflections.

my hitherto adventures—bears somewhat the air of romance. And yet, reader! when we look around us in the course of our every day lives, or go out among our neighbors, and investigate what is transacted there, you might come to the knowledge of things far more improbable and inconsistent.

Upon my arrival at my destination, (at which it was probable I should have to stay the better part of the season.) I was gratified in being received with the greatest kindness by Mr. Bourne. Though he was a bachelor, he lived in a style of ample comfort—and was evidently a man who understood how to enjoy life.

47. This clause is omitted in FC. Considerable revision—though often carelessly done—was required in this part of the tale because of the altered relationship in FC of Evans, Bourne, the creole Margaret, and Louis, the little slave.

48. The remainder of the chapter following this paragraph is omitted in FC. Omitted also are Chapter XVI and the first four paragraphs of Chapter XVII.

CHAPTER XVI.

> They say 'tis pleasant on the lip,
>   And merry on the brain—
> They say it stirs the sluggish blood
>   And dulls the tooth of pain.
> Ay—but within its glowing deeps,
> A stinging serpent, unseen, sleeps.
>
> Its rosy lights will turn to fire,
>   Its coolness change to thirst;
> And by its mirth, within the brain
>   A sleepless worm is nursed,
> There's not a bubble at the brim
> That does not carry food for him.
>   WILLIS.[49]

AMONG the slaves on Bourne's estate lived a young woman, named Margaret, a creole. She had once been owned by a lady, at whose decease she had been purchased, with others, by the planter, for his farm. The lady had made something of a favorite of the girl, and given her a good education for one of her class. She was of that luscious and fascinating appearance often seen in the south, where a slight tinge of the deep color, large, soft voluptuous eyes, and beautifully cut lips, set off a form of faultless proportions—and all is combined with a complexion just sufficiently removed from clear white, to make the spectator doubtful whether he is gazing on a brunette, or one who has indeed some hue of African blood in her veins. Margaret belonged to the latter class: and she only wanted an opportunity to show, that the fire of her race burnt with all its brightness in her bosom, though smothered by the necessity of circumstances.

The overseer of the business of the plantation, was a man named Phillips. I never liked him—though, as he always treated me well, I could have no occasion to be rude toward him. He was from the north, too—my own section of the country—and with much prudence and industry, he had some of the smaller vices of the human character. His dwelling was a mile, or thereabout, from Bourne's own residence.

Phillips, it seems, had frequently noticed the beauty of the young slave Margaret, and with a licentious eye. The advances which his situation gave him the means of making, however, had been repulsed, and not always without some appearance of scorn.

49. From "Look not upon the wine when it is red"; in Cheever, where it is attributed to N. P. Willis.

It happened, about a week after I took up my abode at the planter's, that Margaret being employed in the field, Phillips came, and as formerly, offered proposals which the indignant creature rejected with terms of anger. Irritated at her severity, the overseer proceeded to such lengths, that the passionate slave lifted the instrument of labor she had been using, and felled him to the earth with a heavy blow. He lay there senseless, and blood flowed from his wound.

A moment's reflection convinced Margaret of the dangerous nature of the act she had committed. With promptitude, she immediately made up her mind what course to pursue. She came at once to the homested, and asked for her master. We were sitting together at the time upon the verandah, our usual afternoon retreat. Margaret was ushered there, and told her story. As she went on, I could not help being struck with her beauty, and the influence of the liquor from the bottle by my side, by no means contributed to lessen my admiration.

"If it were to do over again," said the angry girl, her black eye lighted, and her cheek mantling with the rich blood, "I would act the same. He knows well enough what I have said before, when he has spoken his wicked words to me, and the consequence of his deeds he can only lay to himself."

My countenance, perhaps, expressed the feelings of admiration I have spoken of; for she looked at me, as if appealing to my influence with Bourne in her behalf. The glance I gave her, in return, conveyed that whatever might be the result of her hasty conduct, she would at least have one defender and advocate—perhaps one whose word would be effectual.

In the course of an hour, Phillips made his appearance at the house, with his head bandaged, and his face quite pallid. He had lost some blood, and that, joined with the hate which now appeared in his face toward the offending slave, gave him an appearance anything but inviting. I did not wonder, as I looked at the man, that Margaret had been so obstinate in her conduct toward him.

The room being turned into a kind of judgment-hall, and each party's side having had its say, Mr. Bourne was perplexed in no small degree as to the decision he should give. Margaret had evidently had more of his good will, as she had of the justice of the dispute; but the planter feared the danger of making a precedent by letting her off triumphantly. He could not bring his conscience to chastise her, and yet something was necessary in the way of punishment. So, leaning partly to justice and partly to expediency, he put on a severe face, lectured the girl upon the enormity of her offence, added a few words and threats—which the grumbling overseer thought smacked far too much of being done merely for effect—and then signified his desire to hear no more upon the subject, by dismissing each one to his or her avocations.

In a day or two the occurrence seemed forgotten. *Seemed* forgotten— but in fact, the pride of Phillips had been wounded too deeply for forgiveness. His breast rankled with feelings of hate toward her who had defied him, and made him a theme of ridicule. There was one other, too, in whose mind the beautiful creole had roused strong thoughts, though of a nature very different from those which dwelt in the soul of the overseer.

I don't know whether I have intimated, in the preceding course of my narrative, that my nature was not wanting in susceptibility to female charms. The truth was so, however. And moreover, I had imbibed not a few of the pernicious notions which prevail among young men in our great American city, upon conjugal matters. My safety, hitherto, had been from the swiftness with which my passion passed over. Often had I been struck with a pretty face—remembered it for four or five days— and then recovered from my delusion to smile at my own folly.[50]

The loveliness and grace of Margaret had fascinated me; but she was one, not of my own race, and her very liberty was owned by another. What had I to do with such as she? Every feeling of prudence and self-respect, spoke loudly in opposition to my allowing any sentiment akin to love for the girl in my bosom, or to express it by my conduct. And yet, strangely enough, I thought nothing of all this; but in my wine-drinking interviews with Bourne, frequently alluded to the subject, and spoke of the regard I had for *his slave.*

There seems to be a kind of strange infatuation, permanently settled over the faculties of those who indulge much in strong drink. It is as frequently seen in persons who use wine, as in them that take stronger draughts. The mind becomes, to use an expressive word, *obfusticated*, and loses the power of judging quickly and with correctness. It seems, too, that the unhappy victim of intemperance cannot tell when he commits even the most egregious violations of right; so muddied are his perceptions, and so darkened are all his powers of penetration. And the worst of it is, that even in his sober moments, the same dark influence hangs around him to a great degree, and leads him into a thousand follies and miseries.

Something of this kind, I presume, was the cause of my conduct, as I am going to relate it. Certainly, a man with his senses about him would never have acted in so absurd a manner. But, *does* an habitual wine-bibber have his senses about him? Not one day out of the weekly seven, but saw Bourne and myself for long hours at the bottle!

50. This paragraph is incorporated in FC's substitution for this chapter. See Note 52.

In one of these revels, I told my host that my affection for the creole had induced me to come to the determination of marrying her. Instead of placing so singular a proposal in its true colors before me, Bourne expressed his opinion, that if I liked the girl, it would all be perfectly proper; and he declared, as an evidence of his friendship for me, that he would give her her freedom that very day. Moreover, a young lad, a brother of Margaret, named Louis, whom the planter also owned, was to be given over to me, as I would probably not like to have it said that a *connection* of mine was a bondsman. For some time we discussed the matter, and arranged it highly to our satisfaction. In truth, before we rose from the table, we were neither of us in a state to know whether we were acting the part of fools or wise men.

Will it be believed? That very afternoon, Bourne, who was a justice of the peace, united myself and the creole in matrimony. The certificate of manumission also, was drawn out and signed, and given into Margaret's own hand. A couple of apartments in the homested were assigned to her use—and I signalized this crowning act of all my drunken vagaries, that night, by quaffing bottle after bottle with the planter.

CHAPTER XVII.

> Haply, for I am black;
> And have not those soft parts of conversation
> That chamberers have.
>
> SHAKSPERE.[51]

IT needs not that I should particularize the transactions of the next few days. As may reasonably be expected, not a long time elapsed before I awoke from my lethargy. And *when* I awoke! What disgust with myself filled my mind at view of the conduct I had been pursuing! Though since my first chance interview with Bourne, but four or five short weeks had passed away; it seemed, as I looked back over the time, more like an age.

Then I reviewed the uninviting circumstances of my marriage, and my distaste arose toward the creole, *my wife*, who, I felt sure, had done her best to entrap me into all this. The more I thought upon the subject, the more did my dislike to Margaret gain strength. She whom but a little while before, I had looked on with the deepest admiration, was now almost an object of hate to me.

51. *Othello*, III: iii.

Whatever aversion I felt toward the woman, however, I could not but be conscious of her evident affection to me, as it was exhibited from day to day. She saw and was pained with my conduct. She tried a thousand fond arts to gain back the love I had once shown for her. She conducted herself in the most decorous and humble manner. But all to no avail.

Was my former love for the creole, then, become totally extinct? Ah, human love, to be lasting, must be pure and worthily bestowed.

The course of my narrative needs now that another character should be introduced upon the stage.[52] My evil destiny would have it, that an old city acquaintance of mine, Mrs. Conway, a widow lady, visited the neighborhood at this time, and took up her quarters in the house of the overseer Phillips,[53] to whom she was distantly related. I had met the lady often at the house of persons whom I knew in New-York; and of course, nothing was more natural than for me to call upon her.

Mrs. Conway was about twenty-five, and very handsome; not with unformed and unripened loveliness, but in the rich swell, the very maturity of personal perfection. Her light hair, blue eyes, and the delicacy of her skin, formed a picture rarely met with in that region; and perhaps on this very account, the more prized. She was a woman of the world, however. Gifted with such singular charms, and her mind ornamented with the most needful and complete culture; she had but one aim, the conquest of hearts. And seldom did she determine to make any individual addition to her adorers, but what her efforts were crowned with triumph. Luckless were the stars that led her southward!

The very next day after this woman came among us, she made up her mind to bring *me* to her feet. Probably it was partly from natural inclination, and partly to find herself some agreeable method of dissipating monotony, that caused the lady to form this determination. She (I afterward found out all this) mentioned the project to her relative, Phillips,

---

52. FC resumes the story with this paragraph (see Note 48) after substituting the following for the omitted matter:

I must also introduce to the reader one other personage who has much to do with the adventures soon to be related. This personage was a half sister of Mr. Bourne, a creole girl, whom he called, (and I soon became familiar enough to call,) Margaret—a dark eyed, handsome maiden, whose grace and voluptuousness fascinated me the first time I saw her—and with whom, before I had been a week in the house, I was on the footing a declared suitor—a situation of things on which Mr. Bourne appeared to look with entire indifference, for from some reason he never seemed to like his half sister—and never took any more interest in her affairs, than in those of an entire stranger. He thought, I believe, much more of me than he did of her. Margaret had a special attendant, a handsome little slave-boy named Louis—who, though a slave, could hardly be discriminated from a dark-complexioned American.

who approved of it, and promised to give it any aid in his power. He had never forgotten the indignity bestowed on him by Margaret, before she became raised to her present situation. Policy afterward led him to disguise his feelings; but they were by no means effaced.[54]

It needs not to explain all the artifices which were used for effecting what the plotters desired to accomplish. Fortunately for them, they had a willing subject to work upon; and in much less time than they could have anticipated, I was indeed in the toils.

I do not think I admired Mrs. Conway; at least, I did not at first. But I felt no small disposition to feign that sentiment, if it were merely to mortify my ill-assorted wife. For my dissatisfaction at the marriage was of much longer continuance than my love for the creole; and though I felt ashamed to show the people of the household how bitterly I repented of my drunken rashness—for the marriage deserved no other name—I felt sick at heart whenever I thought upon it. We lived together, Margaret and I, but there was often little of peace and pleasure between us.[55]

"I fear that northern beauty has bewitched you," said Margaret, with a smile, as I returned one evening from calling at the overseer's; "you did not use to be so partial to Mr. Phillips's pathway."

"Matters of business," answered I, a little confused; "nothing but business."

"But is she really as handsome as I hear? I have been told by our people, that fancy can hardly conceive any creature more perfect."

"You have been told the truth," said I; "she is wonderfully fair, not dark and swarthy, which I detest!" and I turned away, sure of the effect of the sharp arrow I had winged.

"Indeed!" burst from the surprised Margaret; and she would have spoken further, but her pride came to prevent her.

Surely, a few short days could not have made this sudden change in

The young lady was very fond of the child—and would have braved anything for him. I don't know whether I have intimated, in the preceding course of my narrative, that my nature was not wanting in susceptibility to female charms. The truth was so, however. And moreover, I had imbibed not a few of the pernicious notions which prevail among young men in our great American city, upon conjugal matters. My safety, hitherto, had been from the swiftness with which my passions passed over. Often had I been struck with a pretty face—remembered it for four or five days—and then recovered from my delusion to smile at my own folly. Ah! how flippantly we are apt to give the sacred name of *Love* to some temporary silliness, which is as evanescent as the clouds!

53. in the house of the overseer of Mr. Bourne's plantation, a person named Phillips FC
54. The last two sentences of this paragraph, naturally, are omitted in FC.
55. This paragraph is omitted in FC.

my affections. And then the creole thought of many little things that had before been airy trifles, but were now too sure a groundwork for her suspicions.

The fears of the jealous woman were to be consummated but too soon, leaving her no further ground to doubt. I shortly made no secret of my attachment to Mrs. Conway. Indeed, I believe that, as it often happens in similar cases, the feeling I began by dissembling,[56] I after awhile really felt in truth. Like an actor who plays a part, I became warmed in the delineation, and the very passion I feigned, came to imbue my soul with its genuine characteristics.

Poor Margaret! it was a wild and fearful storm that raged within her bosom, when she came fully to know the truth of her desertion. I have no doubt she had loved me tenderly, ever since the time of my interference in her behalf when she was arraigned for striking Phillips; and with all the fiery disposition of her nation,[57] she now felt torn with strong passions, to think that another had supplanted her. I do not think I have given a faithful transcript of the creole's character in all its strong points. She was, indeed, a very woman, with some of the most beautiful traits, and some of the most devilish that ever marked her sex.[58] Her ambition of rising above the low level of her companions, had been gratified by the act wherein Bourne conferred freedom upon her. Such freedom had been one of the dearest dreams of her life. And to be the wife of one who occupied a respectable station among the masters of the land, was an exalted destiny beyond which her hopes could hardly rise.

She felt that her being a free woman, gave her much power by the law; and that I was bound to her by indissoluble ties. But with excellent policy, she never allowed her knowledge of this to appear in her conversation or conduct. She had a most difficult part to play; and, as I have in late years, cast my mind back, I could not help being struck with wonder at the dexterous manner in which she avoided many a quicksand, and kept from an open rupture with me, where we had so little in common. Hapless girl! I would that her destiny might have been a more fortunate one!

56. by dissembling, (for I cannot say I loved the widow at first) FC
57. I have no doubt she had loved me tenderly, and with all the fiery disposition of her soul FC
58. The rest of the chapter following this sentence is omitted in FC.

CHAPTER XVIII.

No man is safe, who drinks. Actions which are the height of injustice are often committed under the influence of liquor, to those whom we are bound to cherish.

TEMPERANCE ADDRESS.

WHETHER Mrs. Conway returned my admiration, and whether she would have accepted the offer of my hand, had I been in a fit condition to give it, I cannot say. The probability is, however, that in our intercourse the same current of events took place which I have described in my own case. In the first stages, she no doubt acted the part of a most unqualified coquet. But in our subsequent meetings, she may have been touched by the ardency of my love, which was more intense, as it might have been called more legitimate, than that I had borne the creole.[59]

As I gazed on the widow's bewitching beauty—her soft sunny complexion, and her mild eyes—as I listened to her conversation, charming for itself alone, and doubly so from the musical tones it flowed in—I felt myself steeped indeed in the extacy of passion.

One day, after drinking with Bourne,[60] I had been visiting the widow, and pouring into her ears some of those wild thoughts and protestations which wine and love can generate. The beauty listened complacently, for when was homage distasteful to a woman? All of a sudden, a capricious thought entered her brain.

"Come!" said she to me, "I wonder if you would prove, by something more tangible than words, the reality of all this fine sentiment?"

"If there is anything, lady, you wish done," I replied, "that mortal man can do, I will attempt it."

And I spoke with an energy that showed my mind.

"In a stroll I took two or three days since," continued the widow, "I saw a fine boy of some eight or nine years old. They told me he belonged to you.[61] Now I fancy I should like just such a little fellow to be my page, after the fashion of the damsels of old."

"What was his name?" asked I.

"They called him Louis. And now I think of it, some one said he was the brother of the woman Margaret, who lives at your dwelling."[62]

59. which was more intense, than that I had borne the creole. FC
60. "after drinking with Bourne" is omitted in FC.
61. "They told me he belonged to you, or to your friend, Mr. Bourne, which is the same thing." FC
62. "They called him Louis," was her answer. FC

I started, and felt the blood rushing up in my face like fire. Could the widow have intended to strike that chord? Louis was indeed the brother of the creole, and was beloved by her, as a woman might cling to her own child.[63]

The widow waited for an answer several moments in vain.

"How soon gallantry cools when its labor or its money is required!" she said at length, with a contemptuous smile.

"Forgive me, lady, it is not that," and I spoke very earnestly, "it is not that. Ask of me something else. There are reasons," added I, in a quick and confused voice, "reasons I may not mention why that request must be denied. But some other surely will do as well. There are many children among the slaves, and you shall have your choice of them all."

The widow knew the reasons I alluded to full well.

"My choice is made," she replied, calmly and coolly; "it was but an idle notion, and I have done wrong to trouble you with it."

"I beg you," rejoined I, "let some other take the boy's place in your wish."

"Speak no more about it, sir;" the lady answered, in a tone as if intended to cut short the subject; "it is not worth your while to think of a silly woman's whims. Though I don't know, indeed, which are worse— false words, or foolish fancies. I beg you, speak no more about it."

But I did speak further about it. I entreated her to select some other, any dozen others, instead of Louis. Her answer was still the same.

Those who have read the preceding chapters of this narrative, and who know the great failing which has attended me from my very outset of life —weakness of resolution, and liability to be led by others—can conceive the result of this interview. Before I left the widow, I promised to comply with her request about the boy. He was mine, I argued, and why should I not do with my own property as I liked, and bestow it as I listed?[64]

The creole, I have said, loved her young brother very fondly. Who may describe, then, what took place in her bosom when this matter was broken to her? At first it caused a kind of stunning sensation of surprise, almost of incredulity. Then came the tempest. All the fearful propensities which had slumbered so long in her soul, were aroused. Was this stranger —this fair-faced interloper from abroad, not only to destroy the love which had been to her as life; but her very brother to be taken away and made a servant, for *her* beck and command? What right had she, this delicate

63. This paragraph is omitted in FC.
64. This sentence is omitted in FC.
65. This paragraph is omitted in FC.

child of another climate, to invade the privileges and the happiness that had been so pleasant? The spirit of her fiery race swelled in the creole's breast, as she thought of these things: and she cursed her rival with a sharp and bitter tongue.[65]

Louis was sent to his new mistress. Before the time of his departure, his sister was observed[66] to have several long and close interviews with him. What the subject of those interviews was, they alone knew.

At length came the capstone of the misfortunes of Margaret. Rumors floated to her ear of preparations for an intended divorce between myself and her, and of a marriage in prospect of the widow and me. The latter part of the story was an addition of the busy tongue of common report.

The creole occupied the same apartments in the homested yet: but their accommodations were no longer shared by me. I spent a great portion of my time at the overseer's. Bourne was busy with his plantation, it being a season when its weal depended on his active supervision. We had our daily drinking-bouts, however, and our friendship was as firmly knit as it had ever been.[67]

As I sometimes glance back[68] at this period of my life, I think with more regret and dissatisfaction upon it, than upon any other portion of my conduct. My early follies were the result of inexperience in the ways of the world, and of the errors of impulse; hardly any of them but have some excuse. They were either committed or begun when I was under the influence of liquor, and had lost the control of my faculties; or were forced upon me by circumstances, and might be attributed to the great failing I have before alluded to—weakness of resolution. But my acts during the few weeks I resided at Bourne's, were done more in the method of deliberate and premeditated folly. I had my eyes open, and still went on, as though I were blindfolded.

The true explanation of the mystery is, I think, to be found in my former, and present habits of drinking spirituous liquors. Those habits were of the most insidious, sly, and fatal detriment to me. They relaxed my energy of character, what little I had, and left me like a ship upon the ocean, without her mainmast. I was tossed about by every breeze of chance or impulse, and was guilty of a hundred foolish things, which the relation of makes my story appear indeed like a work of imagination, instead of what it honestly is, a record of real events. So evil are the consequences of dissipation![69]

66. Margaret was observed FC
67. This paragraph is omitted in FC.
68. look back FC
69. This paragraph is omitted in FC.

I can trace the outset of all these frailties,[70] as well as all the calamities that have befallen me in my life, to that fatal night when Colby drew me into the drinking place; where, amid music and gayety, the first step in my downward road was taken.

CHAPTER XIX.

> In vain the flattering verse may breathe
> Of ease from pain, and rest from strife;
> There is a sacred dread of death,
> Inwoven with the strings of life.
> BRYANT.[71]

WHILE matters were in the situation described in the last few paragraphs, a danger was preparing, that threatened destruction not only to the love of myself and the widow, but to our lives, and the lives of the whole family and neighborhood. One of those epidemical diseases that prevail in the South made its appearance, and began to spread in all directions. Alarm and consternation fell upon the people. Beginning at first with striking down a man here and there, the fearful Plague Spirit, after a time, became as it were insatiate in his demands.

At the first appearance of the scourge, Mrs. Conway would have flown back to her native north. I, however, to whom her presence had become very dear, represented the evil as far less than rumor attempted to make it. I smiled at her terrors, and though my own heart accused me of untruth, I told the widow that there was little danger.

Thus she remained in fancied security, until it was too late. When the real facts could no longer be kept from her knowledge, it was quite as dangerous to leave as to remain. And yet, so deeply seated was this woman's love of admiration, that she really forgave me for deceiving her, in consideration of the motive that led me to be guilty of it.

One of the last places where the sickness came, was the village near Bourne's plantation. It was a place of not much travel, and being in a more than ordinarily healthy location, its inhabitants had flattered themselves with a hope of escaping the pestilence which desolated their fellow towns. Vain were their hopes. One day authentic information was brought to the

70. And I sometimes think I can trace the outset of all these frailties FC
71. One of the rimed stanzas which formed the prelude of the first version of "Thanatopsis" as it appeared in the *North American Review*, 1817. The stanzas are

planter, that the disease had made its appearance there; and, unfortunately for him, its first stroke was levelled at a poor family whose house stood near the confines of his estate. He was advised to be very cautious, and furthermore enjoined by his medical attendant, who sent the information just mentioned, that fear and anxiety concerning the matter were precisely the things that would bring about the result most dreaded.

All this was kept from Mrs. Conway's ears. I already began to blame myself for my deceit. I took every earthly means to guard her from the dangers that surrounded the place, and never allowed her to hear aught that might produce in her mind those disturbed thoughts which the physician deprecated. New to the climate, and more liable than a native to its deleterious influences, I knew she would stand but little chance of recovery, if once attacked by the dreaded malady.

But amid the general alarm and precaution, there was one person who paid small heed to either. That person was the deserted Margaret. She cared little about bodily danger, for she pined in a deeper rooted sorrow, and not only pined, but with feelings of one much injured, she fostered in her soul the desire of retribution on her injurer. Me, she could not bring herself to regard with any other passion than fondness; but her rival was hated with as deep a loathing, as ever swelled the soul of a jealous woman.

When she heard of the epidemic, her first thought was a desire that the widow would be one of its victims. When the news was brought that it had broken out in our immediate neighborhood, she arranged in her mind a scheme, subtle and worthy the brain whence it sprung—a scheme of revenge. The whole of the thoughts and conduct of the woman, though at the time unknown to me, were afterward fixed too firmly in my knowledge and my memory.

The next day, Louis, her brother, came[72] to the planter's house on some errand for his mistress. Whether that errand required his sister's personal attention or not,[73] I cannot say; but for a long time the child was closetted with Margaret[74] in her apartment. As he left the place, there flashed in his eye a spice of lurking devil, which spoke him to be not a slack partaker of his sister's soul.[75]

Down one of the winding-lanes of Bourne's plantation, that very afternoon, two figures were slowly walking. One was a lady, passing beautiful; the other was a boy, a fine-looking youth, his cheeks tinged with a slight

given in a note in Cheever.

72. Louis came FC
73. required the child's personal attention or not FC
74. with her FC   75. not a slack partaker of mischief. FC

color, betraying though feebly his taint of African blood. The lady was Mrs. Conway; the boy, her attendant Louis.

"It is pleasant," said the widow, "to get once more a taste of the open air; I have been cooped up so long, that it comes to me like something strange and unwonted."

The boy walked on near her in silence.

"Do you not think, Lewy, we are strangely kept in by Mr. Bourne's and Mr. Evans's whims? It was but the other day the latter told me not to stir out of the house to a distance on any account. You don't have robbers here, I hope?"

"I never knew of one about the place, in all my life," answered the child.

"And this sickness," said the lady, "what a fearful thing if it should appear among us! They say, boy, such as I, coming from another clime, stand a double danger from it."

The child looked up in his companion's face with a strange look; and continued to walk on in silence.

"How sweet the air is!" continued the lady. It was more like talking to herself than a listener; but the foible of her sex is proverbial, and Mrs. Conway was no exception to any of her sex's foibles. "How sweet the air is! Life seems pleasant in the South, if it be only for the mild, warm air. Then, the beautiful flowers bloom all around, and are reared with so little trouble; and you have rich fruit here, such as never grows in the rigor of our stormy north. But as much as anything else, I love to hear the birds —the sweet singing birds of the South!"

"What do you think of a bird that can sing tunes?" asked Louis, suddenly.

"I think he would be well worth owning," said the lady.

"Would you like to see such a bird?" rejoined the boy, looking up into Mrs. Conway's face, and with something like a tremor in his voice.

"Certainly," said she, smiling at what appeared to be his childish earnestness; "I would like any variation, however small, of the sameness of this quiet life. Where shall we find the curiosity of which you speak?"

"Through the path yonder," answered Louis, "a little beyond that wood. Andy Warner lives there, and he has the bird hung up in a cage in his room."

"Come on then," said the widow, laughing: "Andy Warner shall show us this prodigy."

And she motioned to go; but the child stirred not. His eyes stared in a wild manner, and he trembled from head to foot.

"How, boy?" exclaimed the lady. "What is the matter? You are sick, Louis, you are sick, I fear!"

"No, I am quite well," answered he, recovering his former appearance. "Come, let us go on to Andy's."

They walked down the lane, and along the path which Louis pointed out. It led to a kind of bye-place. The house he had mentioned was situated at some distance from the principal wagon-way, and on the present occasion, exhibited no sign of tenancy or life. They knocked at the door, which after a moment or two was opened by a woman, who received them with a look so full of startling surprise, that Mrs. Conway knew not what to make of it. They told the woman the reason of their visit—and then she stood looking at them again, in a second long stare of wonder and wildness.

"There!" said Louis, pointing with his finger, "there is the bird!"

Mrs. Conway glanced up, and beheld one of the southern mocking birds, in a cage attached to the wall. The little songster seemed in a sulky vein, however; he hung his head and was totally without cheerfulness or animation.

"Could you make him sing some gay, lively strain now?" said the visiter, turning to her hostess with a sprightly air.

As she looked more fully in the face of the one to whom she spoke, Mrs. Conway started back in alarm. The woman seemed like a ghost —her face pale, and her whole aspect bearing an indescribable appearance of strangeness and insanity. Mrs. Conway was instantly impressed with the idea that she was deranged, and turned in alarm to leave the room.

"Good God!" exclaimed the pale-faced female, "she talks here of singing gay strains!"

Fairly terrified, the widow now made a quick exit, and only recovered her self-possession when she found herself in the open air with Louis by her side. They walked swiftly along the path on their return; for the day was now somewhat advanced, and they had strayed quite a distance from Phillips's house.

That very afternoon I had called at the overseer's, and been told that Mrs. Conway was out on a walk. I started forth to look for her, that I might accompany her back. So it happened, that as she came by the dwelling of Bourne, near which she had to pass, I met her.

She immediately began telling me of her afternoon's adventure. As she mentioned the course of her walk, I started, for a dim fear took possession of my mind, to which I dared not give credit, and yet thought too probable.

"But never mind," exclaimed the widow, in continuation, as she finished her story, "I suppose Andy Warner will be at home himself some day, and then I shall, no doubt, get treated with more politeness."

"Did you," gasped I faintly, as the name struck my ear, and a feeling of deadly sickness crept over my heart—"did you say Andy——?"[76]

I staggered and clutched the air, as a man grasping support to keep from falling.[77]

"Did you say Andy Warner?" came up again from my throat in a hoarse whisper.[78]

"Yes, yes, that was the name, I think;" and the alarmed lady turned with an inquiring look to Louis.

"Then are you lost, indeed," cried I, in tones of shrieking horror.[79] "In that house was the first case of the horrid fever. Andy *died* this very morning, and if you had looked farther, you would no doubt have found his corpse, for it lies there yet!"

One moment more, and a wild shrill cry sounded out upon the air, waking the echoes, and sailing far off in many a sharp cadence. Another followed—and another—and the widow sank down upon the grass in a senselessness so deep, that I thought the contagion would have no chance of working its effect upon her. I was almost out of my senses with agony and alarm. But time pressed, and lifting that form so dear to me, in my arms, I bore her into the planter's residence, and there had those attentions paid which the urgency of the case demanded. In an hour, the widow was somewhat recovered from her fit. But she was still as languid as a babe, and the physician who had been summoned, spoke strongly against the propriety of carrying her the mile's distance which intervened between the house, and Phillips's residence.

So I had it arranged that she should not be removed. In the south range of apartments, there was one with long low windows, opening to the ground. That room was prepared for her reception and there I had her carried.

76. "did you say Andy Warner?" FC
77. This sentence is omitted in FC.
78. This sentence is omitted in FC.
79. in tones of horror. FC
80. This chapter, which FC omits, is obviously out of place and should follow

CHAPTER XX.[80]

> I'll tell you friend, what * * *
> Where'er I scan this scene of life
>   Inspires my waking schemes,
> And, when I sleep, * * *
> Dances before my ravished sight,
>   In sweet, aerial dreams.
>   PROFESSOR FRISBIE.[81]

How refreshing it is to pause in the whirl and tempest of life, and cast back our minds over past years! I think there is even a kind of satisfaction in deliberately and calmly reviewing actions that we feel were foolish or evil. It pleases us to know that we have the learning of experience. The very contrast, perhaps, between what we are, and what we were, is gratifying. At all events, it is acknowledged that retrospection becomes one of the delights of people immediately after arriving at mature years. When merely on the verge of manhood, we love to think of the scenes of our boyish life. When advanced in age, we fondly turn our memory to the times of the early years, and dwell with a chastened pleasure upon what we recollect thereof, beheld through the medium of the intervening seasons.

From no other view can I understand how it is, that I sometimes catch myself turning back in my reflection, to the very dreariest and most degraded incidents which I have related in the preceding pages, and thinking upon them without any of the bitterness and mortification which they might be supposed to arouse in my bosom. The formal narration of them, to be sure, is far from agreeable to me—but in my own self-communion upon the subject, I find a species of entertainment. I was always fond of day-dreams—an innocent pleasure, perhaps, if not allowed too much latitude.

For some days after Mrs. Conway's death, I shut myself up in my room, and hardly went out at all, except in the evening, or early morning. A kind of morbid peculiarity came over me during this while, which, though it fortunately passed off with a change of scene, was very powerful for the time. It was the result, no doubt, partly of my confine-

Chapter XXI, though it fits awkwardly and illogically anywhere in the rest of the tale. This dream sequence—very plainly a reworking of "The Last of the Sacred Army," which had been published in the *Democratic Review* in the early spring of 1842—is evidence, along with the other tales inserted for padding, of the pot-boiling haste in which *Franklin Evans* was written.

81. From Frisbie's "A Castle in the Air"; in Cheever.

ment and the sombre reflections I held—and partly of my former intemperate habits. It was a species of imaginative mania, which led to giving full scope to my fancy—and I frequently remained for two hours at a time in a kind of trance, beholding strange things, and abstracted from all which was going on around me. On one of these occasions, the incident occurred which I shall now relate.

I was sitting in an easy chair at twilight one evening, near the open window. Upon my knees lay a newspaper, which I had been reading. It contained some extracts from an eloquent temperance address. The quietness of the scene, and the subdued light, and the peculiar influences that had been surrounding me for a few days past, had their full chance to act at such a time, as may well be imagined.

Methought I was wandering through the cities of a mighty and populous empire. There were sea-ports, filled with rich navies, and with the products of every part of the earth, and with merchants, whose wealth was greater than the wealth of princes. There were huge inland towns, whose wide and magnificent avenues seemed lined with palaces of marble—and showed on every side the signs of prosperity. I saw from the tops of the fortresses, the Star-Flag—emblem of Liberty—floating gloriously abroad in the breeze!

And how countless were the inhabitants of that country! On I went, and still on, and they swarmed thicker than before. It was almost without boundary, it seemed to me—with its far-stretching territories, and its States away up in the regions of the frozen north, and reaching down to the hottest sands of the torrid south—and with the two distant oceans for its side limits.

With the strange faculty of dreams, I knew, that two-score years had elapsed, as I stood amid this mighty nation. I was in one of their greatest cities—and there appeared to be some general holyday. People were hurrying up and down the streets. The children were dressed in gay clothes. Business seemed to be suspended—and each one given up to the spirit of the time.

"Is it not," I heard one of the passers by say to a companion, "is it not a glorious thing?"

"Most glorious!" said the second.

I lost all further hearing of their remarks, for they walked on, smiling in each other's faces.

Before long, following a crowd, I came into a wide open kind of amphitheatre, where a man stood up in the midst addressing the assembly. The address seemed to be preparatory to something which was to take place at its conclusion.

"The Snake-Tempter," said the man who was speaking, "is this day to be deprived of his last vassal! Long, long have we looked for the coming of this day. It has been our hope, our beacon of encouragement through seasons of toil and darkness. Who would have supposed, years ago, that it could so soon have arrived?

"Now man is free! He walks upon the earth, worthy the name of one whose prototype is God! We hear the mighty chorus sounding loud and long, Regenerated! Regenerated!

"Oh, could those who have wrought and sickened for the coming of this hour—could they but be present with us—how would their hearts leap with joy! But do we know that they are *not* present with us? Who can tell that their spirits may not be soaring in the viewless air near by, and looking down pleasantly upon us, and blessing us? Who can say, but that they are rejoicing in their hearts, and praising the Almighty that these things have come to pass?

"The last vassal of the Tempter is indeed lost him. This day, our charter receives the name of him who finishes the Great Work! We can say then, that of all who live among us, there is none but has his title upon the bond, and his claim to its prerogative."

For some time, the man went on in this strain. Then the assembly dispersed, apparently for the purpose of engaging in the other ceremonies of the occasion.

I had wandered to and fro for an hour or more, when I came out in a wide street, to the sides of which I saw the people flocking from every quarter. Away in the distance there sounded bands of music, which grew louder and louder, as if they were coming toward us.

At length a long and splendid procession was seen, marching with stately pace. First came a host of men in the prime of life, with healthy faces and stalwart forms, and every appearance of vigor. They had many banners, which bore mottoes, signifying that they had once been under the dominion of the Tempter, but were now redeemed. Then I saw a myriad of youths, with blooming cheeks and bright eyes, who followed in the track of those before, as in time they no doubt would occupy their stations in the world. There were rich equipages, also, containing the officers of the state, and persons of high rank. Long, long it stretched, and still there seemed no end.

Not the least beautiful part of the procession, was composed of bands of women and young girls, dressed with taste, and lending their smiles to enliven the scene. I saw many children also, whose happy and innocent looks were pleasant to behold.

All through the long sweep of the multitude, there were innumerable banners, and mottoes, and devices, expressive of triumph and rejoicing. One of them, I noticed, had the figure of a fair female, robed in pure white. Under her feet were the senseless remains of a hideous monster, in whose grapple thousands and millions had fallen, but who was now powerless and dead. The eyes of the female beamed benevolence and purity of heart; and in her hand she held a goblet of clear water.

Toward the end of the march came a large car, upon which was a single personage, a man of middle age, who, as he passed along, was saluted by the shouts of the crowd. He seemed to be the theme, in fact, of all the ceremonials and the rejoicing.

"Who is he?" said I to a by-stander. "Who is he, for whom the people raise their voices so loudly?"

The man turned to me in amazement.

"Have you not heard," he answered, "of the great triumph of this day? The one upon the car is the Last Vassal of the Snake-Tempter; and he goes now to make a formal renunciation of his old allegiance."

"And is this the cause, then, of all the public joy?" said I.

"It is," answered the man.

How it was, I cannot say, but I understood his meaning, though he spoke with strange phrases.

So, yielding myself to the passage of those about, I wended on, until at last we came into a wide field, in the middle of which was an uncovered scaffold. Upon it was the person whom I had noticed in the procession—the Last Vassal. Far around, on every side, countless multitudes of nothing but human heads were to be seen, in one compact body.

"Rejoice!" cried a man from the crowd. "Our old enemy is deserted, and we triumph!"

Then there arose such mighty shouts from the huge concourse, that it seemed as if the sound might pierce the very heavens.

And now, he who stood on the scaffold spoke:

"It gladdens me," he said, "that I shall this day make one of the Army of the Regenerated. You have wrought long and faithfully, and your reward comes in good time. It is well."

Loud shouts evinced the pleasure of the multitude at hearing him utter such remarks.

"We welcome you!" they cried, as with one voice.

"This day," continued he, "I throw off the chains, and take upon myself the pleasant bondage of good. It may not be a truth to boast of, that I am the *last* of the serfs of Appetite; yet I joy that I occupy my position before you now, as I do!"

A venerable old man came forward upon the scaffold, and presented a document to the speaker. He received it with evident delight; and snatching a pen from a table, he wrote his name under it, and held it up to the view of the people.

It were impossible to describe the thunder-peal of hurrahs that arose in the air, and sounded to the skies, as the Full Work was consummated thus. They cried aloud—

"Victory! victory! The Last Slave of Appetite is free, and the people are regenerated!"

CHAPTER XXI.

> Thou sure and firm-set earth,
> Hear not my steps which way they walk for fear;
> The very stones prate of my whereabout;
> And take the present horror from the time,
> Which now suits with it.
>
> SHAKSPERE.[82]

COULD it be possible that the widow might escape the fatal effects of her visit to the cottage? Whatever chance there might have been for some other more equable mind, I saw that her agitation and ceaseless fear left none for her.

Before the end of the second day after that hapless walk, the signs of the coming horrors appeared on her cheek. They were the signals for a general desertion on the part of the attendants. So great was the panic struck to the souls of people by the stories they had heard of the pestilence, that I found it difficult to get for Mrs. Conway the attentions absolutely necessary to her existence. Even before the disease had made its complete appearance, the servants refused to go near her. The unhappy woman had, however, one most devoted servant. Night and day was I ready at the entrance of her apartment, holding a sleepless watch over its inmate.

I shall not think it worth while for my story, to give a minute account of the lady's illness. The sick chamber is a scene which few love to look upon, or to have pictured for them. The sight of this beautiful tabernacle with its foundations broken, and its mysterious furniture out of place, and its strength bowed down in weakness—whose eye has such unhealthy craving as to delight in the grievous spectacle? The soul of a man loves its dwelling, and though itself not thereof, looks on when that dwelling is harmed by evil, and feels in its recesses a sympathizing sorrow.

82. *Macbeth*, II: ii.

At length the time arrived, which at some period or other arrives for all cases of bodily disease—the time of the crisis. The doctor came, and with a wise look, told the listeners that his patient was at the most dangerous part of her malady. He prepared some mixtures of his nauseous drugs, gave directions about the order of their being administered, and then closed by remarking to me that, in the course of the evening or night, the suffering lady would probably fall into a continued slumber, from which she would awake to a new life, or to death.

And where was Margaret of late? The wretched creole lived in her former situation, as far as locality was concerned; but her heart and her happiness were fled for ever. She seldom left her rooms, staying there almost alone, and brooding over her griefs and her injuries, which fancy made many times greater than they really were.

It seems to have been the case, that with this creature's good traits her heart had still a remnant of the savage. When Mrs. Conway's illness appeared favorable, Margaret's bosom felt heavy and sorrowful; and when the sick woman was hovering on the confines of the grave, the other's soul danced with a joyous feeling of life.[83]

When the creole heard that the doctor announced the critical period to have arrived—and heard also what was said about the probable lethargy—the discarded favorite asked her informant again. Receiving the same account, she sat a full minute, apparently gazing on some vision in the air. At length, it seemed to melt from her sight; she drew a heavy breath, and resumed her ordinary appearance.

The God of Mysteries only can tell what passions worked in the woman's breast then, and during the rest of that fearful night. What deep breathings of hate—what devilish self-incitements—what unrelenting, yet swaying resolves—what sanguinary brain-thoughts—what mad, and still clearly defined marking out of fiendish purposes—what of all these raged and whirled in the chambers of that unhappy creature's soul, will ever stay buried in the darkness of things gone: a darkness which falls alike on the dreadful motives of the murderer, and the purity of hearts filled with abundance of good!

Midnight hung its curtains round about the planter's dwelling. Sleep and Repose were there with their pleasant ministerings, and Silence, the handmaiden of both. In the chamber of the sick one there was a lamp, sending forth its feeble beams, and looking as if it were about to gasp its last gasp—ominous emblem of the life that lay flickering near. From the bed which held the beautiful sufferer, sounded breathings faint but regular. There was no nurse or watcher there, for the physician had said it

83. This paragraph is omitted in FC.

was of no importance, and all were worn out with their long-continued attending upon the invalid. Even I myself had sunk into a deep sleep at the door of the room, exhausted nature refusing to allow any further demand upon her powers.

One of the long windows was partly open, and only a thin piece of gauze was between the ground to which it led, and the room. At that window appeared, time and again, two bright small orbs, fixed, and yet rolling in fire. Ever and anon they would draw back into the shadow; then again they would peer inward upon the room, their direction ever being to the bed whereon the sick one lay.

It was wrong to say that couch had no watcher! Three long hours did those glittering things, which were human eyes, continue to keep the vigils of that noiseless spot. Three long hours, while hardly a motion, except the swaying back and forth, before spoken of, disturbed the constancy of their gaze, or a sound broke the solemn stillness.

In the deep hour of that night the widow awoke; and as she awoke, her cool blood, for the first time during five days, coursed through veins that did not throb with loathsome heat. Then she knew that she should live.

All around was motionless and soundless, and the lady felt glad that it was so; for her heart was in that mood of blissful calm to which the least jar produces pain.

"Thank God!" sounded in a low murmur from her tongue; "thank God! I shall not die!"

The sounds came faintly; but faint as they were, they sank into ears besides those of the speaker. They sank and pierced, with a dagger's sharpness, the soul of Margaret, the creole: for she it was, whose eyes had been during those long three hours almost winkless at the room window.

And was her rival, then, to get well once more? And were all her late hopes to vanish? That pale-browed northerner *married* to him she loved? Never should the sun rise upon that marriage!

Horrid purposes lighted up the creole's eyes as she softly put aside the curtains, and stepped into the room. With a stealthy pace she drew near to the sick woman's bed. One moment she paused. The widow lay there, still very beautiful, and calm as a sleeping infant. As Margaret approached, the invalid turned and looked at her a moment, but it was plain she knew her not, and probably thought her to be some hired attendant.

Still nearer and nearer came the wretched female: and now she stands by the very bedside. Unconscious yet, the lady is quiet and composed— fearing nothing and suspecting nothing. An instant more, and her throat is clutched by a pair of tight-working hands. Startled with terror, she would shriek, but cannot. What torture fills her heart! She turns, and struggles, and writhes; but those deadly fingers loosen not their grasp.

The murderess presses upon her. Poor lady! Her soul feels very sick, as in one little minute whole troops of remembrances, and thoughts, and dreads come over her. She grows fainter and fainter. Her struggles become less energetic, and her convulsive writhings cease. Still those terrible hands release not. Their suffocating span is continued yet for several minutes.

And now, no longer is it necessary that Margaret should keep her hold; that last faint gurgle tells the consummation of the fell design. Her deed is done. Her revenge triumphs!

Like some ghost condemned to wander on earth for the actions done there, a figure stalked about the garden and the grounds near by, during the remainder of that night. Bright stars shone down, and the cool breeze swept by; but the Shape heeded them not, walking swiftly on in zigzag directions, apparently without any particular point of destination. Sometimes stretching off down a lane, and stopping by the fence, and leaning thereon, and looking at the cattle that lay doubled on the grass reposing: sometimes bending over a flower, and taking it very carefully and inhaling its fragrance;[84] and sometimes standing like a marble statue, motionless, and gazing vacantly for a long time in the bodiless air: these were the freaks of the strange figure.

It was the murderess who wandered there and thus. And as the first streak of light appeared in the east, she started like the guilty thing she was, and returned to her abiding place.

CHAPTER XXII.

> This even-handed justice
> Commends the ingredients of our poisoned chalice
> To our own lips.
>
> SHAKSPERE.[85]

UPON the distraction which filled my breast, when it was found in the morning that the widow had died—and the burial of the body—and the cunning smoothess of the Creole during the intervening time—I shall bestow no more than this passing mention. Whether any suspicions of foul play were as yet aroused in the breasts of other persons, is more than

84. "sometimes bending . . . inhaling its fragrance" omitted in FC.
85. *Macbeth*, I: vii.   86. Louis, the former page of Margaret FC

I can say. As far as I was concerned, however, I had not the most distant idea of the kind; and taking all things into reflection, the likelihood is that no one thought Mrs. Conway's death, under the circumstances, aught more than was to have been expected.

But guilt has a vital power, which gives it life, until it is held up to scorn. It happened so in this case. Louis, the brother of Margaret,[86] was taken sick with the same disease of which the widow was supposed to have died. Strangely enough, when the Creole plotted with the boy to entice his mistress into the infected cottage (for that occurrence was the result of design,) she did not think how the danger would be shared by Louis too. Her soul had strained its gaze with the single purpose of revenge; and she saw not each incidental effect. Thus it is with evil intentions. I have noticed that the bad are always short-sighted:[87] in the plots they form, and the manoeuvres they engage in, some little thing or other escapes their view, and proves, after a while, to be a seed of punishment and remorse.

Again the curtains of darkness hung around the planter's dwelling; and again had the balancing point of the sickness arrived for a sufferer there. That sufferer was little Louis. He had left the house of the overseer, and now lived at his old abode. There was the same breathlessness and the same want of movement, as on the preceding occasion; but instead of the sick room being almost deserted, as in the former case, many persons waited there. Perhaps they had become more callous to fear, because it was not a new thing; perhaps it was, that they thought the influences of a sick child's apartment more gentle and less dangerous than the former one. Margaret stood in a position so quiet, and with eyes so stony in their gaze, that she seemed like one entranced. On the result of the pending sleep of her brother,[88] it seemed as if her reason and her life were wavering.

At last the slumberer awoke. The Creole shrieked! for it was plain Louis but aroused himself a moment, to sink shortly in that deep senselessness which knows no waking here on earth. He shifted himself uneasily on his bed. A film came over Margaret's eyes—a film of fear and agony; and when it passed off and left her sight clear, she saw, laying before her, the quiet ghastly corpse of her brother.[89]

Those who were present felt awed by her terrible grief. She screamed aloud, and threw her arms around the boy, and pressed his forehead to her lips. She called him by all the old endearing epithets, and seemed crazed with her sense of desperate sorrow. The wild exclamations that started from her mouth, the listeners heard with wonder.

87. The bad are always short-sighted FC   88. of her favorite FC
89. the quiet ghastly corpse of the only being who had ever truly loved her. FC

"Do not go!" she said, looking on the inanimate form of the boy. "Do not go. The pleasant days are not all past. If you leave me, my heart will crack!"

Then in a whisper:

"O, never tell me of her kindness. Lead her into the hut I say. She is a witch, and can steal hearts."

She paused, and looked intently at some phantom before her.

"Why, how long she sleeps! She shall sleep longer, though, and, deeper, after to-night. Softly! softly! softly!"

The heart-strings were too much wrought, and the Creole sank heavily down upon the floor, in a fit. Those who stood by looked strangely into each other's faces, but no one spoke.

It was evident that something wrong had been done, and weighed heavily on the wretched woman's mind. Her words, and her strange gestures could not but have a meaning to them. Gossipping tongues, once started upon such matters, are not easily put to rest; and before long the dark rumor came to Mr. Phillips's ears, that his kinswoman had been murdered[90]—murdered by her, too, on whom, of all who lived around, he wished an opportunity of showing his dislike.

The overseer, whatever might have been his deficiencies, was a shrewd clear-headed man, and in ferretting out a mystery, had few equals. In the present instance, his wits were sharpened by a sense of duty toward the dead widow, and a desire for revenge.[91] He worked with sagacity, and allowed no incident to escape him, small or large. As might be expected, he soon discovered enough to make his surmises a positive belief.

Many of what the people would have called trifles, were noted down by this man; and the sum of these trifles presented an array dangerous enough to warrant the suspicions even of the most incredulous. The strange appearance of Mrs. Conway's body was remembered—how the bed was all disordered, as if from a violent struggle—the livid spots upon her neck—the open window—and the tracks of some person's feet from the grounds without, through the room—even the fact that Margaret's couch had the next morning borne no sign of occupancy the preceding night—were hunted out by the indefatigable observer. Many other minor and corroborating incidents were also brought to light—the whole making the case of the suspected woman a dark one indeed.

Mr. Phillips applied to the proper authorities for a warrant, and had

90. The rest of this sentence is omitted in FC.
91. This sentence is omitted in FC.
92. The remainder of this sentence is omitted in FC.
93. From "Water *versus* Alcohol"; in Grosh.
94. This paragraph is preceded in FC by the following paragraph:

Margaret lodged in prison, as one who, at the very least, was involved in deep clouds of suspicion.

In the meantime, I myself was as one petrified. Never in all my life did I receive such a shock, as when authentic information was first brought me of the charge against the creole! I could not join the overseer in efforts to worm out the facts of the case; neither could I do aught to screen the murderess of one whom I had so loved. I shut myself up in my room for several days, waiting the conclusion of all these horrible circumstances.

Let me hasten toward that conclusion. I have already dwelt long enough, and too long, on this part of my history,[92] which, notwithstanding the space I have given it, did not occupy more than five or six weeks from the commencement of my acquaintance with Bourne. And I feel glad that I have arrived at the end of the chapter, for my mind revolts at the ideas the narration of these things has already called up in most disagreeable distinctness.

The overseer continued his investigations, but he might as well have spared himself the trouble. From some train of motives which the great Heart-Viewer alone can fathom, the creole soon after sent for Phillips and myself, and made a full confession. Upon her story as she told it me, and her own acknowledgment, I have given many of the incidents in the preceding two chapters, which, at the time they took place, were totally unknown to me. That very night she committed suicide in her cell. I never saw her again.

CHAPTER XXIII.

> What can mar the sweetest peace?
> Alcohol!
> TEMPERANCE SONG.[93]

THINKING over what had taken place, as I prepared for my journey back to New York, I sometimes fancied I had been in a dream. The events were so strange—and my own conduct, in respect to some of them, so very unreasonable, that I could hardly bring myself to acknowledge their reality.[94]

> Under any circumstances, I should have now desired to return to New York, forthwith. But this return was hastened by my receiving a letter from Mr. Lee's oldest and most confidential employee, conveying peremptory orders from my kind benefactor to make all speed back—for he was very ill, and it was not improbable he might die.

Bourne was loth to part with me. Our short friendship had been in many ways very pleasant to us both. It was seldom, indeed, that his retirement was enlivened with the voice of a stranger, or his lonesome hours made glad by the company of one he loved.[95] At the last interview but one which we had before my departure, we discussed in soberness the transactions of the past month. I think that both of us, though we did not so express ourselves at the time, arrived at the conclusion that the drinking-bout, where I and he settled the wretched step of marriage between myself and the creole, was the starting point of all the late evils.

I had hardly arrived in the city, and was at my home there, before a messenger came with a request that I would visit Mr. Lee,[96] my old antiquary friend, who lay very ill. I went, and found him quite as sick as was reported. He knew me at once, however, and rose in his bed to give me a cordial shake of the hand.

"The reason I have sent for you," said he, "is to prepare you for an evidence that, notwithstanding what has passed between us in days gone by, I have thought proper to bestow upon you a portion of that wealth, which it has been my honest pride to gain."

I was amazed with wonder.[97]

"Sir," said I, "what reason can you have for such favor toward one who is to you almost a stranger?"

"My own fancy, Evans," he answered, "my own whim, perhaps. But we are not strangers. And I have always taken blame to myself, that I did not watch over you with a more fatherly care, when you were first thrown, as it were by the hand of Providence, under my charge."

"Indeed, sir," said I, agitated and affected almost to tears, by the old man's kindness, "I did not expect this."

"No matter," said he, "I have made inquiries, from time to time about you, though you knew it not, and have kept the track of your course of life. I feel assured that your wild days are over—that experience has taught you wisdom, and that the means I shall place at your command will not be put to improper uses."

The sick merchant, raised himself, and propped against his pillow, enjoined me to listen a few minutes, and he would briefly relate the story of his life—and why it was that in his old age, he was alone in the world, without family or intimates. I shall give his story in my own words.

Stephen Lee, at an early age, received from his father a sufficient capital to enable him to start himself in business, in the mercantile profes-

---

95. The rest of the paragraph following this sentence is omitted in FC.
96. The remainder of the sentence is omitted in FC.

sion. Though he was ambitious, he was prudent, and soon sailed on the forward and brilliant track to success. Fascinated by the charms and accomplishments of a young female cousin, he paid his addresses to her, and they were shortly married.

For several months happiness seemed hovering over them, and all prospects were fair for a life of cloudless content. A year elapsed, and Lee's wife bore him a son. The delighted father now thought that the measure of his joy was full. A few days after her confinement, there began to be a strange lassitude about the young merchant's wife—her health was as good as is ordinary in such cases, but as the time passed, her countenance grew more pallid and sickly and her eyes lost their lustre. The physician could give no satisfactory account of all this; and Lee himself for some time was in the dark also. But too soon did the fatal truth come to his knowledge, that *ardent spirits* was the cause of that pallor and that lassitude. His wife was an habitual gin-drinker![98]

Lee, though shocked at this disgusting fact, imagined at first, that the habit had been formed by using drink as a stimulus to keep up her powers of body in her sickness. But it was not so. During the time that had intervened between their marriage, the miserable woman, for very shame, had desisted from the practice. But a single taste, revived the old appetite in all its strength.

It happened one day, when the infant was some ten weeks old, that the mother, stupified by excess of liquor, let her babe fall against some projecting article of furniture, and received a blow from which it never recovered. In the course of the week the child died, and though the physician never stated the exact cause of its death, it was well understood that the fall from the arms of its drunken mother had been that cause.

Two or three years passed on. Another infant was born to Lee—but it met with a fate not much better than the first. Its death came from neglect and ill nursing.

And the mother—the lovely and educated wife, with whom the merchant had expected to see so much happiness, she was a drunkard. She lingered not long, however, to bear witness to her own and her husband's shame. She sank into the grave the victim of intemperance.

It was many years before Lee recovered his former tone of character. Naturally cheerful, however, he could not long remain that gloomy being which his misfortunes had for a time made him. He was fond of sporting, and loved the country, which he frequently visited. He loved, too, the old

97. This sentence is omitted in FC.
98. But too soon did the fatal truth come to his knowledge, that his wife was an habitual gin-drinker! FC

traditions, and reminiscences of the earlier part of our American history, to which he gave up a considerable portion of his leisure. Thus, and in the affairs of his trade, which he still kept on, he had made life pass as evenly and pleasantly as he could.

"You say you are a stranger," he said to me, before I left him, "but you are not half so much so as the rest of the world. My nearest relatives, who were never friendly to me in life, have long since been laid in the grave; and I can make no better disposition of my profits than to give them to one whom I feel confident will not be unwilling to use some part thereof, for suppressing the fearful fiend Intemperance, that has brought such wo upon us both!"

I mused, as I left the place, upon the singular notion of the old man, in remembering me thus. Of course, it was anything but unpleasant to me that I should inherit a respectable competency; and yet I could not help wondering at the method of it.

Not many days elapsed before Lee died, and was laid away to his repose. His will, though the theme of much grumbling to some far-distant connexions,[99] could not be gainsayed, and I came into possession of the property left me.

CHAPTER XXIV.

> The temperance flag! the temperance flag!
> It is the banner of the free!
> The temperance flag! the temperance flag!
> An emblem of our liberty!
> WASHINGTONIAN MINSTREL.

So, at an age which was hardly upon the middle verge of life, I found myself possessed of a comfortable property; and, as the term is 'unincumbered' person—which means that I had no wife to love me—no children to please me, and be the recipients of my own affection, and no domestic hearth around which we might gather, as the center of joy and delight. My constitution, notwithstanding the heavy draughts made upon its powers by my habits of intemperance,[1] might yet last me the appointed term of years, and without more than a moderate quantity of the physical ills that man is heir to.

99. connections FC
1. (Third Series). by my youthful dissipations FC
2. This paragraph, and the remainder of Evans' conversation with Mrs.

The Marchions were still my firm friends. I visited them often.[2]

"I think, Mr. Evans," said Mrs. Marchion to me one day, "that there is still one thing for you to do, in connection with what has already been your movement upon Temperance. Lately, I find, there is more progress made than we are aware of. People now are not content to abstain merely from the stronger kinds of drinks, but they disuse *all*. I have been reflecting my own mind upon the subject, and I came to the conclusion that *total* abstinence is indeed the only safe course."

I too had been reflecting in my mind upon the same thing, and I had arrived pretty nearly at the same conclusion.

"My dear madam," said I, "there is more truth in your words perhaps, than even you yourself imagine. I have tried the old pledge, and I can conscientiously say that I have adhered to it, ever since the day of my signing it; yet, if I were to tell you all the horrors that have been transacted since that time, in reference to my own life, and which I can trace directly to *wine-drinking*, you would be appalled with fear! Total abstinence is indeed the only safe course, and I will put the principle in effect this very evening."

My deeds were as good as my word. Before the sun rose again I had signed the bond—the holy charter with myself, which has never yet been broken; and which, under the blessing of Providence, shall remain inviolate while I continue among the living.

I do not intend to relate the occurrences of my after life. Indeed, were I so disposed, it would be impossible; for I have brought the chain of events down almost to the very day when the reader will be perusing my story. True, several years have passed since my Virginia visit, which resulted so disastrously to some of those[3] with whom I was brought in contact; but the tenor of action has flowed on so smoothly since then, that I have little to tell which would be interesting.

There is one person, however, who has figured in these pages, on whom I would bestow a paragraph before I close. I allude to my old friend, Colby.

As I was passing one day along a street on the eastern side of the city, my course was impeded by crowd, gathered around a tipsy loafer, who was cutting up his antics in the street. The miserable man, it seemed, had been promised by some idle boys enough money to purchase a drink of gin, if he would dance for their amusement. And there he was, going through his disgusting capers.

Marchion, and the signing of the total-abstinence pledge by Evans are, naturally, omitted in FC.

    3. so disastrous to those FC

Pausing a moment, and looking in the man's face, I thought I recollected the features. A second and a third glance convinced me. It was Colby, my early intimate, the tempter who had led me aside from the paths of soberness.

Wretched creature! Had I even wished for some punishment upon his head, in requital of the harm he had done me, a sight of the kind I saw there, would have dissolved all my anger. His apparel looked as though it had been picked up in some mud hole; it was torn in strips and all over soiled. His face was bloated, and his eyes red and swollen. I thought of the morning when I awoke upon the dock, after my long fit of intemperance: the person before me, was even more an object of pity than myself on that occasion. His beard had not seen the razor for weeks, and he was quite without shoes.

The spectators laughed, and the heedless children clapped their hands in glee—little thinking of the desecration such a spectacle brought upon the common nature all shared. I felt sick at heart, and hurried away from the place. How had it happened, that I myself did not meet with the same degraded fortune? Was it not indeed miraculous that I—instead of being a counterpart of the poor sot whom I had just been witnessing with feelings I shall not attempt to describe—was occupying a respectable station in society, and on the fair road to a remainder of my life, passed in honor and comfort? I blessed my Maker as I thought of these things, and besought His favor on that holy Cause of Reformation, where I had myself cast anchor, and where thousands besides were moored, safe from the wild storm, and from the boiling waves that so threatened to ingulf them.[4]

As it is the usage of story-tellers to give some passing notice of all who have figured in their pages, before those pages are brought to a close,[5] I will here follow the custom; though the small number of such persons, apart from the I, who have been the hero of the tale, will render the task an easy one.

My country relations were not forgotten by me in my good fortune. The worthy uncle, who had kindly housed and fed me when I was quite too small to make him any repayment for that service, received in his old

---

4. This episode of Colby's degradation is condensed in FC to the following brief paragraph:

> As I was passing one day along a street on the eastern side of the city, my course was impeded by a crowd, gathered around a loafer, who was cutting up his antics in the street. It was Colby, my early intimate, the tempter who had led me aside from the paths of soberness.

5. who have figured in their columns, before those lines are brought to a close

FC

age the means to render his life more easy and happy. My cousins too, had no reason to be sorry for the good-will which they had ever shown toward me. I was never the person to forget a friend, or leave unrequited a favor, when I had the payment of it in my power.

The tavern-keeper, to whom the reader was introduced in the first chapter of my story, dragged out a life of intemperance, a discredit to his family and with little comfort to himself. He was found dead, one winter morning, in a room where in a fit of passion the preceding night he had gone, from that which he usually occupied with his wife. An overturned bottle of brandy was at his side. After his death, the tavern was closed.[6]

My friend, the driver of the market-wagon, became by chance an attendant at some meetings of the temperance advocates. He was a sensible fellow, and listened with open ears to their arguments. In a visit I lately paid to the island of my birth, I found him a whole-hearted and most ardent Washingtonian.[7]

Demaine, I have never been able to light upon more than once or twice, and therefore cannot fully say, what are his fortunes. Probably, however, he is to be numbered among those hundreds of men in our city,[8] whose god is fashion and dress; and who, when they are out of sight of their 'genteel' acquaintances, have to practice the most miserable economy to 'keep up appearances,' in the ball-room or the public promenade.[9] Such fellows are as far removed from true gentlemen, as the gilded sun, in stage melo-dramas, from the genuine source of light himself.

The Marchions continued to prosper, as their kindness of heart and their honorable benevolence to the needy, deserved. They are among the most respectable and respected families in the city.[10]

I hear now and then from Bourne. Things are going on in the old way. Phillips has left him, and bought a plantation of his own.[11]

Andrews, my old master, died of grief at the failure of some stock-jobbing operations, wherein a cunning fellow-broker overreached him. His immense possessions, after his death, were found to be as fallacious as the basis on which they had been reared.

The landlord, by whom I was so swindled in the country village, after my poor Mary's death, was caught at last in one of his tricks; and not hav-

6. This paragraph is omitted in FC
7. This paragraph is omitted in FC.
8. in New York FC
9. and who, are miserable out sight of their 'genteel acquaintances,' in the ball-room or the public promenade. FC
10. This paragraph is omitted in FC.
11. This sentence is omitted in FC.

ing been as cautious as with me, he now has to repent his wickedness within the walls of the county jail. I hope he will be taught better, by the time he is at large again.[12]

I have never heard any thing further of the Picaroon, or either of his two companions. Undoubtedly, they reached the confines of Sing-Sing before long, after I had the honor of their acquaintance.[13]

Boarding-houses are no more patronized by me. The distaste I formed from them in my memorable search for quarters, when I first came to New York, was never entirely done away with. The comforts of a home are to be had in very few of these places; and I have often thought that the cheerless method of their accommodations drives many a young man to the barroom, or to some other place of public resort, whence the road to habits of intoxication is but too easy. Indeed, the thought has long been entertained by me, that this matter is not sufficiently appreciated. I would advise every young man to marry as soon as possible, and have a home of his own.

Reader! I have brought my narrative quite to an end. I may be presumptuous to flatter myself that it has been of much amusement to you, though I have had that partly in view. Partly—but not wholly. For I have desired, amid the path we have travelled together, and which is now at an end—that a few seeds of wholesome instruction might be dropped at the same time[14] that we gathered the fruits and the flowers.

CHAPTER XXV. . . . CONCLUSION.

As works of fiction have often been made the vehicle of morality, I have adopted the novel experiment of making one of the sort a messenger of the cause of Temperance. And though I know not what the decision of the reader may be, I am too strongly armed in the honesty of my intentions, to suppose that there can be any doubt as to the propriety of the *moral* intended to be conveyed—or to fear any attack upon the story, as regards its principles.

To expatiate upon the ruins and curses which follow the habitual use of strong drink, were at this time almost a stale homily. A great revolution has come to pass within the last eight or ten years. The dominion of the Liquor Fiend has been assaulted and battered. Good men and strong

---

12. This paragraph is omitted in FC.
13. This paragraph is omitted in FC.
14. The sentence and the tale ends with the word "time" in FC.

have come up to the work of attack. Warriors, with large hands, and with girded loins, are waiting with resolution, and their energies are devoted to the battle. They are taking the place of those who are wearied, and in their turn give way to others, who have new and greater strength. Will the old fortress yield? It *must*, sooner or later. It may be compared to some ivy-crowned castle, some strong tower of the olden time, with its flanked battlements, and its guards pacing on the top of its walls, and laughing to scorn all the devices of those who came against it. The red banner floated on its topmost height—inscribed with its fearful watchword, "Disgrace and Death!" And a million victims came every year, and yielded themselves to their ruin under its control. But the foes of the Castle of Orgies stepped forth in array, and swore to one another that they would devote their lives to the work of reform. Long did that haughty structure resist every blow—firmly did it defy every besieger. But the might of a good motive is more than the highest strength of wickedness; and at last the bars of the gates began to give way, and the thick walls cracked. An outpost was driven in, and a tower fell. How tremendous the shout then that arose from the men who were fighting the good fight, and the faces of their antagonists paled with fear! So they kept on. And other parts of the foundation were undermined, and the heavy stanchions were burst asunder, and the forces of the Red Fiend have been routed, band after band, until but a little are left; and they will soon have to retreat, and go the way of their brethren.

The good of the present age are smiling upon the cause of Temperance. It is indeed a holy cause. How many widows' tears it has assuaged—and how many poor wretched men it has taken by the hand, and led to reputation and comfort once more. It seems to me, that he who would speak of the efforts of the Temperance Societies with a sneer, is possessed of a very heedless and bigoted, or a very wicked disposition. It is true, that the dictates of a classic and most refined taste, are not always observed by these people; and the fashionable fop, the exquisite, or the pink of what is termed 'quality,' might feel not at home among them. But to persons with clear heads, and with breasts where philanthropy and a desire for the good of their fellows have a resting-place, I am fully content to leave the decision, whether, after all, there be not a good deal of *intellectuality* engaged in the Temperance movement.

The Reformers have one great advantage, too, which makes up for any want of polish, or grace. They are sincere, and speak with the convictions of their own experience. In all ages, a revolution for the better, when started, has found its advocates among the poorer classes of men. From them, it gradually rises, until it pervades all ranks of society. It has happened so in this case. The few men who met together in Baltimore, and formed a compact with themselves to abstain from those practices which had been so injurious to them, little thought how their principles were to spread, and how they would be pointed back to with admiration, from the rich as well as the poor—the learned as well as the ignorant.

They called themselves "WASHINGTONIANS." Long may the name be honored—and long may it continue to number among those who are proud to style themselves by the title—upright and noble spirits, determined never to turn back from the work, or to discredit the name they bear, and the Society to which they belong!

Any one who has attended the meetings of the temperance people, cannot but be amazed and delighted at the enthusiasm which pervades them. It is not confined to one sex, or to any particular age or class. It spreads over all. Men and women join in it. Young people, even boys and girls, are inoculated with the fervor, and are heard about the streets, singing the temperance songs, and conversing upon the principles of the doctrine, by which their fathers or brothers have been regenerated and made happy. The enthusiasm I mention, has not been limited, either, to one City, or one State. It is felt over every part of this Republic, and accounts come to us of the wondrous doings of Temperance in Maine, while the same hour, in the Western mail, we receive the story of how many new converts there are in Illinois. Perhaps on no occasion has there been a spectacle so full of moral splendor. A whole nation forsaking an evil mania, which has hitherto made it the mark of scorn to those who, coming from abroad, have noticed this one foul blot in contradistinction to all the other national good qualities—and turning a goodly portion of its mighty powers to the business of preventing others from forming the same habits; and redeem, as far as practicable, those who have already formed them: I consider it a sight which we may properly call on the whole world to admire!

In the story which has been narrated in the preceding pages, there is given but a faint idea of the dangers which surround our young men in this great city. On all sides, and at every step, some temptation assails them; but all the others joined together, are nothing compared with the seductive enchantments which have been thrown around the practice of intoxication, in some five or six of the more public and noted taverns called "musical saloons," or some other name which is used to hide their hideous nature. These places are multiplying. The persons engaged in the sale of ardent spirits are brought to see that their trade, unless they can join something to it, as a make-weight, will shortly vanish into thin air, and their gains along with it. Thus they have hit upon the expedient of MUSIC, as a lure to induce customers, and in too many cases, with fatally extensive success.

I would warn that youth whose eye may scan over these lines, with a voice which speaks to him, not from idle fear, but the sad knowledge of experience, how bitter are the consequences attending these musical drinking-shops. They are the fit portals of ruin, and inevitably lead thither. I have known more than one young man, whose prospects for the future were good—in whom hope was strong, and energy not wanting—but all poisoned by these pestilent places, where the mind and the body are both rendered effeminate together.

To conclude, I would remark that, if my story meets with that favor which writers are perhaps too fond of relying upon, my readers may hear from me again, in the method similar to that which has already made us acquainted.

THE AUTHOR.

THE END.

The Madman[1]

"Lo! See his eyeballs glare!"
Monk Lewis[2]

THE little tables of one of the large eating houses in the upper part of Fulton street, were crowded. It was an hour past noon. At that time, all classes of our citizens, except they who aspire to rank among the fashionable, or in the neighborhood of fashionable, either are engaged in the pleasant business of eating, or taking measures for soon being so. The waiters, in their shirt sleeves, hurried to and fro, obeying the mandates of the customers. The carvers and cooks, at a little place partitioned off in a corner in the back part of the room, were tasked to their utmost. Knives and forks jingled, plates clattered, the names of the variety of dishes were sung out without a moments cessation.

It might have been noticed, by the curious eye, that nine out of ten who sought the accommodation there, *gulped* down their food with the most alarming haste, and in a manner which inferred that the crisis of some important transaction were just on the eve of happening—and its favorable conclusion depended on the celerity of mastication and swallowing. The large plain clock, at the top of the back wall, received many a hurried glance—as though the eaters timed themselves, and sought to get through the dining operations, within a given movement of the minute hands.

And there were two features which an observer might have noticed with great satisfaction. Each customer, upon finishing his meal, walked up to the counter and paid for it, according to his own computation —his own honesty being the only bar between a little petty cheating and the fair payment for what he had been served with. It is asserted that the instances of deception, from customers, are so rare as hardly to deserve mention. What a pleasant commentary on the attacks of foreign slanderers with respect to our national integrity! The second feature was the absence of any ardent liquors—no temptation existing for any one to

1. This fragment appeared in the New York *Washingtonian and Organ* (formerly the *Washingtonian*), January 28, 1843, and was discovered by Professor Emory Holloway several years ago (see Footnote One, "Reuben's Last Wish"). No issues of the *Washingtonian* containing any further installments of the tale have been found. It seems probable, since the *Washingtonian* was an organ of the Washingtonian temperance movement, that *The Madman* was intended to be a temperance

nullify the healthy action of the powers of the stomach upon what had been eaten, by drinking the unwholesome draught.

When the business and the confusion were at the highest, the door opened and admitted Richard Arden. Who was Richard Arden?

Any one who has been familiar with life and people in a great city cannot have failed to notice a certain class, mostly composed of young men, who occupy a kind of medium between gentility and poverty. By soul, intelligence, manners, and a vague good taste, they assimilate to the former method. By irresolution of mind, evil acquaintances, a kind of romance which pervades the character, an incapacity for the harder and tougher and more profitable purposes of life, they attach to the latter. Poverty, too, many times, is the source of much meanness. It causes the commission of a thousand things which result at last in the brushing off from the unfortunate poor one, of that fine sensitiveness which forms the most exquisite trait in the character of a *true gentleman*—that character which it ought to be our highest ambition to attain. I don't know, either, whether it may not be wrought out as well by a person surrounded by the disagreeables of want, and ill-breeding—as by one who has all the advantages of society and fashion. Let me make an impression in this passing remark, good reader.

Richard Arden had but fifteen cents in his pocket—and with that he intended to purchase his dinner. He had no certainty that he could get another meal afterward. Yet he was not cast down in spirit. He held his head well aloft. He bore upon his countenance the expression of one whose mind was but little agitated. He was a philosopher.

"Pork and beans, No. 8!" sung out Irish John, the waiter.

The words themselves may seem identified with any thing in the world but refinement and romance. But they involve quite an amount of comfort, nevertheless. The smoking plate was brought—the crispy brown[3] upon one side, and the rich fat slice of meat upon the other. Young Arden applied himself with great cheerfulness to the matter of devouring the savory viand.

What a hubbub! What a clatter of knives and forks!

One of the surest tests of good breeding is the manner of performing the little duties of meals and the table. A person whose fork dashes into the food before him, and whose knife divides it with the ferocity of

novel or novelette. If so, the fact that *The Madman* began publication less than three months after the appearance of *Franklin Evans* indicates that Whitman did indeed "cut a chip off that kind of timber again." Following the title of the tale is "By the author of '*Franklin Evans.*'"

2. I have been unable to locate this epigraph in "Monk" Lewis.

3. Read "beans" after "brown"?

a wild beast, has been unfortunate in his earlier education; and one remnant, at least, of the manners of a clown is still resident with him. Hurry is a vulgar trait, at best. At the table it becomes doubly so—inconsistent with health and prudence, as with decorum and enjoyment.

Our hero—for the reader has doubtless seen that the person to whom he has been introduced is so—our hero was unexceptionable in the matter to which we have just alluded. Though in our establishment, and surrounded by companions, that would have shocked the fastidious delicacy of an Astor House boarder, or one whose dining hour was five or six o'clock, Arden comported himself with the quiet and deliberation which are at the root of good taste. So we think we have established for our principal character a claim to be considered a gentleman—an important point.

At the opposite side of the table sat a man of rather pleasant countenance, whom Arden had seen some few times previous, and with whom, on the present occasion, he happened to enter into some light talk. As they discussed their dinner, they discussed one or two of the ordinary topics of conversation. For some ten or fifteen minutes per......... tinued.[4]

How strangely we form acquaintances! How strange, indeed, and how complete a matter of chance, are many of those incidents and occurrences which have a lasting influence on a future destiny—trivial, as they seem at first, but potent for good or evil, in the future.

Arden and the pleasant-faced man, whose name was Barcoure, happened to get through their meal at the same time—to pay at the counter together—and to walk forth into the street together. Then they happened to be going a block or two in the same direction.

Why was it that they became acquaintances—and, are[4.1] long, friends?

I cannot tell. At first they saw little or nothing—the one in the mind or manners of the other—to attract an admiration or respect in unwonted degree. Yet the next day, when they happened to meet, they bowed. The next day, each gave the other his name. The next week, they were on the footing of intimacy and familiarity.

4. The unique copy of the *Washingtonian* is mutilated here. Holloway suggests the reading—"perhaps this continued."
4.1. "ere"?

CHAPTER II.

Barcoure was a young man—like my hero. Indeed it may be found, before the end of my story, that the right of main personage may lie between the two. He was of French descent—his father having come to America just after the downfall of the Napoleon dynasty, imbued with that fierce radicalism and contempt for religion which marked the old French revolution, and which still lingers among a by no means small portion of the people of that beautiful and noble country. The son inherited the sentiments, with the blood, of his father. His infidelity and his disregard of all the ties which custom and piety have established, more[4.2] tempered with more discretion than his father had possessed—but they were none the less firm.

Perhaps I am not fully justifiable in calling Barcoure an *infidel*. He had ideas of morality and virtue, and, to a degree, practiced them. His system was a beautiful and a simple one—in theory—based upon a foundation of stern and strict and rigorous correctness of conduct. He rejected all of what he called the *superstitions* of mankind. He held that each code of religion contained more or less excellence—and more or less fanaticism. A strange and dreamy creature was Pierre Barcoure.

And before I advance any farther, it were well for me to remind the reader that I seek to paint life and men, in my narrative—describing them in such manner, and putting such words into their mouths, as may seem to make the portratures[4.3] truthful ones. In what they say, I hold no responsibility.

So[5] these two—Pierre and young Arden—became near and dear to one another.

Their friendship was not of that grosser kind which is rivetted by intimacy in scenes of dissipation. Many men in this great city of vice are banded together in a kind of companionship of vice, which they dignify by applying to it the word which stands second at the beginning of this paragraph. How vile a profanation of a holy term!

(To be continued.)

4.2. "Were" was probably carelessly omitted by the typesetter before "more."
4.3. So spelled in the original.
5. "To" in the original; certainly erroneous.

The Love of Eris: A Spirit Record[1]

WHO says there are not angels or invisible spirits watching around us? O! the teeming regions of the air swarm with many a bodiless ghost —bodiless to human sight, because of their exceeding and too dazzling beauty!

And there is one, childlike, with helpless and unsteady movements, but a countenance of immortal bloom, whose long-lashed eyes droop downward.—The name of the shape is Dai. When he comes near, the angels are silent, and gaze upon him with pity and affection. And the fair eyes of the shape roll, but fix upon no object; while his lips move, but a plaintive tone only is heard, the speaking of a single name. Wandering in the confines of earth, or restlessly amid the streets of the Beautiful Land, goes Dai, earnestly calling on one he loves.

Wherefore is there no response?

Soft as the feathery leaf of the frailest flower—pure as the heart of flame—of a beauty so lustrous that the sons of Heaven themselves might well be drunken to gaze thereon—with fleecy robes that but half apparel a maddening whiteness and grace—dwells Eris among the Creatures Beautiful, a chosen and cherished one. And Eris is the name called by the wandering angel,—while no answer comes, and the loved flies swiftly away, with a look, of sadness and displeasure.

It had been years before that a maid and her betrothed lived in one of the pleasant places of earth. Their hearts clung to each other with the fondness of young life, and all its dreamy passion. Each was simple and innocent. Mortality might not know a thing better than their love, or more sunny than their happiness.

In the method of the rule of fate, it was ordered that the maid should sicken, and be drawn nigh to the gates of death—nigh, but not through them—Now to the young who love purely, High Power commissions to each a gentle guardian, who hovers around unseen day and night. The office of this spirit is to keep a sleepless watch, and fill the heart of his charge with strange and mysterious and lovely thoughts.[2] Over the maid

---

1. This story was first published in the *Columbian Magazine*, March, 1844, with the title of "Eris: A Spirit Record." The version followed here is that reprinted under its present title on August 18, 1846, in the *Brooklyn Eagle*, which Whitman was editing. There are a few unimportant differences in punctuation and capitalization in the two versions; only the verbal variants of the 1844 text are shown in the footnotes that follow.

2. This paragraph is followed by this one-sentence paragraph: "To the immortal,

was placed Dai, and through her illness the unknown presence of the youth hung near continually.[2]

Erewhile, a cloud was seen in Heaven.[3] An archangel with veiled cheeks cleaved the air. Silence spread through the hosts of the Passed Away, who gazed in wonder and fear. And as they gazed, they saw a new companion of wondrous loveliness among them—a strange and timid creature, who, were it not that pain must never enter those borders with innocence, would have been called unhappy. The angels gathered around the late comer with caresses and kisses, and they smiled pleasantly with joy in each others' eyes.

Then the archangel's voice was heard—and they who heard it knew that One still mightier spake his will therein:

"The child Dai!" said he.

A far reply sounded out in tones of trembling and apprehension, "I am here!"

And the youth came forth from the distant confines, whither he had been in solitude. The placid look of peace no more illumined his brow;[4] and his unearthly beauty was a choice statue shrouded in smoke.[5]

"Oh, weak and wicked spirit!" said the archangel, "thou hast been false to thy mission and thy Master!"

The quivering limbs of Dai felt weak and cold.—He would have made an answer in agony—but now[6] he lifted his eyes and beheld the countenance of Eris, the late comer.

Love is potent, even in Heaven! And subtle passion creeps into the hearts of the Sons of Beauty, who feel the delicious impulse, and know that there is a soft sadness sweeter than aught in the round of their pleasure eternal.

When the youth saw Eris, he sprang forward with lightning swiftness to her side. But the late comer turned away with aversion. The band of good-will might not be between them, because of wrongs done, and the planting of despair in two happy human hearts.

At the same moment, the myriads of interlinked spirits that range step by step from the throne of the Uppermost, (as the power of that light and presence which is unbearable even to the deathless, must be tempered for the sight of any created thing, however lofty,) were conscious of a mo-

days, years and centuries are the same."

3. This sentence is followed by: "The delicate ones bent their necks, and shook as if a chill blast had swept by—and white robes were drawn around shivering and terrified forms." A new paragraph begins with "An archangel . . ."

4. with silver light

5. was a choice statue enveloped in mist and smoke

6. but at that moment

tion of the mind of God. Quicker than electric thought the command was accomplished! The disobedient angel felt himself enveloped in a sudden cloud, impenetrably dark. The face of Eris gladdened and maddened him no more. He turned himself to and fro, and stretched out his arms—but though he knew the nearness of his companions, the light of Heaven, and of the eyes of Eris, was strangely sealed to him. Dai[7] was blind forever.

So a wandering angel sweeps through space, with restless and unsteady movements—and the sound heard from his lips is the calling of a single name.—But the loved flies swiftly away in sadness, and heeds him not. Onward and onward speeds the angel, amid scenes of ineffable splendor, though to his sight the splendor is darkness. But there is one scene that rests before him alway. It is of a low brown dwelling among the children of men; and in an inner room a couch, whereon lies a young maid, whose cheeks rival the frailness and paleness of foam. Near by is a youth; and the filmy eyes of the girl are bent upon him in fondness. What dim shape hovers overhead? He is invisible to mortals; but oh! well may the blind spirit, by the token of throbs of guilty and fiery love beating through him, know that hovering form! Thrust forward by such fiery love, the shape dared transcend his duty. Again the youth looked upon the couch, and beheld a lifeless corpse.

This is the picture upon the vision of Dai. His brethren of the Bands of Light, as they meet him in his journeyings, pause awhile for pity; yet never do the pangs of their sympathy, the only pangs known to those sinless creatures, or arms thrown softly around him, or kisses on his brow, efface the pale lineaments of the sick girl—the dead.

In the portals of Heaven stands Eris, oft peering into the outer distance. Nor of the millions of winged messengers that hourly come and go, does one enter there whose features are not earnestly scanned by the watcher. And the fond joy resides in her soul, that the time is nigh at hand; for a thread yet binds the angel down to the old abode, and until the breaking of that bond, Eris keeps vigil in the portals of Heaven.

The limit of the watch comes soon. On earth, a toil-worn man has returned from distant travel, and lays him down, weary and faint at heart, on a floor amid the ruins of that low brown dwelling.—The slight echo is heard of moans coming from the breast of one who yearns to die. Life, and rosy light, and the pleasant things of nature, and the voice and sight of his fellows, and the glory of thought—the sun, the flowers, the glittering stars, the soft breeze—have no joy for him. And

7. The youth

the coffin and the cold earth have no horror; they are a path to the unfor-
gotten.

Thus the tale is told in Heaven, how the pure love of two human beings is a sacred thing, which the immortal themselves must not dare to
cross.—In pity to the disobedient angel, he is blind, that he may not
gaze ceaselessly on one who returns his love with displeasure. And haply
Dai is the spirit of the destiny of those whose selfishness would seek to
mar the peace of gentle hearts, by their own intrusive[8] and unhallowed
passion.

8. unreturned

My Boys and Girls[1]

THOUGH a bachelor, I have several girls and boys that I consider my own. Little Louisa, the fairest and most delicate of human blossoms, is a lovely niece—a child that the angels themselves might take to the beautiful land, without tasting death. A fat, hearty, rosy-cheeked youngster, the girl's brother, comes in also for a good share of my affection. Never was there such an imp of mischief! Falls and bumps hath he every hour of the day, which affect him not, however. Incessant work occupies his mornings, noons and nights; and dangerous is it, in the room with him, to leave anything unguarded, which the most persevering activity of a stout pair of dumpy hands can destroy.

What would you say, dear reader, were I to claim the nearest relationship to George Washington, Thomas Jefferson and Andrew Jackson? Yet such is the case, as I aver upon my word. Several times has the immortal Washington sat on my shoulders, his legs dangling down upon my breast, while I trotted for sport down a lane or over the fields. Around the waist of the sagacious Jefferson have I circled one arm, while the fingers of the other have pointed him out words to spell. And though Jackson is (strange paradox!) considerably older than the other two, many a race and tumble have I had with him—and at this moment I question whether, in a wrestle, he would not get the better of me, and put me flat.

One of my children—a child of light and loveliness—sometimes gives me rise to many uneasy feelings. She is a very beautiful girl, in her fourteenth year. Flattery comes too often to her ears. From the depths of her soul I now and then see misty revealings of thought and wish, that are not well. I see them through her eyes and in the expression of her face.

It is a dreary thought to imagine what may happen, in the future years, to a handsome, merry child—to gaze far down the vista, and see the dim phantoms of Evil standing about with nets and temptations—to witness, in the perspective, purity gone, and the freshness of youthful innocence rubbed off, like the wasted bloom of flowers. Who, at twenty-five or thirty years of age, is without many memories of wrongs done, and mean or wicked deeds performed?

1. This somewhat allegorical sketch, which appeared in *The Rover*, April 20, 1844, appears to describe Whitman's sisters and some of his brothers, though one of the sisters is depicted as a niece. Mary, Louisa, Andrew Jackson, George Washington, and Thomas Jefferson correspond in actual names as well as in relative ages to Whitman's sisters and three of his brothers. Whitman speaks of Mary as being "in her

Right well do I love many more of my children. H. is my "summer child." An affectionate fellow is he—with merits and with faults, as all boys have—and it has come to be that should his voice no more salute my ears, nor his face my eyes, I might not feel as happy as I am. M., too, a volatile lively young gentleman, is an acquaintance by no means unpleasant to have by my side. Perhaps M. is a little too rattlesome, but he has qualities which have endeared him to me much during our brief acquaintance. Then there is J. H., a sober, good-natured youth, whom I hope I shall always number among my friends. Another H. has lately come among us—too large, perhaps, and too near manhood, to be called one of my *children*. I know I shall love him well when we become better acquainted—as I hope we are destined to be.

Blessings on the young! And for those whom I have mentioned in the past lines, oh, may the development of their existence be spared any sharp stings of grief or pangs of remorse! Had I any magic or superhuman power, one of the first means of its use would be to insure the brightness and beauty of their lives. Alas! that there should be sin, and pain, and agony so abundantly in the world!—that these young creatures —wild, frolocksome, and fair—so dear to me all of them, those connected by blood, and those whom I like for themselves alone—alas, that they should merge in manhood and womanhood the fragrance and purity of their youth!

But shall I forget to mention *one* other of my children? For of him I can speak with mingled joy and sadness. For him there is no fear in the future. The clouds shall not darken over his young head—nor the taint of wickedness corrupt his heart—nor any poignant remorse knaw him inwardly for wrongs done. No weary bane of body or soul—no disappointed hope—no unrequited love—no feverish ambition—no revenge, nor hate, nor pride—no struggling with poverty, nor temptation, nor death—may ever trouble him more. He lies low in the grave-yard on the hill. Very beautiful was he—and the promise of an honorable manhood shone brightly in him—and sad was the gloom of his passing away. We buried him in the early summer. The scent of the apple-blossoms was thick in the air—and all animated nature seemed overflowing with delight and motion. But the fragrance and the animation made us feel a deadlier sickness in our souls. Oh, bitter day! I pray God there may come to me but few such!

fourteenth year," which makes it possible that this sketch was written in 1835, the year Mary reached fourteen. In the same year Louisa was twelve; Andrew Jackson, eight; George Washington, six; and Thomas Jefferson, two. The baby girl who died a month after her birth could be the child born to Whitman's parents who died in 1825 a few months after its birth and before it was given a name. It is impossible to identify the other dead child or those children designated only by initials.

And there is one again:—and she, too, must be in the Land of Light, so tiny and so frail. A mere month only after she came into the world, a little shroud was prepared, and a little coffin built, and they placed the young infant in her tomb. It was not a sad thing—we wept not, nor were our hearts heavy.

I bless God that he has ordained the beautiful youth and spring time! In all the wondrous harmony of nature, nothing shows more wisdom and benevolence than that necessity which makes us grow up from so weak and helpless a being as a new-born infant, through all the phases of sooner and later childhood, to the neighborhood of maturity, and so to maturity itself. Thus comes the sweetness of the early seasons—the bud and blossom time of life. Thus comes the beauty which we love to look upon—the faces and lithe forms of young children.

May it not be well, as we grow old, to make ourselves often fresh, and childlike, and merry with those who are so fresh and merry? We *must* grow old—for immutable time will have it so. Gray hairs will be sown in our heads, and wrinkles in our faces; but we can yet keep *the within* cheerful and youthful—and that is the great secret of warding off all that is unenviable in old age. The fountain flowing in its sweetness forever, and the bloom undying upon the heart, and the thoughts young, whatever the body may be—we can bid defiance to the assaults of time, and composedly wait for the hour of our taking away.

Dumb Kate[1]

NOT many years since—and yet long enough to have been before the abundance of railroads, and similar speedy modes of conveyance— the travelers from Amboy village to the metropolis of our republic were permitted to refresh themselves, and the horses of the stage had a breathing spell, at a certain old-fashion'd tavern, about half way between the two places. It was a quaint, comfortable, ancient house, that tavern. Huge buttonwood trees embower'd it round about, and there was a long porch in front, the trellis'd work whereof, though old and moulder'd, had been, and promised still to be for years, held together by the tangled folds of a grape vine wreath'd about it like a tremendous serpent.

How clean and fragrant everything was there! How bright the pewter tankards wherefrom cider or ale went into[2] the parch'd throat of the thirsty man! How pleasing to look into the expressive eyes of Kate, the landlord's lovely daughter, who kept everything so clean and bright!

Now the reason why Kate's eyes had become so expressive was, that, besides their proper and natural office, they stood to the poor girl in the place of tongue and ears also. Kate had been dumb from her birth. Everybody loved the helpless creature when she was a child. Gentle, timid, and affectionate was she, and beautiful[3] as the lilies of which she loved to cultivate so many every summer in her garden. Her light hair,[4] and the like-color'd lashes, so long and silky, that droop'd over her blue eyes of such uncommon size and softness—her rounded shape, well set off by a little modest art of dress—her smile—the graceful ease of her motions, always attracted the admiration of the strangers who stopped there, and were quite a pride to her parents and friends.[5]

---

1. The text followed here is that of *Collect*. The tale was originally published in the *Columbian Magazine* for May 1844, as "Dumb Kate.—An Early Death." Whitman later reprinted the story in the *Brooklyn Eagle*, which he was editing, on July 13, 1846. The *Eagle* version exactly follows the *Columbian* version except for its omission of two sentences which will be noted later. As usual, the *Collect* text differs from the original in its elision of the "e" in the past forms of most regular verbs; however, the only change in punctuation is the omission of one comma. The verbal variants of the *Columbian* text are given in the footnotes that follow.
2. rolled through the lips into
3. delicately beautiful
4. brown hair
5. In the original text, this paragraph follows: "Dumb Kate had an education which rarely falls to the lot of a country girl. She had been early taught to read, and notwithstanding her infirmity, had most of those accomplishments which usually fall to the lot of the daughters of wealth and prosperity."

How could it happen that so beautiful[6] and inoffensive a being should taste,[7] even to its dregs, the bitterest unhappiness?[8] Oh, there must indeed be a mysterious, unfathomable meaning in the decrees of Providence which is beyond the comprehension of man; for no one on earth less deserved or needed 'the uses of adversity' than Dumb Kate. Love, the mighty and lawless passion, came into the sanctuary of the maid's pure breast, and the dove of peace fled away forever.[9]

One of the persons who had occasion to stop most frequently at the tavern kept by Dumb Kate's parents was a young man, the son of a wealthy farmer,[10] who own'd an estate in the neighborhood. He saw Kate, and was struck with her natural elegance.[11] Though not of thoroughly wicked propensities, the fascination[12] of so fine a prize made this youth[13] determine[14] to gain her love, and if possible, to win her to himself. At first he hardly dared, even amid the depths of his own soul, to entertain thoughts of vileness[15] against one so confiding and childlike. But in a short time such feelings wore away, and he made up his mind to become the betrayer of poor Kate.[16] He was a good-looking fellow, and made but too sure of his victim. Kate was lost!

The villain[17] came to New York soon after, and engaged in a business[18] which prosper'd well, and which has no doubt by this time made him what is call'd a man of fortune.

Not long did sickness of the heart wear into the life and happiness of Dumb Kate. One pleasant spring day, the neighbors having been called by a notice the previous morning, the old churchyard was thrown open, and a coffin was borne over the early grass that seem'd so delicate with its light green hue. There was a new made grave, and by its side the bier was rested—while they paused a moment until holy words had been said. An idle boy, call'd there by curiosity, saw something lying on the fresh earth thrown out from the grave, which attracted

6. so innocent and beautiful
7. was made to taste
8. the bitter cup of unhappiness
9. At this point in the original text, the following two sentences, deleted in the *Eagle* reprint, completed a paragraph: "What heart, what situation in life is superior to love? Even this young country girl, retired from the busier and more exciting scenes of existence, was made to know the sweet intoxication, as well as the madness, that comes with the attacks of that boy-conqueror." Whitman reprinted "Dumb Kate" in the *Brooklyn Daily Eagle* on July 13, 1846. The *Eagle* version exactly follows the *Columbian* version except for its omission of the lines quoted above.
10. a gentleman farmer
11. with her beauty and natural elegance
12. the merit   13. this man
14. determine, without intending marriage,
15. of vileness or harm
16. In the original, this sentence is followed by these two paragraphs:

his attention. A little blossom, the only one to be seen around, had grown exactly on the spot where the sexton chose to dig poor Kate's last resting-place. It was a weak but lovely flower, and now lay where it had been carelessly toss'd amid the coarse gravel. The boy twirl'd it a moment in his fingers—the bruis'd fragments gave out a momentary perfume, and then fell to the edge of the pit, over which the child at that moment lean'd and gazed in his inquisitiveness. As they dropp'd, they were wafted to the bottom of the grave. The last look was bestow'd on the dead girl's face by those who loved her so well in life, and then she was softly laid away to her sleep beneath that green grass covering.[19]

Yet in the churchyard on the hill is Kate's[20] grave. There stands a little white stone at the head, and verdure[21] grows richly there; and gossips, sometimes of a Sabbath afternoon, rambling over that gathering-place of the gone from earth, stop a while, and con over the dumb girl's[22] hapless story.

As the girl's evil genius would have it, the youth was handsome and of most pleasing address. He laid his plans with the greatest art. The efforts of wickedness triumphed. It is needless to transcribe the progress of this devil in angel's guise. He had made but too sure of his victim. Kate was lost!

Look not with a frown, rigid moralist! Give not words and thoughts of contempt, you whose life has been pure because it has never been tempted, or because you had the wisdom of the serpent to resist temptation! There is an Eye which looks far beneath the surface of conduct, and forgives and pities the infirmities of mortal weakness. To that Eye, it not seldom appears that they upon whom the world has placed its ban, are the fittest for entering the abodes of heaven itself—while others, to whom men look up with reverence and admiration, might make their appropriate home amid spirits of darkness.

17. The successful villain
18. a respectable business
19. laid away to that repose which, after life's fitful fever, comes so sweetly.
20. Dumb Kate's   21. the grass   22. the poor girl's

The Little Sleighers[1]

A SKETCH OF A WINTER MORNING ON THE BATTERY

JUST before noon, one day last winter, when the pavements were crusted plentifully with ice-patches, and the sun, though shining out very brightly by fits and starts, seemed incapable of conveying any warmth, I took my thick overcoat, and prepared to sally forth on a walk. The wind whistled as I shut the door behind me, and when I turned the corner it made the most ferocious demonstrations toward my hat, which I was able to keep on my head not without considerable effort. My flesh quivered with the bitter coldness of the air. My breath appeared steam. Qu-foo-o! how the gust swept along!

Coming out into Broadway, I wended along by the Park, St. Paul's church, and the icicle-tipped trees in Trinity grave-yard. Having by this time warmed myself into a nice glow, I grew more comfortable, and felt ready to do any deed of daring that might present itself—even to the defiance of the elements which were growling so snappishly around me.

When I arrived at Battery-place—at the crossing which leads from that antique, two story, corner house, to the massive iron gates on the opposite side—I must confess that I was for a moment in doubt whether I had not better, after all, turn and retrace my steps. The wind absolutely roared. I could hear the piteous creaking of the trees on the Battery as the branches grated against one another, and could see how they were bent down by the power of the blast. Out in the bay the waves were rolling and rising, and over the thick rails which line the shore-walk dashed showers of spray, which fell upon the flag stones and froze there.

But it was a glorious and inspiriting scene, with all its wildness. I gave an extra pull of my hat over my brows—a closer adjustment of my collar around my shoulders, and boldly ventured onward. I stepped over the crossing, and passed through the gate.

Ha! ha! Let the elements run riot! There is an exhilarating sensation —a most excellent and enviable fun—in steadily pushing forward against the stout winds!

The whole surface of the Battery was spread with snow. It seemed

1. This sketch appeared in the *Columbian* Magazine, September 1844. Whitman had been working and living in New York in 1844 and had been for about three years.

one mighty bride's couch, and was very brilliant, too, as though varnished with a clear and glassy wash. This huge, white sheet, glancing back a kind of impudent defiance to the sun, which shone sharply the while, was not, it seemed, to be left in its repose, or without an application to use and jollity. Many dozens of boys were there, with skates and small sleds—very busy. Oh, what a noisy and merry band!

The principal and choicest of the play tracks was in that avenue, the third from the water, known to summer idlers there as "Lovers' Walk." For nearly its whole length it was a continued expanse of polished ice, made so partly by the evenness of the surface and partly by the labor of the boys. This fact I found out to my cost; for, turning in it before being aware that it was so fully preoccupied and so slippery, I found it necessary to use the utmost caution or run the certainty of a fall.

"Pawny-guttah!" Gentle lady, (I must here remark,) or worthy gentleman, as the case may be, whose countenance bends over this page, and whose opportunities have never led you to know the use, meaning and import, conveyed in the term just quoted—call to your side some bright-eyed boy—a brother or a son, or a neighbor's son, and ask *him*.

"Pawny-guttah!" I stepped aside instinctively, and, with the speed of an arrow there came gliding along, lying prone upon a sled, one of the boyish troop. The polished steel runners of his little vehicle sped over the ice with a slightly grating noise, and he directed his course by touching the toe of either boot, behind him, upon the ice, as he wished to swerve to the right or left.

Who can help loving a wild, thoughtless, heedless, joyous boy? Oh, let us do what we can—we who are past the time—let us do what we may to aid their pleasures and their little delights, and heal up their petty griefs. Wise is he who is himself a child at times. A man may keep his heart fresh and his nature youthful, by mixing much with that which is fresh and youthful. Why should we, in our riper years, despise these little people, and allow ourselves to think them of no higher consequence than trifles and unimportant toys?

I know not a prettier custom than that said to be prevalent in some parts of the world, of covering the corpses of children with flowers. They pass away, frail and blooming, and the blossom of a day is indeed their fittest emblem. Their greatest and worst crimes were but children's follies, and the sorrow which we indulge for their death has a delicate refinement about it, flowing from ideas of their innocence, their simple prattle, and their affectionate conduct while living. Try to love children. It is purer, and more like that of angels than any other love.

Reflections somewhat after this cast were passing in my mind as I

paused a moment and gazed upon those little sleighers. What a minia-
ture, too, were they of the chase of life! Every one seemed intent upon
his own puny objects—every one in pursuit of "fun."

The days will come and go, and the seasons roll on, and these
young creatures must grow up and launch out in the world. Who can fore-
tell their destinies? Some will die early and be laid away in their brown
beds of earth, and thus escape the thousand throes, and frivolities, and
temptations, and miserable fictions and mockeries which are interwoven with our journey here on earth. Some will plod onward in the
path of gain—that great idol of the world's worship—and have no higher
aspirations than for profit upon merchandize. Some will love, and have
those they love look coldly upon them; and then, in their sickness of
heart, curse their own birth-hour. But all, all will repose at last.

Why, what a sombre moralist I have become! Better were it to listen
to the bell-like music of those children's voices; and, as I turn to wend
my way homeward, imbue my fancy with a kindred glee and joyous-
ness! Let me close these mottled reveries.

The Half-Breed: A Tale of the Western Frontier[1]

CHAPTER I.[2]

LOUDLY rang merry peals of laughter from a group of children, of almost every age and size, as they emerged, one afternoon, through the door of the rude log school-house, in the little town of Warren, a place situated on one of the upper branches of the Mississippi. Less than seven years[3] previously, the site on which the dwellings of the Warrenites now stood, had been a tangled forest, roamed by the savage in pursuit of game. An adventurous settler purchased a few hundred acres there, and with some companions, took up his abode, and gave it the name I have mentioned. The place numbered nearly three hundred inhabitants.

Loudly rang the laughter of the liberated children. Master Caleb, the teacher, stood in the door of his school-house, and gazed with a cheerful smile upon their noisy merriment. He was a pale young man, from the East—and, because that his strength did not allow him to engage in the heavy labours of his comrades, (for in the West, all men are comrades) he gladly accepted an offer from the fathers of the village to take charge of the education of the small people.

"Hurrah!" said one harum-scarum young elf, who was running and tearing like a mad tiger, "Hurrah! the master has given us a holiday,

---

1. This tale first appeared in print under the title of "Arrow-Tip," in the March issue of *The Aristidean*, edited by Thomas Dunn English for the few months of its existence in 1845. The version printed here appeared in the *Brooklyn Eagle*, edited by Whitman, June 1–6, 8, 9, 1846, under its present title, "by a Brooklynite," as an "Original Novelette." The first installment of the tale initiated the literary page of the *Eagle*, thereafter a daily feature. There are only minor differences between the two texts. In the format of *The Aristidean*, all proper nouns were printed with the initial capital and the rest in small capitals. The *Eagle* version eliminated many of the commas of the first version, but added a few. These and minor variants in punctuation have not been noted. The notes that follow list the verbal variants of the *Aristidean* text.

2. In the original version, each chapter has a title: I, A Hunchback and His Errand; II, The Entrance of the Main Character; III, Crime, and Its Detection; IV, A Story, an Alarm, and a Disagreeable Conclusion; V, Wrong Done—But Not So Bad As Might Have Been; VI, One Person's Wicked Hopes Blasted, and Another's Fervent Desire Gratified; VII, The Truth, Known to One Who Might Have Made Many Happy By Telling It, Kept Back For Revenge; VIII, A Hasty Judgment—A Criminal's Story—And the People's Decision; IX, Summing Up of the Case.

3. Less than three years

next Thursday, because he is going to Peter Brown's wedding! Hey! Hurrah!"

"But Bill!"[4] said a larger and more sedate looking youth, addressing the elf, "Bill! be quiet, and do n't act so foolish. Can't you see Mr. Caleb is looking at you?"

"Well," rejoined the other, "What if he—?"

The sentence which the exuberant child was about to utter was cut short suddenly, by a loud shout from seven or eight of his companions.

"Boddo! Boddo!" they cried, "Boddo is coming!" And they pointed with their mischievous fingers, to a turn in the road, at about ten rods distance, where a figure was seen slowly walking, or rather limping, towards them.

More than half the party started off on a gallop, and in a few moments they were[5] at the side of him who had attracted their attention. Boddo, as the youngsters called him—and that was[6] the name he went by all over the settlement—appeared to be a man of about seven-and-twenty years of age. He was deformed in body—his back being mounted with a mighty hunch, and his long neck bent forward, in a peculiar and disagreeable manner. In height he was hardly taller than the smallest of the children who clustered tormentingly around him.—His face was the index to many bad passions—which were only limited in the degree of their evil, because his intellect itself was not very bright; though the sedulous care of some one had taught him even more than the ordinary branches of education. Among the most powerful of his bad points was a malignant peevishness, dwelling on every feature of his countenance. Perhaps it was this latter trait which caused the wild boys of the place ever to take great comfort in making him the subject of their vagaries. The gazer would have been at some doubt whether to class this strange and hideous creature with the race of Red Men or White—for he was a half-breed, his mother an Indian squaw, and his father some unknown member of the race of the settlers.

"Why, Boddo," said the elf, Bill, "how-d'e-do? You lovely creature I hav'nt seen you for a week!"

And the provoking boy took the hunchback's hand, and shook it as heartily as if they had been old friends forever. Boddo scowled, but it was of no avail. He was in the power of the lawless ones, and could not escape.

"What's the price of soap, Boddo?" said another urchin, pointing to

4. "Bill!"   5. and in a few moments were
6. that indeed was   7. at last, exclaimed
8. the passionate half-breed, goaded beyond endurance;
9. any but a child, heedless as the one on whom he gazed.

the filthy hands and face of the Indian. And they all laughed merrily.

"Devils!" exclaimed[7] the passionate half-breed, making an impotent attempt at blows, which they easily foiled;[8] "why do you pester me? Go! —go away—or I shall turn upon you."

"O, Boddo! dear Boddo! do not let your sweet temper rise!" said little Bill, and he patted the Indian on his head, as a man would do to a child.

Boddo glanced *up* to him with an expression of hate which might have appalled any but the heedless one on whom he gazed.[9] He turned round and round, like a wild beast in the toils; but wherever he cast his look, he saw nothing but villainous little fingers extended, and roguish eyes flashing. The poor fellow was indeed sadly beset, and was rapidly working himself up to a pitch of rage, which might have cost some of the thoughtless crew a broken head. At this moment, the tall boy who had reproved Bill in front of the school-house, came up, and, beholding the plight of the tormented one, offered his gentle interference.

"Boys! boys!" he cried, "don't let us bother this poor friend of ours any more. Come, now, are you not willing that he should go?"

He paused, and it was plainly a doubtful case, whether his mediation would be successful. The boys had just come from a three-hours' confinement to their lessons, and they felt disposed for any thing in the shape of mirth. So, like a prudent arbiter, Quincy Thorne, the tall lad, offered a kind of compromise[10] between both difficulties:

"I'll tell you what!" said he, "Boddo shall say all about where he has been this afternoon, and what after; for I see he is just returned from a long tramp—and then we'll let him go. Hey, boys?"

"Agreed!" said the band.

And the hunchback, garrulous by nature and glad no doubt, to be let off thus easily, at once commenced his recital—which we shall take the liberty, however, for our readers' sake, of giving in our own style:[11]

"You know," said he, "of Peter Brown, the blacksmith's marriage, which is to take place soon. Well, even this could not be managed, it seems, without the help of Boddo. A marriage needs a priest—and hereabouts one of that kind is not often met with. Now I, who so love to see my neighbors happy," the hunchback grinned, "could not bear that the pretty sport should all be spoiled for want of a priest. And so—"

"Rather say," interrupted the elf, Bill, "you feared the loss of some drinks of rum, and meals of pork,[12] you had set your heart upon getting at the wedding."

10. a kind of compromise which would steer
11. And the hunchback, glad, no doubt to be let off thus easily, commenced his recital:
12. "meals of food"

Boddo snarled at the saucy boy, and continued:

"And so I said to Brown, that my worthy teacher and friend, Father Luke, the Lonesome Man, at Oak Creek might be brought hither. They say he is a priest; one not exactly of the right sort to suit the people here, perhaps—but when the nearest town is distant a three days' journey, we are not apt to stand on trifles. This priest, then—this Catholic monk, I think, he calls himself—being the only one near at hand, and even the place where he lives not known to many of the people, Mr. Peter bid me go and seek him out, and deliver to him a message, written on paper. More than ten hours have I been wandering up and down the banks of the river, and through the wood, to discover the house of the Lonesome Man. I, Boddo, to whom every tree in the forest, I thought, was known—and every dent in the shore—and every swamp and thicket—could hardly find that place. Not that I have ever taken pains to search for it before; for I defy any of you—the cunningest boy of all—to hide a dead squirrel within five miles, where I shall not ferret it out—so well do I know every spot.[13]

"Well, after a long time,[14] and when I had more than once thought of giving up the search and coming back—which I might have done, had I not reflected on the disappointment to Mr. Peter and the rest—what should——"

"Don't lie, Boddo," interrupted the elf, again, "you can't deny it was the fear of the trouncing you might get—and nothing else—that made you keep on."

The group did not laugh at[15] this sally as at the former ones—for they were anxious to hear the end of the story.

"What should I see, as I came out of a thicket, about two hours' walk from here, but Father Luke[16] himself. He was standing on the bank, at a high place and looking down into the stream—quiet as one of the trees back of us. I approached, and told him my errand.

"Though I knew not his residence, we were old acquaintances in times by-gone; so I thought it strange that he should start, and tremble like a frightened girl, before I spoke a word. He took my letter—and then asked me into his hut; for it was near at hand. He led the way and I followed. A few rods brought us to the side of a crag, all covered with bushes and hanging trees—he parted them at a place where not one eye out of a thousand would have suspected aught else than the brown ground to lie

---

13. In the *Aristidean* this is followed by the following paragraph: "The children were evidently becoming interested in the narrative. They gazed in the hunchback's face—and eagerly drank in every word that he uttered."

14. "Well," continued he, "after a long time"

underneath—and we were in a room, dimly lighted in some way from above, whose sides were stone and dirt,[17] half hidden by some few domestic utensils.

"There stood a table in the middle of the room, covered with books and paper. He sat down there, and, taking a pen, told me he would write an answer to the request I brought. In a few minutes it was ready. He put before me some drink and meat, and then, though he spoke not, I saw he wished my departure. Carefully noting the place, as I emerged, in order that I might tell it again, if occasion required, I bent my steps homeward.

"And now you have all of my story—and I must go, for it is time Peter Brown received his answer."

The children made no opposition to his departure, with the exception of little Bill, who gave Boddo an extra pinch, and a stout pull of the hair, ere he scampered off to engage in some new mischief.

The house of Peter Brown was situated at one end of the village—a pleasant place,[18] where the beams of the sun, of a clear day, dazzled the gazer's eye, as they were reflected from the stream. Peter, contrary to the advice of his neighbors, had, in clearing up his land left a number of the finest trees standing close to his dwelling—which divested it of that rather disagreeable aspect of newness which a lately settled town almost invariably possesses. The house, too, was of a better build and material than most of its fellows; it was of logs, to be sure, but it had a number of good glass windows, and two tall chimneys, and doors which swung on hinges, and fitted tightly.

The blacksmith lived in it now alone. A day or two more was to see him with a companion, however—and that companion, a wife, the daughter of a respectable man, of his own grade in life.

Some three or four rods distant, on the other side of the road, was the shop of the blacksmith, with its smoky fire, and bellows, and the anvil which every morning was heard to clink with rapid and ponderous blows. Leaning idly on the handle of the bellows, stood the master of the establishment himself. He was a stout, well-made, strongly-jointed young man, with light hair, and clear grey eyes.—Though not what is called handsome, he was far from being ill-looking. His lips were beautifully cut, and his neck might have been taken by the most fastidious sculptor as a model of that part of the human form in some fine work of art.

15. did not laugh so long at
16. "but the Lonesome Man"
17. "and we were in a dark room, whose sides were stone and dirt"
18. at one end of the village, near the river, in a pleasant place

What were Peter's thoughts about? Nothing more or less than *love*. He had despatched Boddo many hours previous, and he feared the malicious creature had forgotten or disregarded the duty—and would not perform his bidding. A dozen times during the half hour, would he step to the door of his smithy, and strain his gaze to catch any glimpse of the returning hunchback—and in vain.

When at last he beheld his messenger, and looking into his face, saw the expression of one who returns to a master with news he is sure will be pleasant—he forgot his determination[19] to wring Boddo's neck, and beat him with a bar of iron, and so on—and eagerly demanded the result of his mission.

The Hunchback told the story which the reader has already heard—as related to the school-children—and then gave to Peter the note which had been sent him from the monk. Impatiently breaking the seal, and opening it, the blacksmith read as follows:

"*In answer to Peter Brown, the Blacksmith.*

"A wretched man has come to me with a demand that I should perform the ceremonials of marriage between yourself and a maiden of your town. The messenger explains that no holy minister of heaven, of your faith,[20] is at hand—and entreats me, in your name to refuse him not.

"I am a Catholic monk—for reasons of piety and choice, holding myself aloof[21] from any communion with my kind. But in this matter, though a strict interpretation of my priestly allegiance might keep me from granting what you ask—uniting two members of a church we condemn, in bonds of marriage—I have thought fit, taking all things into consideration, to do as you desire.

"On the morrow, I shall visit the village, and will hold further conference with you on the subject. THE MONK"

"A plague on the roundabout way of his saying Yes!" exclaimed the blacksmith, with a laugh: "as if it made any difference whether our fathers sat in a meeting-house, or heard mass before papal altars—in such a case as this!"

Then briefly informing Boddo that as he had been faithful and successful, he should be rewarded still farther, the happy Peter gave him a small coin, and prepared to shut up his shop, for the purpose of walking over, and telling the news to the family of his intended bride.

---

19. his various determinations
20. "of your own faith"   21. "much aloof"
22. "favourites." In the *Aristidean* text, the "our" spelling of such words pre-

CHAPTER II.

Master Caleb, the teacher, as usually happens in schools, had his favorites[22] and his more especial likings, among the young flock whose education he controlled. Of all the rest, Quincy Thorne, the tall gentle boy, was the one whom he loved, and whose company he preferred. Any other choice would have created some envy and jealousy—but all the children themselves were attached to the teacher's favorite, and gladly yielded to his good fortune without demur.

It happened on the Thursday, when Peter Brown's wedding took place, that Master Caleb and Quincy stole away from the revellers in the middle of the afternoon, and took a quiet round-about stroll, bringing up, at last, at the dwelling of Quincy's father. The whole family had gone to the wedding—as in fact had all the inhabitants of the village, old and young; for the generous-hearted blacksmith would have it so—and the house was therefore quite deserted. The boy and the teacher took a seat on the door-step in front, and gazed at the pleasant prospect before them.

A little and verdant grass-patch, only, intervened between them and the river, which the dwelling fronted toward. They amused themselves by watching the gambols of the water-fowl, wild, but with their wings clipped, and thus partly domesticated;[23] and by counting the various objects that glided along the stream[24]—logs, and torn-up trees, and now and then a fish leaping above the surface.

"Master Caleb," said the boy suddenly, "is not that the figure of an Indian yonder on the hill?"

He pointed as he spoke, to a spot forty or fifty rods distant, on the same side of the river where they were seated.

"It is indeed," answered the teacher, "and he is coming this way. Poor fellow! he seems worn and sick."

As the figure advanced, they had full leisure to survey him. He was one of the finest specimens of the Red People—or rather had the evidence of having once been so—for his gait was now slow and uneven, his eyes dim, and without brightness or glitter—and his cheeks sunken.

"It is Arrow-Tip!" said Master Caleb and the boy simultaneously, as they had a review of the savage; "it is our old friend, Arrow-Tip!"

---

dominates over the "or" spelling, though there is some inconsistency. Whitman makes an evident effort in the *Eagle* text to follow Webster, and the "or" spelling predominates. These spelling changes have not been individually noted.

23. and thus domesticated   24. along the current of the stream

Quincy rose from his seat, and stepped toward the new comer with words of welcome. He led him to the door, and into the house, and bade him rest himself. The Indian took these little kindnesses with the apathetic method of his race. It was plain, however, that they could but be acceptable[25] to him—for he gasped with pain and exhaustion.

"We have not seen you here in Warren for many weeks," said Caleb, after a pause, "and you are ill, it seems."

"I am," replied the savage: "A dull-heat—like the air of your iron-warmed rooms in the settlement—fills me from head to foot. Strength has gone—and Arrow-Tip might be beaten by a young boy."

"How long has this been?" inquired Caleb.

"It first came," was the answer, "when the buds started on the trees, Now the forest is all green and dark with leaves."

"You have a fever," said Master Caleb, "which I dare say some trifling medicine[26] from our common physic-chest, in the land agent's room, would cure at once."

Arrow-Tip made no reply.[27]

"Surely," said young Thorne, looking at the worn moccasins upon the feet of his guest, "surely you have not made this journey from your dwelling alone? Where was your brother, who ever came with you on your former visits?"

The dull eyes of the Indian glanced devoutly upwards:

"He who is your Great Spirit and ours," said he, "lives in the still forest, and was with the sick chief. My people knew not of my coming— none but my brother's wife, to whom I confided my purpose, lest they might think evil had befallen me. I had heard that the white man knew a hundred remedies for ills, of which we were ignorant—ignorant both of ills and remedies. The love of life was strong in my soul. I could not bear to pine away, as a tree whose trunk had been girdled by the hatchet. I felt my arm, and said to myself, perhaps in the village of the pale-faces, there may be something that will bring back its thickness and its nerve. In the night, when all were sleeping, I came out from our lodge, and bent my steps toward your town. The sun is now on his third journey over our heads, since I started."

Both Quincy and the teacher felt their sympathies strongly enlisted for the unfortunate savage. The boy assured him that he might no doubt be welcome to stop with them, as at home, for a season, during which all

25. could not but be acceptable   26. "medicines"
27. answer   28. about what was Arrow-Tip's ailing
29. something, which he knew not, had taken place in former years—and now served as a memento

should be done for his recovery. And Master Caleb averred that Ezekiel Barrett, the store-keeper of Warren, had in his youth spent half of an apprenticeship with a New-England apothecary—and would probably be able to tell all about Arrow-Tip's ailing,[28] and what would effect his recovery.

Toward night-fall, when Mr. Thorne and the members of his family returned from the wedding, it was readily arranged that Arrow-Tip should remain with them, as Quincy had suggested.

"Shame were it to me and my wife," said Thorne, "did we let one who has saved a life very dear to us, ask shelter here, and be refused."

And he looked at his son Quincy, while he spoke. Master Caleb saw that something, which had taken place in former years now served as a memento[29] of good-will between the settler and the chief. He made inquiry, by a glance toward Thorne.

"Yes," said the latter, "we have indeed reason to be grateful to this sick man—for many years ago[30] he saved Quincy's life."

And he told the teacher how it had happened.—It was before[31] they came to live in Warren; for their acquaintance with Arrow-Tip dated many years back.[32] The child, then small,[33] was swept away by a freshet in a river, and Arrow-Tip had dashed into the foaming waters, and brought him safe back again. As may readily be supposed, Thorne and his family were unbounded in their expressions of gratitude—and through all the future years of their existence, never lost an opportunity of showing that gratitude.

Arrow-Tip—as he was called in the figurative style of his people—though possessing now but little of the power of a chief, was descended from the sachems of his tribe. He and a younger brother, named from his swiftness the Deer, frequently had intercourse with the white settlers of that region in the way of trade. They brought the furs and skins collected by their people, and exchanged them for powder, blankets, hardware and other things which habit had made necessary to them.

The Deer generally accompanied his brother on these excursions. The two loved each other—for they were the remnants of their family, and had none else to distract their affection. Boddo, the hunchback, had a claim also to be considered as indirectly of the same tribe with Arrow-Tip and the Deer. But no one knew exactly his relationship; and few thought it worth investigation.

30. "for not many years ago"   31. It was long before
32. This clause does not appear in the original version.
33. then quite small

CHAPTER III.

A week must have passed[34] away since the events of the last chapter. In the course of that time, another personage had arrived upon the stage where our little drama is being enacted, the village of Warren. This personage was Arrow-Tip's brother, the Deer. Informed by his wife of the course intended to be taken by the sick chief, a few days after the departure of the latter, and thinking of a thousand mishaps that might possibly befall him on the road, the Deer filled a pouch with food, strapped his bow and quiver on his back, and commenced a rapid progress toward the settlement.

He arrived in time to witness the favourable change in Arrow-Tip's illness, which was but the precursor of still more improvement. It needed, indeed, but that he should continue a few days longer in the hospitable house of Thorne, and under the medical auspices of Master Caleb and the store-keeper, Barrett, to have his health and strength wholly restored.

One morning when Mr. Thorne came in to partake with his family of their early meal, he looked disturbed and somewhat agitated. To the inquiries of his wife, he for a time returned no answer.

"But I don't know," said he at length, "why I may not as well inform you of the cause of what moves me. For two or three mornings past, on going as I usually do at daylight to take care of my cattle, and feed them, I have missed something from the storehouse where I keep my grain and farming utensils. Occasionally I find merely that matter not very valuable is taken away; but, then, again, an article of great use to me is stolen. I certainly have no idea who is the thief; but it becomes us all to be on the look-out, and see if we cannot discover him."

It was a painful thing for Arrow-Tip, who sat in the chimney-corner, while Mr. Thorne was speaking, that the eyes of nearly every one in the room, with the exception of Thorne, himself, and his eldest son, were turned upon *him*. He was too proud to answer any suspicions; and he moved not or spoke under their gaze.

"This morning," continued Mr. Thorne, "a large piece of bear-meat, which I purchase yesterday of a man sent here by Boddo, and which I intended for our dinner today, is taken off—where and by whom, it is impossible to say."

Again were the eyes of the group directed toward Arrow-Tip. The sav-

34. must pass   35. This

age was deeply pained, but, as before, he evinced it by no sign. In truth, the suspicion, if any such were harboured, was unjust, and in no small degree unreasonable, from the nature of the articles purloined. They[35] could have been of no value to the Indian, unless he sold them, and that were a difficult undertaking, without risk of discovery. Arrow-Tip rose and left the room, uttering not a word.

For the first time, Mr. Thorne reflected on the grief he must have inflicted by his remarks. With true good taste, however, he forebore to make the matter worse by attempting an apology. He bade his children abstain in future from any allusion to the subject, and particularly any sign that they looked upon Arrow-Tip himself as an object of doubt.

In the course of the afternoon, Peter Brown, the lately married blacksmith, came over to Thorne's to speak of a contemplated hunting party the next day, in the forest.

"I am told," said Peter, "that there is a fine herd of deer which some of our folks have several times seen in the neighborhood of Oak Creek. What say you? If the day be fair, will you join us?"

"Certainly," was Thorne's answer; "and our friend, Arrow-Tip here, shall make another of the party, if he will."

"The chief," rejoined the one last spoken to, "will be glad to go."

Quincy stood near while this conversation was taking place.

"Father," he said, "do you not remember your promise that I might hunt with the next party?"

Thorne smiled upon his eager boy, and assented. So it was arranged that soon after sunrise they should all start together—a number of men from neighboring houses having agreed[36] to join them.

As Arrow-Tip retired that evening to a kind of out-house, where he slept, (Thorne would have had him, on his first arrival repose in the main dwelling, but the savage pertinaciously refused,) Quincy tapped him on the arm, and bade him, with a smile, to be up in time.

"And lest I should oversleep myself," said the boy, "come to my window, which opens on[37] the river, and knock upon it to wake me."

It were hardly amiss to guess that the dreams of the young hunter that night were interwoven with huge buffaloes, and springing deer, and mighty bears, in most admired confusion.

Arrow-Tip rose some time before daylight. He pushed open, a small, swinging door, and stood a few minutes gazing over the river, in the direction of his distant tribe. His thoughts were with them—with his brother, whom he expected to visit him that day, (the Deer had his abode

36. having also agreed   37. "opens toward"

at a dismantled hut in the neighborhood of the village,) and with his far off friends.

Of a sudden, while his gaze was thus fixed, he saw a figure stealthily stepping, or rather crawling, through the farm-yard, toward the building used by Thorne for a granary. His sight convinced him that it was none of his host's family; the figure was smaller than Quincy or his father, and much stouter than any of the younger children. The savage immediately remembered what had been said respecting the thefts, the preceeding day; and he felt sure that he should now be able to clear up the mystery, and also remove any doubts that might have been held, respecting his own integrity. The Indian silently drew back into the shadow and watched the figure.

Like a thief, indeed, did it move, and directly toward the door of the granary—which it opened and passed. Arrow-Tip cautiously emerged from where he had been standing, and favoured by the shadow of a huge tree, he stood near the door which the figure had entered, and waited his coming forth. He had not to wait long. With the same halting and stealthy gait, the thief appeared directly, staggering under a bag, borne upon his shoulder, and evidently containing grain.

When he had got a couple of rods forward, Arrow-Tip sprang upon him, as a cat would spring on a mouse.

"Now!" said he, "who comes forth like an owl in the night, to take his brother's goods?—I have him!"

A dismal howl sounded out from the startled thief, and he struggled to get free—but his struggles were useless. Arrow-Tip held him with a grasp of iron, and dragged him to the dwelling of the family, where he knocked loudly.

Not many moments elapsed before Thorne and his people, disturbed by the racket, came rushing together into the porch in front. Arrow-tip, in brief terms, explained the matter to them, and shoved his prisoner toward them.

"As I hope I may shoot a deer to-day!" said Quincy, with a loud burst of laughter, "it is no other than Boddo!"

The boy spoke truth, indeed. The mischievous and now detected hunchback stood before them.—He hung his head in stupid obstinacy, and spoke not a word in excuse for his crime.

"It is very wicked," said Arrow-Tip as he stood with folded arms, and a flush of shame passed over his face, "and it sickens the chief's soul, that one who owns blood of an honest tribe, should be caught thus!"

Boddo looked up, and scowled on the Indian with a furious expression

of deviltry and hate, that plainly said he would lose no convenient opportunity of revenge, if such occurred.

"Come! come!" said Mr. Thorne. "Though I did not expect such conduct, even from Boddo, I am willing to let it pass. We all know the infirmity of the poor fellow—and I dare say this will be a salutary lesson
to him. Come! we forget that to-day we hunt the deer. And our breakfast
is to be prepared, and a dozen matters attended to yet, which we had best
set about immediately!"

As the hunchback turned from the spot, to walk away, he cast another
glance at Arrow-Tip. It was full of malice and hate. But the chief did
not deign to heed it by the slightest notice. He calmly set himself about
the necessary business of the hour.

CHAPTER IV.

Who could be more happy then Peter Brown's bride? She was a
young and handsome woman, possessed of much good sense, and a
strong faculty of making people become attached to her. On no occasion
was this latter trait illustrated more pleasantly than in the intercourse and
friendliness between her husband and herself on the one part, and him
who has been spoken of in a preceding page as the Lonesome Man, on
the other. Ever since the hour when the monk, or Father Luke, as he was
also sometimes called, united them in marriage, he had apparently found
a new impulse to be sociable, by visiting the house of the blacksmith.

There was considerable of mystery about the character of the holy
man. No one knew his life. Sometimes he would be absent for months,
and then would suddenly appear in his rude dwelling once more, as if
returned from a distant journey. It was generally supposed that in these
intervals he went away to the convents of his brethren in Canada. No one
sought to pry into his designs or wishes. Yet he was by no means of an
austere disposition, and might probably have answered their questions,
had they seen fit to proffer any. But in the west, where every one is in some
degree or other an adventurer, few wish to investigate the former history
of their neighbours. Inquisitiveness does not prevail there, as in some
other sections of our republic.

Much more frequently than before, as has been intimated, the monk
now sought communion with the villagers, and most of all the Browns.
On the day of the hunting-party, he came there, and though Peter himself was absent, he was invited by the young wife to rest himself, and
remain and chat with her. So kindly were her requests proposed, and so

yearning, if the truth be told, were the Lonesome Man's wishes for some kind of companionship, that he made little demur to accepting the invitation. The hours passed on quite pleasantly—each mutually entertained with the presence and cheerfulness of the other.

"Father Luke," said the hostess, after a long pause in her[38] conversation, "I know you will not be offended, if I tell you I have wondered how you can be comfortable in that cold cave of yours, where they say you reside."

The monk smiled, quietly.

"I have long learned," said he, "to be content with coarse fare and coarse accommodation. It is part of the duty of such as I."

"And were you always content?"

"Not always," was the subdued answer.

The monk saw that his companion would probably have spoken further, had she not feared intruding on his wish for concealment.

"Daughter," said he, "perhaps I have been looked upon, by the good people hereabout, too much as a being of mystery. I have little that I wish to conceal. I will, if you have patience to bear it, tell you my story. Some few items, your own good sense will inform you, it were better[39] to pass no further."

The young woman was certainly not so far superior to the foibles of her sex, as to turn away from any thing in shape of a secret. She made a gesture of assent, and the monk proceeded:[40]

"I was born in a country town in Ireland. My parents were in the humbler walks of life, and of all their children I alone received what might be called a respectable education. Even in my early boyhood, I was destined for the church.

"When I was about eighteen years old, my mother died—a sad loss to us all. A year passed away, before the end of which, my father finding the cares and troubles of his family to press heavily upon him took unto himself another wife.

"I had a sister—a lovely girl, some two years younger than myself. My sister possessed in her character some of the most excellent, as well as some of the weakest propensities of her sex. She was capricious and headstrong—but tender, and very affectionate. Her beauty gained her many suitors—whom her whim induced her to discard, as they were generally of our own lowly condition.

"One summer, there came to reside, for a few days, in our village, a citizen, named Arnold. It was a dark hour for poor Mary, when he made his entrance there. He was handsome, fascinating, and a confirmed rake.

"They met—this man and my sister. Arnold saw what a prize the place had hitherto unconsciously contained, and determined to win it. Ah, if she would but have taken warning—for she *was* warned!

"To make the tale short, Mary, refusing to hear the advice of her well-wishers, received Arnold to her love. He protracted his visit to many weeks. Before he returned to the city, he added another to his *triumphs*. My sister fell! O, when will the false tone which pervades society, make it needful to hold beyond the pale of its promiscuous communion, the man who acts as Arnold acted?

"But what am I saying? From whom could such sentiments come with more ill grace than me—*me*, who have been guilty of a similar, and even worse, course of conduct!

"A few months passed on, and my sister's frailty could no longer be concealed. Our step-mother was a severe woman. Her cold and haughty looks, and her sharp taunts, drove poor Mary almost insane. My father, too, when he knew his daughter's disgrace, expressed[41] a determination to cast her off forever. Had our own mother been alive, the case would no doubt have resulted differently. *She* might have stormed for a time—but at least the fatal termination which, as things were, came to pass, would have been prevented!

"One day my sister was missing. She had decamped in the night, and no doubt was wandering about homeless and shelterless. We caused a search to be made, which, at the end of a couple of days, ended in the discovery of the lost one. She was completely deranged—and, when found, was seated upon a bank in a wide forest. She died within a week from that time.

"Death, they say, blots out all misdoings. We were all grieved and agonied at the fate of our hapless Mary—but none with that passion which filled my own bosom. I pondered, night and day, upon the wickedness of her seducer, Arnold. A hundred schemes for revenge were fixed upon in my mind, and then abandoned.

"Happening to go, about this period, upon business in a neighboring city, I was accidentally called upon, at my lodgings, by an itinerant teacher of sword fencing. Suddenly, a new method of vengeance struck me. Upon the instant, I engaged the man to give me lessons. I applied myself diligently to my new study, and within a short time had the satisfaction of hearing my teacher pronounce me one of the most proficient pupils he ever had. I challenged Arnold to combat. He accepted my challenge.

41. "half expressed"

"Perhaps you may wonder that in view of the profession I intended to follow, I should have thought fit to act thus. I was blinded by my hate for my sister's betrayer. I was engrossed by no other thought than that of revenge!

"Arnold met me, as I demanded. Whether it was that a just cause nerved my arm, or that his was powerless with conscious guilt, I know not —but he fell. When I left the place of the fight, he lay there a stiff and senseless corpse!

"My antagonist had relatives and friends of rank; and it was plainly dangerous for me to remain in Ireland. I gathered together what funds I could raise on so sudden an emergency, and fled. I directed my course to this general country of refuge for the oppressed and the unfortunate, America.

"Good daughter, I am now coming to a part of my fortunes which I must fain hurry over with a rapid and casual narration.

"My desire for adventure led me West—even to this region, which at the time I speak of, nearly thirty years since, was far more wild and un-cultivated than at present. A party of hunters and traders with whom I travelled, encamped on this very spot during one entire winter. We were in the neighborhood of a tribe of Indians whom they wished an op-portunity of extended intercourse with, in the way of traffic.

"There was a young maiden of the tribe of—. Bah! why does the tell-tale colour rush up into my face, and mantle it with the hue of shame!

"An Indian girl, who visited our camp now and then, saw something in the young Irishman that awoke in her breast the flame which burns as brightly in the midst of the great new world forests, as in the populous places of the old[42] hemisphere. She loved me—and I—I had nothing[43] to interrupt the tedium of our long stay. We were both with the hot blood of young veins. At the coming of the spring, I left the place.

"Some four or five seasons afterward, I came hither again. They showed the child of the Indian girl—my son!—I almost shrieked with hor-ror at the monstrous abortion! The mother herself had died in giving it birth. No wonder. Never had my eyes been blasted with[44] so much ugli-ness as that hunchback boy!

"Daughter, that child even now moves among you, an object of pity and disgust. Can you wonder[45] when I tell you it is no other than the half-idiot, half-devil, Boddo?

"My wild and wayward course of life, for the next few years, I shall not pause to dwell upon.

42. "olden"   43. "naught"

"In the course of time, a poignant sense of my ill deeds, and a sickened feeling of the vanity of all human enjoyments, led me to take the vows of the order I now form an humble member of.

"One of the rules of our rigorous piety is, that a full and open confession of any sins that lie upon the breast, shall be given ere a man can become one of our community. By the advice of my superior, and prompted too by my own conscience, I have been aware that the least return I can make the wretched Boddo, for having been the author of his existence, is, to do my best toward opening his mind to the blessing of the True Faith.

"For this purpose I come every few months hither. I have laboured diligently to educate and imbue with devout feelings the unfortunate young man—but his besotted nature and wilful peevishness lead me to believe that my labours will too probably be in vain.

"Your look seems to ask me why I do not take him to a more congenial region for giving him the benefits of religion. Of what use would it be? —Now, no one knows the degree of relationship that exists between us, except yourself, and my holy intimates. Boddo, himself, is, of course, totally ignorant of it.

"Leaving the matter in the hands of Providence, and painfully conscious that naught which I could do, would benefit the condition of the poor creature—I have made up my mind that when I leave this place, as I shall shortly do, to return to my convent and my brethren, it will be to spend the rest of my days there, and to see this spot and my miserable offspring no more."

Toward the latter part of Father Luke's narration, he had been somewhat interrupted by sundry distant shouts, and sounds of tumult. Mrs. Brown, deeply interested in his story, had paid but little attention to them—but now the clang came nearer and nearer, and loud and agitated voices sounded out in the road near the door.

A moment longer, and the door opened quickly, and a man, the elder brother of the young wife, rushed toward her with his face very pale, and every sign of horror and agitation.

"O, sister!" he cried, "Peter Brown is murdered, in the forest, by the Indian, Arrow-Tip!"

The startled woman looked a moment in his face, as if to assure herself that she heard aright. She saw crowding in at the door, and out upon the road, the forms of many of the neighbours. Then all swam before her eyes, and she fainted in her brother's arms.

44. "blasted by the spectacle of"   45. "wonder at my feelings"

CHAPTER V.

Just out from the village, when the hunting party started that morning, they had been joined by Arrow-Tip's brother, the Deer. He, accompanied by a favourite dog, was watching the evolutions of a large bird that lazily skimmed near the surface of a cascade near by—a charming spot, that, were it in the neighbourhood of our eastern cities, would be visited by thousands for its beauty.

"Call the dog from me, brother," said the Deer, "He frightens the bird."

Arrow-Tip did as he was desired. The party had passed on, bidding the two Indians to follow. And the chief sat himself down a moment, at the foot of a large tree, and waited till the successful aim of the Deer should bring the bird to the ground. One hand grasped his hunting-bow, and with the other he caressed the dog.

The plot of the narrative makes it preferable not to detail minutely here all the events that took place during the day. One of those events— a startling and bloody one—has already been intimated to the reader, at the conclusion of the last chapter.

Soon after Arrow-Tip and the Deer came up with the rest of the party, whom they found proceeding onward with light and buoyant steps[46]— they all arrived at the destined point of their enterprise. It is usual[47] in such cases for a band to be sub-divided into smaller groups, each having its section, or look-out spot. The animals to be hunted are thus encompassed and met at every turn, and seldom fail of becoming, sooner or later, a prey to the sportsmen.

"I think," said Mr. Thorne, "it will be the best for Quincy to come with my party. Arrow-Tip, suppose you and Peter Brown take the Bend at Oak Creek for your station?"

"That will suit me," answered the blacksmith.

Arrow-Tip also expressed his consent to the arrangement.

Four or five other groups, of two or three in each, were despatched to their various posts—and the business of the day soon commenced in good earnest.

It was fine sport—and the young villagers of Warren, in this case, found their labours attended with that alternate good and ill-fortune which

---

46. step
47. The *Eagle* has "unusual," which is obviously an error since it contradicts the

makes such amusement more agreeable even than a continued current of success.

A hunt in the western forests! To those who have tasted of the fun, and know its pleasures, we need say but little! With the great woods all about, and no sign of man's neighborhood except the cheerful voices of your companions; with the wide, solemnly wide, stretching of unpeopled territory to a distance which it would take the journey of months to compass; with the blue sky overhead, clear, and not murky from the smoke of a million chimneys; with that strange, and exhilirating,[48] and pervading sense of *freedom*, which strikes into all your sense and body, as it were, from the illimitable, and untrammelled, the boundless[49] nature of every thing about you—is it not a right manly and glorious sport? There are no appearances of the artificial about such a hunt—no park walls and no cultivated and regularly-laid-out grounds to be crossed. It is all nature—all wild, beautiful, and inspiriting business, which no systematic chasing of a poor deer, within fences, and by trained packs, can equal! One week of such fine and wholesome recreation would do more good to our enervated city gentry, than a hundred gymnasiums, or all the medicines of the drug-shop!

During the morning, and the earlier half of the afternoon, the various groups of the party saw each other at intervals; and those who had been most successful threw out merry gibes against their less fortunate companions.

The day advanced, and the sun wanted but a couple of hours to his setting. Mr. Thorne, and one or two others, who, being the elder and more experienced, had, by general consent, been called upon to act as leaders of the party, began to think of collecting their scattered forces and returning homeward.

It was at this period that the following incident happened—casting a gloom over the occasion and throwing the whole of the village, when it became known, in a paroxysm of agitation and horror.

Two of the hunters, young men who had come out with the rest of the party, had to pass, on their return to the general rendezvous, near the station assigned to Peter Brown and the Indian. The young men made themselves a rude raft, and were floating down the river toward their destination—for this was an easier and more agreeable method of travelling than breaking their way through the thickets of the forest. As they came off against the mouth of Oak Creek they heard sounds of human voices in the wood, in loud and angry talk. They paused and listened.

sense of its context; the *Aristidean* reads "usual."

48. So spelled in both versions.   49. and boundless

They soon distinguished the voices to be those of the blacksmith and Arrow-Tip.

From where they were situated, the hunters could not distinctly see the quarrellers—but the latter were within a few rods, and their voices, and much of what they said, might be easily heard.—Brown was plainly wrought up to a high pitch of passion, and swore most terribly. Not many moments elapsed before the two men upon the raft were convinced that the dispute had ended[50] in a scuffle. Fearful that some more than ordinary harm might be the consequence, they seized their poles, and rapidly pushed the raft to the shore. Upon landing there, to penetrate the wood, and reach the place of the combatants, took them but a few moments.

They started in alarm as they came in close view of the spot. No scuffling or angry words were there now. Brown, the blacksmith, lay upon the ground with a heavy gash on the side of his head—and Arrow-Tip stood leaning calmly and sullenly against a tree.

"Good God!" exclaimed one of the intruders, "he has murdered him."

They stepped quickly to Brown's prostrate form, and raised him up in a sitting posture—but it was too late. All sense was gone, and they saw that what they could do to restore him, would be of little avail.

Horror-struck at the terrible nature of the whole affair—the impulse of both the men was first to fly the place and bring some of their companions.—Then a very natural sentiment of indignation arose in their bosoms towards[51] the murderer, who stood there with so much apathy. They feared that if they left the spot, he would escape.

"Chief!" said he who had first spoken, "you have done a dammed[52] action—and must go with us to answer for it!"

Arrow-Tip made no sign of repugnance. Had he done so, indeed, the result might have been somewhat unfavorable to the others. He was a strong and agile man, and held in his grasp the gun which they recognized as belonging to Brown. Once only, as a remark was passed between them, about the propriety of binding his arms, the savage looked towards[53] their faces with a glance which caused them to desist from their intention.

Arrow-Tip then, as they signed him to follow, walked after them. He spoke not a word, and offered nothing in the shape of remonstrance, excuse, or justification.

Ere they left the ground, one of the hunters took a blanket, which he happened to have with him, and threw it over the senseless body. It was to be there but a few minutes—when they would return, and bear it to the village, in company with the criminal, whom they desired first to place in security.

50. had resulted   51. toward   52. "damned"

CHAPTER VI.

Return we to the scene of the conflict, and to the senseless body. The hunters were mistaken in supposing it dead. Though severely injured, Brown was not deprived of life—the blow had stunned him, and the loss of blood had made[54] him faint.

Some fifteen minutes elapsed, and the flickering consciousness of existence came back to the wounded man. It came at first, painful and dream-like—then fuller and with more distinctness. When he awoke to a knowledge of his situation, and realized why it was that he lay there with a bloody gash upon his temple, and his hair clotted, and his limbs quite nerveless—he remembered the altercation, and the blows passed between himself and the Indian. Cooler in temper now, he thought of twenty little things wherein he had been in the wrong, and he determined to make up the quarrel, the first time he and the chief met. He shut his eyes a moment, conscious of a drowsy and disagreeable sensation.

What impish creature was that who met Brown's gaze as he looked again? The leaves and the twigs crackled, and a form which mocked the outlines of humanity bent over him. It was Boddo.

"Hah!" said the half-breed, an expression of dissatisfaction settling upon his face; "is he alive?—I thought the blow had killed him outright!"

And a second time, and more plainly, disappointment was evinced upon his features.

"How came you here?" said Brown in a weak voice.

"I saw it all," answered the hunchback, chuckling. "O, I saw it all. I have followed him—curse him forever! since the morning; and I thought he had killed you. Don't you call that murder?"

The wounded man made a sign of assent.

"And then he would have been hung! O, that it might—"

Boddo paused, for he saw he was going too far. He had a species of cunning, not withstanding his natural dulness—and that taught him, on the present occasion, to repress the remarks[55] he was going to make, nothing more or less than sorrow because the savage had not indeed made himself amenable to the severest punishment of the law.

"I am as weak as a baby," said Peter. "O, what would I give for a drink of cool water, and a quiet rest of an hour or two!"

And a spasm of agony passed over the countenance of the speaker. He was evidently under much suffering.

53. toward   54. blood made   55. remark

"There is a place," rejoined Boddo, "nearer at hand, perhaps, than you imagine, where you might get what you wish."

The blacksmith looked up with a mute glance of inquiry in the other's face.

"Yonder," continued Boddo, "where you see the crooked oak, is the cave of Father Luke. I have been there, and know the spot."

"Help me thither," said Brown, "and when I am taken home, I will remember your kindness."

He slightly raised his body, and waited for the hunchback's further assistance.

"See!" said that malicious personage, grinning, "how important is your Boddo, in cases of extremity! All along, no people care for him, except to mock him, until they are harmed, and then they ask his aid."

Brown, had he possessed his strength, would have found a summary way of replying to the provoking speech; but he was now fain to submit, and silently wait his pleasure.

The hunchback bent at the side of the blacksmith, and assisted him to rise. It was hardly until that moment that Brown felt how much injured he had really been. He could hardly hold himself up—and he shivered with a chill, and felt deadly sick.

So with slow and unsteady pace, leaning upon Boddo, and often stopping to rest against the trunk of a friendly tree, he traversed the few rods which intervened between the place of the quarrel and the rude dwelling of the Lonesome Man.

Boddo parted the shrubs around its entrance, and showed his companion the method of the safest ingress—for, either by accident or from its occupant's labour, there were certain thorny plants, and various twistings, and dark turns, which required some heed to tread uninjured.

When they came into the room of the monk, they found it untenanted, without[56] life or noise. They saw from the appearance of things that its dweller had probably left it that morning, and no doubt would[57] be back ere long.

"Take that vessel," said Peter, faintly, pointing to a large tin cup which hung on the wall, "and bring me some water, from the nearest spring. I am dizzy and thirsty."

Boddo did as he was desired; and the sick man threw himself on a heap of bear skins[58] that lay in one corner. He felt strangely, and miserably.— Perhaps, even now, the death Arrow-Tip had failed of inflicting, might not be far distant. He would have given half his little estate, had he been at home, and with his wife to soothe his sickness.

56. and without   57. he would   58. heap of skins

The indolent half-breed, loitering on his way to the spring, notwithstanding the emergency of the time, heard a step along a[59] path near by, and, turning, saw Father Luke wending his way with hasty strides, and agitated features.

"Know you aught of this terrible business, my son?" said he, addressing Boddo, with a title which the poor wretch little knew his right to, in a worldly sense, as well as from the usage of the church.—"They tell me in the village that Peter Brown is murdered by Arrow-Tip!"

"What they say in the village is often false as true," replied Boddo, with a sneer.

The monk saw that the hunchback could relate more of the business—and a hope sprung in his mind that he should perhaps hear a refutation of the fearful rumor.

"Good son," said he, "do not tamper with me. Describe what you may of the matter, at once."

"Well then," continued the other, "the plain truth is, that the Indian would have killed Peter, and did so try. But Peter, having a very thick skull, his life was saved. I saw it[60] myself. They came and took Arrow-Tip away; and probably have him at[61] the village, at this moment, where—"

"I know that," interrupted the holy father, impatiently; "I am just from Warren myself, and know all about that. Tell me where is Brown now?"

"Seeing the poor fellow in such distress," Boddo went on, "though to tell the fact, he did not know it himself for quite a long while—I, with my usual good kindness, walked round him and round him, and prayed for his recovery."

The hunchback leered.

"Blaspheme not!" said the monk, sharply. "Hasten with your narration, and use no more such wicked ridicule!"

"Shortly he came to himself, and I have taken the liberty of showing him the way to your luxurious dwelling, where he is at this moment reposing. Being dry, he wished a cup of water, which I am now to bring."

"God in heaven be blessed!" was the fervent ejaculation of the monk, as he heard Boddo's recital. "The curse of the Avenger of Blood will not fall on the chief's head—and the misery and crime be saved!"

Then bidding Boddo make speed, he turned toward the cave with a lighter heart.

59. the   60. "it all"   61. "in"

CHAPTER VII.

Peter Brown was indeed much injured. When the monk looked upon him he saw that it would be dangerous to have him carried the distance between the cave and the village. Father Luke, as is frequently the case with those of his profession, had considerable knowledge of surgery and medicine—and he determined to tax that knowledge to its utmost for the benefit of his guest.

He prepared a simple plaster, and washing the wound, bound it round the blacksmith's head. Some cooling drinks were then given him, and he felt less faint.

"Tell me," said he to the monk, "what was done in the village, where you say you heard of this silly matter."

Father Luke thought the talk might wile away his patient's thoughts from his suffering, and he readily acceded to his request.

"You may imagine," said he, "with what horror we first heard the story of your death, and in such a manner. Your poor wife, with whom I had been for a couple of hours, was like one distracted—and wished at once to start forth for the scene of the calamity. We of course prevented her, for that would have done no good, even had the case been as bad as stated.[62]

"Shortly, on going into the heart of the village, I saw the hunting party themselves. Arrow-Tip was there, in custody between two of your neighbors, of whom I inquired more particularly with respect to your death. They stated that it was too true—that they had themselves seen your corpse. From what Boddo there has told me, it must have been while you were lying senseless after the blow. Bitterly grieving that such sad things should disturb the happiness of our peaceful settlement, I questioned the men over and over again with regard to the details of their story. But they told that story with evident truth—and I could not but believe them.

"It was hastily arranged that a party should be immediately despatched for your dead body. And in the mean time Arrow-Tip was to be strictly guarded, and prevented from any chance of escape, until proper measures could be taken for his punishment. Judging from the fierce glances of your neighbors towards him—and their strongly-uttered sentiments of revenge—the poor Indian's fate, had you indeed been killed, would have proved quite as painful as yours; and, indeed, he would have followed you before many hours. A band of six are to keep watch day and night, in the strong room where he is confined."

62. as was stated

Painful as was the situation of the blacksmith, he could not help feeling some sympathy for Arrow-Tip, to whose proud nature he knew the scoffs and threats of the villagers would be scathing agony. Confinement, too, even for a few hours, was a terrible infliction to such a being as the Indian chief—apart from the disgrace—which in itself, was no small matter.

"Let Boddo go at once to the village," said the blacksmith, "and tell the truth of the story. And I would not have my wife come hither, at least at present—for I think of no good she can do. Now let us talk no more; for I feel a strange drowsiness all over me, and would sleep. Tell me, Father Luke, how long do you think will be the duration of my illness?"

"That," answered the monk, looking reverently upward, "is in the hands of God. But judging from the best of my knowledge, I may be able to recover you in three days, so that you can travel to your own house. At present you are not fit to walk a rod. At this very moment you are falling into a fever which will require all my watchfulness. Now, my son, compose yourself to sleep."

Drawing down a rude curtain that served the double office of door and of shade—if the latter were needed in so obscure an apartment— the monk took Boddo by the hand, and stepping into the outer part of the hut, gave him his directions, and his message and bade him hasten to the village. The hunchback sullenly listened, and made no rejoinder, as he started forth on his errand. Then softly stepping in again, the Lonesome Man took his seat beside the blacksmith, who already slumbered. He saw that his patient would indeed need his closest and most unremitting care.

Let us go with Boddo toward the village. Why as this hapless creature arrived beyond sight of the entrance to Father Luke's dwelling— why did he stop, and gaze cautiously around a moment, sit himself down upon a bank, and remain there a long hour apparently buried in the profoundest meditation? What thoughts passed through the miserable young man's brain as he rested there? What strange wishes, or petty resolves of evil, or hopes for revenge?

In the early light of that very day, it will be remembered, the hunchback had been detected by Arrow-Tip in the[63] theft, and exposed before all of Mr. Thorne's family. Boddo, used as he was to all kinds of scorn and insult—had times when the bestowal of such insult would plant itself so deeply within his breast that it could never be blotted out, but by signal revenge. Once he was known to have kept for nearly two years, the memory of a blow given him by a boy, and taken vengeance for it, at last, by destroying a pet dog of his young injurer. Another time when refused by an irritable dame a drink of water, he, ten months afterwards, frightened the woman half to death, by wrapping a white garment around him, and starting out before her as she returned home alone[64] one evening from a tea-party with some of her gossips. Numerous were the instances in which he would suddenly verge from his sometime patient endurance of contempt—such as that related at the opening of this tale—and resolve upon a signal scheme of retaliation.

The present case as he turned it over in his mind, might afford him an opportunity of repaying Arrow-Tip for the shame of the event of the morning.—The chief was now in custody in the village, and, according to Father Luke's account, surrounded by those who had little goodwill toward him. Boddo felt sure that the course of "justice"[65]—were the people allowed to remain with the unquestionable[66] belief of Peter Brown's death—would neither be very lenient, nor wait very long to be carried to its consummation. Suppose he should *not* do his errand, as enjoined upon him by Brown and the monk? The monk himself, in all probability, would be unable to leave the cave to visit the village—and they had desired him to request the absence of the immediate friends of the blacksmith.[67] Would not his revenge then triumph?

The malignant hunchback laughed in his heart, as he determined upon carrying out his[68] plan. He rose, and with the swiftness of a deer, more than that of man, he soon gained the neighborhood of the village.

Within a hundred rods, or thereabout, of the outermost house, Boddo beheld a party of eight or ten men approaching him with sedate and gloomy demeanour. Among them was Quincy Thorne.—They paid no attention to the hunchback, although he was directly in their path. But that personage, suspecting their errand, determined on accompanying them. He attached himself to Quincy, entered into conversation with him, and walked on with the rest.

"You have seen the body you say?" asked the boy, in rejoinder to something the hunchback was telling him; "and you are sure it was quite dead?"

Without design, Quincy looked full into the other's eyes. Boddo, resolute and impudent[69] as he was, could not stand that gaze. His countenance expressed something from which young Thorne strongly judged he knew more of the matter than he felt disposed to tell.

"It was cold and stiff as a nail," answered Boddo, "and I was frightened, and run away from the place."

64. returned alone
65. Not enclosed in quotation marks.

Less than an hour brought them to the limits of the spot. The two hunters who had heard the conflict, and carried Arrow-Tip to the rendez-vous a prisoner, were with them, and pointed out the way.

How were they amazed upon coming to the exact place, to find the blacksmith's body missing! There were tracks and signs of a struggle —and the blood lay thick upon the leaves where the hunters told Brown's body had been—but the corpse itself was no where to be seen!

For a minute or two they gazed on one another, without knowing what to do or say.

"Comrades!" said one of them, suddenly, "a new light breaks upon me. We all know that the brother of this cursed Arrow-Tip is near at hand. He was with us in the hunt. Without doubt he has concealed the body, in the hope to give the murderer a chance of escape from justice!"

The glances which, from each to his fellow, followed this opinion, showed that every one assented to it.

CHAPTER VIII.

In many of the towns to the west and south, it is well known, the pun-ishment of crime is without the delays and necessary forms, and statuta-ble restrictions, of our older cities and states. The only law, in fact, to some of the more remote of these places, is public will, and public feeling—a dangerous state of things in a large and vicious city, but far from being attended with the evils which many people imagine, when exercised in the places we allude to. At all events, it is better to be un-der this sovereign and self-constituted power, than to have no law at all.

When the men returned to Warren that evening, with the strange news of the disappearance of the corpse—the same sentiment prevailed among the villagers which has been mentioned in the concluding lines of the last chapter. It served perhaps to deepen their indignation, and make them anxious for a more hasty retribution on the head of him who was considered as the murderer.

"Let us," said they, "let us not wait, in this affair, and give the savage a chance of escape. But let us act as determined men, and have blood for blood!"

The watch, that night, had been arranged for six persons, who were thought a sufficient surety that Arrow-Tip could not get away. But so sanguinary was the spirit of the inhabitants that half the young

66. unquestioned
67. of the murdered one   68. this   69. imprudent

men in the place turned out, and surrounded the strong room, where the prisoner was confined, lest some little opportunity might occur, which would lead to a failure in the fulfilment of their gloomy purpose.

The brother of Arrow-Tip, the Deer, appeared among them. As he approached, they lowered fierce glances upon him, which he returned not.—He made a simple request to be permitted to see Arrow-Tip—which they at once, and without parley, refused. He turned and calmly left the place. One or two among them spoke of the propriety of placing the Deer also in durance—but this, upon further consideration, was abandoned.

No one knew the thoughts of the imprisoned chief, that weary night, but his Great Spirit. He spoke not to those about him—preserving a calm and lofty aspect, and making no answer to their scoffs and taunts.

Day came again. They found him—when they went in the room, at the first streak of light, impelled by a feverish jealousy lest he might still have evaded their vigilance and got away—they found him standing there still, and silent and haughty. His hair, part of it, had fallen down over his forehead and his eyes. He was too abstracted, even, to lift his hand, and push it away.

The morning meal which they gave him, he partook of in moderation. And as the people of the place—men, women and children—came during the course of the forenoon, to gaze in upon him, as upon some strange monster, brought from a distant clime—he preserved the same attitude, and even brushed not the hair away from his eyes where it had fallen again.

About an hour past noon, three of the oldest men in Warren, (the oldest of the three was but five-and-forty years) made their way through the crowd, and came in apparently upon important business connected with the prisoner, and his crime.

"Chief!" said the leader of the trio, "it is needless for us to tell you why you are confined here, and what may be the nature of the punishment for the deed you have committed."

Arrow-Tip glanced upon them with apathy, and made no reply.

"Chief!" said the first speaker, again, "it is ill that you act so obstinately—and preserve this childish silence. A grown man should not be stubborn, like a dumb brute that has no knowledge."

"It is not ill," said the savage, quietly; "I am silent, because I have seen no fit occasion to speak. What would you have me say?"

"My companions and myself have been sent hither," answered the other, "to learn from you what you can tell us of the quarrel and fight which ended so fatally."

70. direction

Arrow-Tip paused a moment, in thought. Then waving his hand toward the door he said,

"I have little to tell, but let it be told to all—not to three only. Let me speak to your brothers and kinsmen also."

"As you desire," was the reply.

One of the three opened the door, and gave some directions[70] to a person without. They then emerged, altogether,[71] and walked onward to an open green, on one side of which was the school-house, and on the other the church. It was a kind of public assembly ground, and there four-fifths of the people were at that moment gathered.

As Arrow-Tip, in company with the three, approached this, what was to be in some sense his tribunal, there was a silence throughout the whole spot, and all eyes were directed toward him.

He told his story. It was a plain tale—and bore not strongly either toward his guilt or innocence.

Brown and he, as most of those present knew, had been despatched together to the Bend station. In the course of the day, they were frequently seen, like the others, and had themselves seen the others.

When they first arrived at the station, (we are giving the substance of the story of Arrow-Tip himself) the chief made a banter with the blacksmith, that the latter would kill no game. In a merry vein, he bet his tobacco pouch against a rude kind of weapon, half-hatchet and half-poinard, that Brown had made himself, and then carried in his girdle. The day passed on, and it was plain that the chief would in all probability gain his wager.—Brown was a man of considerable heat of temper, and his ill success in the sport, and the laughing gibes of Arrow-Tip—(for it is an error to suppose that our American Indians invariably retain their sedateness)—caused him to become more than ordinarily fretful.

At last the signal for their return to the rendezvous was heard, and they prepared to obey it—carrying nothing to the common stock. The chief still continued his provoking raillery, and the blacksmith was rapidly losing all command over his passions.

It was at this unfortunate juncture that Arrow-Tip was heedless enough to attempt seizing the weapon at Peter's girdle, which was now become his prize. The difficulty merged at this point into a scuffle, and in the scuffle the blow was given, which was supposed to have caused the blacksmith's death.

Thus the chief concluded his story. He himself entertained no doubt that Brown was dead. But when told that his brother had taken away the body, he made no answer but a glance of scorn. Of all those there

71. all together.

convened, one only, the hunchback, Boddo, knew the full truth—and could have set the whole matter right, and the prisoner free, and poured joy into the hearts of the wife, and Brown's friends, had he so chosen. But he did not choose.

A short communion took place between the men of Warren. There was no judge, and no jury.—Each grown man was admitted to the conference, and listened to with respect. For each knew that the present case was a matter which touched the happiness and interest of his neighbor as much as himself.

Perhaps the time which was consumed in this deliberation upon the fate of the chief, might have been an hour, perhaps less, certainly not more.—Reader, such deliberations, and such methods of administering justice may perhaps appear to you as fictitious—and part of a tale of fiction. It is not so. There may be found, in the region of the scene of these transactions, many a place where the same course is held in criminal cases. And it may be doubted whether, after all, the result is at the risk of being more inconsistent with justice than in courts of law in our Atlantic towns.

"Chief," said the one who had acted as messenger two hours before, "we look upon you as guilty of murder. We shall take your life for that of our brother. We shall kill you. To-morrow, when the sun is at the highest, you will look for the last time on the light!"

Arrow-Tip's countenance changed not, nor did his lip quiver. One passionate[72] wild glance only he cast around him, as if in quest of his brother, or of some look of sympathy. He found neither.

CHAPTER IX.

"Ha! ha! ha!" came the children's laughter.

It was a simple, and yet awful commentary on the dispositions of human hearts—that laughter! For the merry tones were the same to all appearance, which had been uttered several days previous, when Master Caleb gave his flock a holiday, for Peter Brown's wedding. This second laugh, and just as gleesome, commemorated the bestowal, that morning, of another holiday, for the hanging of Peter Brown's murderer.

The day was warm and sunny. A languid breath of wind, now and then, fluttered the leaves of the trees—but for the most time, the sun shone down as upon a sleeping and lifeless[73] place. Even the laugh of the heedless children soon hushed, of their own accord; for a sombre

72. passionate and   73. and a lifeless

spirit pervaded the people of Warren—a resolute spirit, however—resolute to have the life-blood of him who had taken life.

Let us open the doors of the strong room and go in there. Arrow-Tip stood against the wall, by a window—it was the only one, and a little child's body could not have been twisted through, so small was it—and gazed forth upon the land, and the trees, and a small strip of the bright river beyond.—He could see only a small strip—but it was pleasant; and many minutes glided on as he gazed. Haply, he pondered upon scenes and people far away in the early years—scenes not to come any more, but which it was a great delight to think of. A smile passed over his face then.

The sounds of talking outside, and something like disturbance, interrupted the chief's meditation. His brother, the Deer, entered and stood before him.—They had consented to let him pay this visit, at last. Mr. Thorne had interceded in his behalf.

For several minutes neither spoke. Arrow-Tip himself was as calm as the most placid lake in the forest,—but the features of the other were convulsed in agony.

"Brother!" said the chief, with dignity, "I see the eyes of our parents looking down upon us.—Very soon I shall talk to them. They will ask me of news about my brother. Let me not say, I left him weeping like a girl!"

His remonstrance produced the effect he wished. Shortly, the face of the Deer was as calm as[74] his own.

"The path," said the new comer, "will be dark, and the white man's taunts hot, for the last hour of a warrior's life!"

"I can bear both," was the laconic answer.

"And *my* path," plaintively continued the younger brother, drawing nigh, and resting his face on Arrow-Tip's shoulder, "as I look forth upon the passing of the moons—is bitter and lonesome, not for an hour, but for years. O, brother, the Great Spirit has frowned upon our race. We melt away, like the snows in spring."

"It is the will of the Spirit."

"Yet I am glad," continued the Deer, true to the instincts of his people, "I am glad that you die like an old brave! We will laugh in the very faces of the whites."

Arrow-Tip smiled, quietly. He, too, had been bred in the school of those sturdy stoics.

"Death is but a puff of air," said he, "and in the distance lie the Green Hunting Grounds of the honest Indian. They are fair. Our kinsmen

74. **was calm as**

beckon me to them with smiles and friendly gestures. Why should I fear to go?"

"But the tidings will cloud the faces of our tribe in darkness."

"Tell them," rejoined the chief, "that I met my punishment as a hunter grasps the hand of one he loves. Tell them of the customs of those[75] white people—our own are the same—which require of him who destroys one of their number, his own life as a sacrifice. When I came hither, not many days since, I was near to death, even then—and my fate would have happened to me, but for the medicine-knowledge of two or three kind men of the settlement. Brother, wait till the last is over, and then carry me away a little distance from the sight of these people's dwellings, and bury me with my face toward the Pleasant Hunting Grounds. Let us talk no more!"

The courage of the younger Indian failed him at this speech again. The piteous sight of a man abandoned to the excess of sorrow, is fearful at any time. It could not but be doubly so, in the present case, from the general apathy and haughtiness of the savage character.

It was now ten o'clock, and the sun stood high in the heavens. On the green where Arrow-Tip had received judgment, the day before, the people of Warren were assembled again to witness the performance of that judgment.

While they were waiting thus, some of them chatting in groups, and others vacantly gazing at the rude scaffold and rope—Quincy Thorne came hurriedly in among them, and inquired for Master Caleb, the teacher. Finding him, the two drew aside from the mass, the boy leading his companion. They conferred together a few minutes, with much animation and many gestures of wonder—and then both hurried away toward a path which led from the village along the river's edge.

We will pause here a moment to explain. Two of the school-boys who had received their permission of a holiday that morning, determining to enjoy it to the utmost, agreed to take a ramble in the forest, on some juvenile project or other, which they might do, and still return in time to behold *the sight*—as they termed the event of the day. Unconsciously, in their wanderings, they came upon the very opening where Brown and the chief had fought. The sudden recollections brought up by seeing the place, and the blood which was even yet visible on the ground, frightened one of the children: and in their hasty retreat from the spot, how much more were they alarmed on gaining the banks of the stream, to see, reclining there in the sunshine, the shape of the now wan and pallid-faced Peter Brown himself. To their horrified imaginations, it was

75. these

the spectre of a murdered corpse. They ran, pale and breathless, toward the village, and meeting Quincy there, told him with gasping voices, what they had witnessed. The youth lost not a moment in seeking out his friend, Master Caleb, and in conveying the information to him. Joined with the strange manner of Boddo, and with Quincy's previous strongly entertained suspicions, the teacher and his young intimate had no doubt that the case was, as it in truth was, and as it has been related to the reader. —They immediately determined on[76] their plan of action.

Meanwhile, Brown, wondering that some of his neighbours had not at least called at the cave to see him, was importunate with the monk that he might be allowed to walk home. Solitude had few charms for the blacksmith, whatever Father Luke thought upon the subject. As he returned to the cave from the idle lounge in the sun, where he had unconsciously so alarmed the two school-boys, he again asked the monk when he could safely walk the distance of the village:

"Though judging by the cool kindness of my friends," said he, peevishly, "it will make little difference if I remain away for months."

"Patience my son!" said the holy father; "tomorrow I will myself accompany you thither. As yet your strength is hardly equal to the task."

And the invalid though ill-satisfied was forced to be content.

"But, see!" exclaimed the monk, "as if to reprove you for your ungrateful vexation, yonder comes two of your townsmen—and with a pace which speaks little of indifference for your company."

The two were Master Caleb and Quincy Thorne.

It would be superfluous here, were we to dwell on the rapid and graphic narration of the visitors to Brown and Father Luke. With a flushed cheek, and without speaking, the blacksmith snatched up a blanket—the blanket the two hunters had thrown over his senseless form in the forest —and strode forth from the cave.

At about the same period when the teacher and his companion first appeared to the sight of the monk—the self-appointed guard opened the doors of the room where Arrow-Tip was confined, and bade him come forth. He did so, and his brother with him. What wondrous power those rude savages have over the expression of their features! The condemned Indian, you might have thought, was starting on a hunt, instead of marching to an ignominious death! The other, also, had mastered his agony once more.

They passed through the multitude, and the chief stood upon the scaffold.

O, God of the Innocent! throw strength amid the sinews of that

76. upon

sweaty-faced man in the forest, who, with strained eyes, and unsteady steps, is dashing through the tangled shrubs and the thick underwood—whose thorny and jagged branches have wounded him in many places, though he sees not the trickling blood, nor feels the smart!

All around the scaffold were the dogged and lowering countenances of men—telling of an unrelenting purpose, and of no hope. It was a strange spectacle. Those hewers of the forest—and even the women and children, had gathered there—and the lofty bearing of the chief—and that, still more difficult to uphold, calm aspect of his brother—and all this in the bright glare of a noon-day sun—and the spot, far, far away from the bound of the cities—may it not well be called a strange spectacle?

They arranged the last dread and sickening preparations, immediately preceding the death of criminals by that awful method. Could it be that high heaven should look down and see this unjust doom consummated—and not interpose?

No sound disturbed that horrible silence, except the shuffling movements of two men, to whose lot it had fallen to act in the execution. The men started at the noise they themselves made—for it seemed unnatural, and struck upon the ear with a strange vibration.

O, what a quiver was that which ran through the limbs—and, as it were, the very souls—of all those assembled thereabout! It was followed by *perfect* silence.

Wo-hoa-a!—Wo-hoa-a!—came a faint and hoarse shout from a bend in the road, at some thirty rods distant. Very faint and very hoarse it came. *It was too late!*

Then, with wild and ghastly visage, and with the phrenzied contortions of a madman in his worst paroxysm, Peter Brown dashed along the path and among them. His blood-shot eyes were fixed upon a hideous object dangling in the air. He rushed up to the scaffold—but his limbs failed him, and he could not ascend the ladder. His head vibrated to and fro, like the pendulum of a clock, and he beckoned and tried to speak, though for several moments they could not hear what he said, or rather tried to say.

"Quick! Quick!" came at last from his throat, in a gasping whisper; "cut the rope, he may not yet be dead!"

It was all too late.

Three days after these events, a pilgrim traveller might have been seen, wending his way through the regions of the west, toward the north-east. He was not unaccompanied. An Indian, who seldom spoke, and over whose face a gloom and wildness were spread, trod at his side. They were the monk, called in this narrative Father Luke, and the miserable brother of Arrow-Tip.

—An aged and gentle hearted friar, some few years after, was laid away to his[77] last repose, beloved of his[78] fellows; and at the same time, many hundred miles distant, an Indian leader, the remnant of his family, led his tribe still farther into[79] the west, to grounds where they never would be annoyed, in their generation at least, by the presence of the white intruders.

Scorned and abhorred by man, woman, and child, the half-breed, through whose malicious disposition the fatal termination took place which has been narrated, fled the settlement of Warren. Whether he perished in the wilds, or even now lives a degraded and grovelling life, in some other town, no one can tell.

Master Caleb has risen in his fortunes. As the extent and population of the town wherein we have introduced him, increased, it was thought fit to have an incorporated academy. Master Caleb is at the head of it. Quincy Thorne, a popular and intelligent young man, whom they think of holding up as a candidate for a respectable legislative office, still keeps communion of friendship with his early and excellent teacher. Peter Brown, although he has quite a family of little children, finds time, now and then, to utter eloquent homilies in praise of the young political aspirant—than whom he thinks no one is more worthy.

77. the   78. by all his   79. to

Shirval: A Tale of Jerusalem[1]

EARTH, this huge clod over which we tread, enwraps the lost outlines,[2] the mixed remains,[3] of myriads of human forms that were once as we are now. Nor is the truth a stale one, old as it may be. Also, it is a beautiful and solemn truth.[4]

Those buried men and women lived and loved—wrought and grieved, like us;—had their crimes and their agonies, as the living now have. Death came to their dwellings[5] and struck down those for whom affection was strong. Anger and hate and pride, three wicked ministers of unhappiness, held sway over them;—love and charity, too, stole into their hearts, and found a home there. And thus they were, and thus they passed away. —O Earth![6] huge tomb-yard of humanity! if the brown pall under which are hidden the things of old ages—of ancient generations—of the men who have been folded in thy recesses when thyself wast in the earlier life —if that far-stretching pall could be removed, what eye might look unquailed on the awful wonders of the scene!

Let me go to times and people away in the twilight of years past. It is the pen's prerogative to roll back the curtains of centuries that can have a real existence no more, and make them live in fiction[7]—pleasing thus, and, haply, fostering thoughts which the moralist would smile upon. Such are among the sweetest rewards of us humble bookmen, whose spur comes in the hope that we may gain, not alone for our frail paragraphs, some passing thought of friendliness to ourselves, from a portion of that outer world we love so well.

Very beauteous was the coming of the sun, one day, over the cities of Judah. The tops of the mountains, which received his first warm kisses, smiled down upon each neighboring valley; and the Israelites and dark-eyed women went forth to their tasks with cheerful hearts. The dewy grass, and the olive trees, glittered as with countless diamonds. All nature was glad like a laughing infant.

But in a street in a city of Nain stood the house of tears—the house of the widow Unni, whose son, the preceding night, had been forsaken, by the angels of Life, and now lay a cold corpse in the inner chamber.

1. The text of this tale—which is based on an incident related in Luke vii: 11–18—is that which originally appeared in *The Aristidean* for March 1845. Whitman revised and paged the story for inclusion in *Collect* but did not use it. A unique clipping of the *Aristidean* "Shirval" in the Feinberg Collection, with Whitman's intended revisions, is the source of the variants listed in the following notes.
    2. outline

And there came a young Jewish maid, early in the morning, and went into the chamber. Her cheeks, as she walked through the fresh air, were like the roses of the plains of Sharon; but when she passed the portals, and entered, and saw the dead man, her face imaged the colour of ashes, the emblem of mourning and decay. The maid was Zar, the beloved of Shirval, the widow's son. Her mission was to inquire about his illness: she found it ended.

Noon came.—The preparations for the burial had been made, and ere the daylight should close, the body of the youth was to be put in its sepulchre, without the walls of the town.

He looked beautiful in his manly proportions, even in death. The curls of his hair were drawn back from his forehead, and a linen bandage had been passed under his chin, and tied around his face. And on one side stood his mother, and on the other side Zar, his beloved. Unni wept, and rent the air with shrieks of agony; but the maid was silent and tearless.

Twenty-and-four years had Shirval lived in his native city; and it was known that his mother, to whom he was ever obedient, leaned on him as the staff of her declining age. He was her only child.

"O, God of Judgments!" cried Unni, "what am I that thou hast afflicted me thus!"

And her grey hairs were bowed to the ground, and she would not receive consolation.

So as the young man's body lay there, the day still waned, and the mourners arrived to attend him to the last resting-place. They placed the corpse upon the bier, and set forth.

No one could tell why it was so,—that, as they advanced, many spectators, people of Nain, gathered around them, and walked with them on their solemn errand. The rich men and the officers joined the crowd; and it swelled to many hundreds. Yet none spoke, or understood what mysterious impulse led him thus to honour the funeral-march of the poor widow's son.

Now they came to the gates of the town, and the foremost mourners passed out, and went no farther; for a band of travellers were before them, coming inward, and stopped the way. The travellers paused too—all but a small group who approached the mourners of Shirval. Most of those in

3. remain
4. This sentence and the preceding one are deleted and the next paragraph is continued as part of the first paragraph.
5. The rest of this sentence following "dwellings" is deleted.
6. "Earth" is deleted.
7. The remainder of this paragraph following "fiction" is deleted.

the group were wayworn and coarse in their appearance; but their look imported strange things—and ONE of their number as HE walked a little before the rest, fixed all eyes, while the hearts of the wide assembly throbbed, as at the nearness of an UNDEFINABLE PRESENCE, more than mortal.

The BEING was of middle stature and fair proportions, in every motion whereof was easy grace. His step was neither rapid or very slow; and his look more sought the earth than swept around him with glances of pride. His face was beautifully clear, and his eyes, blue as the sky above them, beamed forth benevolence and love. His brown hair was parted in the middle of his head, and flowed in heavy ringlets down upon his shoulders. The aspect of the stranger was not deficient in dignity, but it seemed far unlike the dignity of princes and captains.

As this PRESENCE came in among them, the haughtiest of Nain were awed: and the concourse paused, with the expectation, as it were, of an unwonted event. It needed not that any one should inform the BEING[8] what had happened. Shirval's corpse was there, borne upon its bier; and the widow was nigh, convulsed in her grief; and Zar, the maiden, followed meekly.

A moment only were the compassionate eyes of the BEING bent upon this sight of agony and death—bent with a mortal look of sympathy. He stept forth, and stood before Unni. He spoke,—and his voice, musical and manly, thrilled to the fine chords of every soul in that multitude.

"Widow of Nain," he said, "weep not!"

And he looked about, and waived[9] his hand gently; and as he touched the bier with one finger, they who carried it put it upon the ground, and stood away. And the stranger[10] bent over the young man's corpse, and gazed upon the face.

O, Nazarine! thou who didst pour out bloody sweat upon the cross, at the Place of Skulls! what feelings of human pity—what yearning for the weal of all mankind—what prophetic horror at the agonies of thine own death—what sympathy with the woes of earth, which the mortality of thy nature gave thee to feel as mortals themselves feel—what soul-tears for that pain and wretchedness, which must still continue through time—what of all these were thine during that fearful minute, it were almost blasphemous to transcribe!

There was a stillness over all the gathering. Even the grief of Unni

8. the stranger
9. Whitman marked out the "i," a typographical error, in his revision.
10. "He" is substituted for "the stranger."

was hushed. The people had given back from around the BEING, and he and the dead form were together—all eyes bent toward them.

A second time he spoke—and at the awful nature of the command he gave, the hearts of the people paused in motion, and the breathings were suspended.

"Live! thou who art dead!—Arise, and speak to the woman, thy mother!"

At the word, the white vestments wherewith they had bound Shirval began to move. His eyes unclosed, and the colour came back into his cheeks. The lips that had been still, parted a passage for the misty breath,—and the leaden fingers glowed with the warmth of life. The ashy hue of his skin was marked by the creeping blood, as it started to fulfil its circulation in the veins—and the nostrils quivered at the inward and outward motion of air. His limbs felt the wondrous impulse—he rose, and stood up among them, wrapped in his shroud and the white linen.

"I have slept!" said he, turning to his mother, "but there have been no dreams."

And he kissed the widow's cheek, and smiled pleasantly on Zar. Then the awe of the presence of the Stranger gathered like a mantle upon him —and the three knelt upon the ground and bent their faces on the earth-worn sandals of the MAN OF WO.

Richard Parker's Widow[1]

WHEN I was in London some years since, I, with another person, went one morning to the police office, with several of the higher functionaries with whom my companion was acquainted. After seeing some of the peculiar sights and scenes that are to be met with at such a place only, we were invited to sit a while in a short of half-private, half-public parlour, attached to the establishment. When we entered, one of the magistrates was talking to an aged, shabbily-dressed lady, (for *lady* she was, by a title superior to dress,) who seemed to be applying for parish assistance, or making enquiries of him about the necessary steps to be taken for procuring it. My companion, the moment he saw her, directed my attention to her by a peculiar movement of the head.

"Look closely at her," said he, in a whisper, "that woman's life has been indirectly involved with the welfare of nations. When we are alone, I will tell you more about her."

The female might at one time have been handsome; but now, years and sorrow had graven deeply on her features and form the evidences of decay. Her eyes had that piercing look which belongs to people whose sight is nearly gone. Her garments were clean, though old, and very faded.

I was interested in the appearance of this female—though I could hardly divine what or who she had been—and when we left the place, I reminded my friend of his promise.

"That woman," said he, "is the widow of a man whose name, forty years ago, rang for many weeks like a death-knell through England, and shook with terror the foundations of the throne itself! Her husband was Richard Parker, the Admiral Mutineer, who headed the sailor's rebellion at the Nore."

He then went on to give me the particulars of this celebrated mutiny, which I had read in my own country when a boy, but which had nearly escaped my memory. As the reader may also have forgotten—or may never have heard it—and as the history of the singular affair is full of interest— I will recapitulate it here. I am of course indebted to English authorities for most of the facts that follow.

In the early part of May, 1797, the British seamen in the vessels about the Nore, (a point of land so called, dividing the mouths of the

---

1. This sketch appeared in *The Aristidean* for April 1845. Mabbott (pp. 17, 121–122) states that the sketch generally paraphrases Camden Pelham's *Chronicles of Crime; or, The New Newgate Calendar*, London, 1841; but he points out that Whit-

Thames and Medway,) indignant at many oppressive restrictions, and at non-payment of their wages, broke out into an organized meeting.[2] They deprived the officers of all command of the ships, though they otherwise treated them with every respect. Each vessel was put under the government of a committee of twelve men; and a board of delegates was appointed to represent the whole body of sailors, each man-of-war sending two delegates, and each gun-boat one. Of these delegates Richard Parker was chosen president. This man was of good family, and had been engaged in Scotland in mercantile business, which proving unsuccessful, he one day in a fit of despondency left his family, took the bounty, and became a common sailor. He was gentlemanly in his manners, well educated, and the bravest of the brave.

The force of the mutineers, which, toward the latter part of May, consisted of twenty-four sail, soon proceeded to block up the Thames—sternly refusing a passage to vessels up or down. In a day or two there was of course an immense number of ships, and water craft of all descriptions, under detention. The appearance of the whole fleet is described by contemporaneous accounts as appalling and grand. The red flag floated from the mast-head of every one of the mutineers.

It may well be imagined that the alarm of the citizens of London was extreme. The government, however, though unable to quell Parker and his fellow sailors by force, remained firm in their demand of unconditional surrender as a necessary preliminary to any intercourse. This, perhaps, was the wisest line of conduct they could have assumed. The seamen never seemed to think of taking an offensive attitude. Being thus left in quiet to meditate on their position of hostility to a whole country, they shortly began to grow timorous—and the more so, as the government had caused all the buoys to be removed from the mouth of the Thames and the adjacent coasts, so that no vessel dare attempt to move away, for fear of running aground. The mutineers held together, nevertheless, till the 30th of May, when the Clyde frigate was carried off through a combination of its officers with some of the seamen; and this desertion was followed by the St. Fiorenzo. Both were fired upon by the mutineers, but no great damage was done.

From the 1st to the 10th of June, all was disquiet on board the fleet. Several more desertions happened during that period. On the 10th, the whole body of the detained merchantmen were allowed, by common consent, to proceed up the river. Such a multitude of ships certainly never

man acknowledges this indebtedness after a fashion in the closing sentence of the sixth paragraph.

2. "Meeting" is perhaps a misprint for "mutiny."

entered a port before at one tide. On the 12th, only seven ships held out—and by the 16th, the mutiny had terminated. A party of soldiers then went on board the Sandwich, and to them were surrendered the delegates of that ship, Richard Parker, and a man named Davies.

Parker, to whom the title of Admiral was given by the sailors and the public during the whole of this affair, occupied from the beginning the principal attention of the government. He was now brought summarily to trial before a naval court martial, on the 22d of June—having been thrown, for the intermediate time, in the black-hole of Sheerness garrison. In his defence, which he conducted himself, he read an elegantly written and powerful paper, setting forth that the situation he had held, had been in a measure forced upon him—that he had consented to occupy it chiefly for the purpose of preventing any bloody or cruel measures—that he had restrained the men from excesses—and that, had he been disloyal, he might have taken the ship to sea, or to an enemy's port.

But nothing could save Parker. He was sentenced to death. When his doom was pronounced, he immediately stood up, and with a firm voice made the following short but most beautiful response: "I shall submit to your sentence with all due respect, being confident of the innocence of my intentions, and that God will receive me into favor: and I sincerely hope that my death will be the means of restoring tranquillity to the navy, and that those men who have been implicated in the business may be reinstated in their former situations, and again be serviceable to their country."

On the morning of the 30th June, the whole fleet was ranged a little below Sheerness, in full sight of the Sandwich, on board of which Richard Parker was that day to suffer an ignominious death. The yellow flag, the signal of death, was hoisted—and the crew of every ship was piped to the forecastle. Parker was aroused from a sound sleep that morning, and attired himself with neatness, in a suit of deep mourning. He mentioned to his attendants that he had made a will, leaving his wife heir to some property belonging to him. On coming upon deck, he was hale,[3] but perfectly composed, and drank a glass of water[4] "to the salvation of his soul, and the forgiveness of all his enemies." He said nothing to his mates on the forecastle but "Good-bye to you!" and expressed a hope that his death would be considered a sufficient atonement, and would save the

3. "Hale" is probably a misprint for "pale."
4. Mabbott (p. 17) says that "Whitman tells nothing that Pelham does not, and where Pelham is at variance with the early pamphlets, Walt is in agreement with Pelham." But in the matter of Parker drinking a watery toast, Mabbott (p. 122)

lives of others. He was then strung up at the yard arm, and in a few moments dangled lifeless there.

Mrs. Parker was in Scotland, among her connexions, and when the rumour came to her ears that the Nore fleet had mutinied, and that the leader was one Richard Parker, she immediately started for London—and on her arrival heard that her husband had been tried, but the result was unknown. Being able to think of nothing better than petitioning the king, she gave a person a guinea to draw up a paper, praying that Parker's life might be spared. She attempted to make her way with this to His Majesty's presence—but was finally obliged to hand it to a Lord in waiting, who gave her the cruel intelligence that applications for mercy in all cases would be attended to, except those for Richard Parker. The distracted woman then took coach for Rochester on the 29th, where she got on board a king's ship, and learned that her husband was to be executed on the following day. Who can imagine her unspeakable wretchedness, as she sat up the whole of that long night of agony! At four o'clock the next morning, she went to the river side to hire a boat to take her to the Sandwich, that she might at least bid her poor husband farewell. Her feelings had been deeply tortured by hearing every person she met talking of that occurrence which was the subject of her distress; and now the first waterman to whom she spoke, answered, "No, I cannot take one passenger; the brave Admiral Parker is to be hung to-day, and I will get any sum I choose to ask for a party!"

After a long trial, the wretched wife was glad to get on board a Sheerness market-boat—but no boat was allowed to come alongside the Sandwich. In her desperation, she called on Parker by name, and prevailed on the boat people, by the mere spectacle of her suffering, to attempt to go nearer, when they were stopped by a sentinel threatening to fire at them. As the hour drew nigh, she saw her husband appear on deck between two clergymen. She called on him again, and he heard her voice, for he exclaimed, "There is my dear wife, from Scotland!"

The excitement of this was too great, and the miserable wife fell back in a state of insensibility—from which she was fortunate enough not to recover until the scene of death was finished, and she had been taken ashore. She seemed to think, however, that she was yet in time; she hired another boat, and a second time reached the Sandwich. Her delirious

remarks that Pelham (and sundry sources) state that Parker drank a glass of white wine as his final toast. Mabbott adds that "the change to 'a glass of water' is a bit of cant."

shriek, "Pass the word for Richard Parker!" rang through the decks, and must have startled all on board. The truth was now made clear to her, and she was further informed that the body had just been taken on shore for burial. She immediately caused herself to be rowed back again, and proceeded to the churchyard; but found the ceremony over and the gate locked!

The key, which she sought from the proper source, was refused her; and she was excited almost to madness at learning that the surgeon would probably disinter the body that night for anatomical purposes. She was now in a situation of mind wherein all the ordinary timidity and softness of her sex left her. She waited cautiously around the churchyard 'til dusk—then, clambering over the wall, she readily found her husband's new-made grave. The shell was not buried deep, and she worked in such a manner that the earth was soon scraped away, and the coffin lid removed. She clasped the cold neck, and kissed the clammy lips of the object of her search!

The necessity of prompt measures to possess the body, aroused this extraordinary woman from the enjoyment of her melancholy pleasure. She left the churchyard, and communicated her situation to two women, who in their turn got several men to undertake the task of lifting the body. This was accomplished successfully, and the coffin was carried to Rochester, and thence to London. The widow stopped with her sad burthen at a tavern on Tower Hill. By express at the same hour, or before it, information had been brought to the capital of the exhumation of the body; and the secret of its locality could not now be kept. A great crowd assembled around the house, anxious to see the dead man's face, which Mrs. Parker would not permit. She had the corpse in her own room, and was sitting disconsolately beside it, hardly knowing what course to pursue, and fearing it would be taken from her by the authorities, when the Lord Mayor arrived to see her. He came to ask what she intended doing with the remains of her husband: she answered, "to inter them decently at Exeter, or in Scotland." The Lord Mayor said the body should not be taken from her; but he prevailed upon her to have it buried in London. Arrangements were accordingly made for that purpose, and finally the corpse of the hapless sailor was inhumed in Whitechapel churchyard. After the closing ceremony, Mrs. Parker gave a certificate that the burial had been conducted to her satisfaction. But, though strictly questioned as to who had aided her in the disinterment, she firmly refused to disclose their names.

For many years afterward, this faithful wife lived on the income she derived from the little property left her by her husband's will. But ultimately her rights were some how or other decided against by a judicial tribunal, and she was thrown into great poverty in London, where she lived. She was in the habit of receiving assistance, however, from the highest quarters. William IV. gave her at one time £20, and at another £10. On the occasion when I saw her in 1836, she was nearly blind, and, as I intimated in the beginning, was making application for some public aid. I was gratified to learn afterward that she received it. Whether she be yet living, I am not able to say.

The Boy Lover[1]

LISTEN, and the old will speak a chronicle for the young.[2] Ah, youth! thou art one day coming to be old, too. And let me tell thee how thou mayest get a useful lesson. For an hour, *dream thyself old*. Realize, in thy thoughts and consciousness, that vigor and strength are subdued in thy sinews—that the color of the shroud is liken'd in thy very hairs —that all those leaping desires, luxurious hopes, beautiful aspirations, and proud confidences, of thy younger life, have long been buried (a funeral for the better part of thee) in that grave which must soon close over thy tottering limbs. Look back, then, through the long track of the past years. How has it been with thee? Are there bright beacons of happiness enjoy'd, and of good done by the way? Glimmer gentle rays of what was scatter'd from a holy heart? Have benevolence, and love, and undeviating honesty left tokens on which thy eyes can rest sweetly? Is it well with thee, thus? Answerest thou, it is? Or answerest thou, I see nothing but gloom and shatter'd hours, and the wreck of good resolves, and a broken heart, filled with sickness, and troubled among its ruined chambers with the phantoms of many follies?

O, youth! youth! this dream will one day be a *reality*—a reality, either of heavenly peace or agonizing sorrow.

And yet not for all is it decreed to attain the neighborhood of the threescore and ten years—the span of life. I am to speak of one who died young. Very awkward was his childhood—but most fragile and sensitive! So delicate a nature may exist in a rough, unnoticed plant! Let the boy rest;—he was not beautiful, and dropp'd[3] away betimes. But for the cause—it is a singular story, to which let crusted worldlings pay the tribute of a light laugh—light and empty as their own hollow hearts.[4]

Love! which with its cankerseed of decay within, has sent young men and maidens to a long'd-for, but too premature burial.[5] Love! the child-

---

1. The text followed here is that of *Collect*. The story was first published in the *American Review* for May, 1845. In revising the tale, Whitman as usual deleted the "e" in the past forms of most regular verbs, made a few minor changes in punctuation and paragraphing, and removed a few passages. The more important variants in the original text will be found in the footnotes that follow.

2. "for the ears of the young." This sentence is followed by "It is a brave thing to call up the memory of fires long burnt out—at least we withered folk believe so—and delight so to act."

3. drooped.

4. This paragraph follows:

The sway of love over the mind—though the old subject of flippant remarks from

monarch that Death itself cannot conquer; that has its tokens on slabs at the head of grass-cover'd tombs—tokens more visible to the eye of the stranger, yet not so deeply graven as the face and the remembrances cut upon the heart of the living. Love! the sweet, the pure, the innocent; yet the causer of fierce hate, of wishes for deadly revenge, of bloody deeds, and madness, and the horrors of hell. Love! that wanders over battlefields, turning up mangled human trunks, and parting back the hair from gory faces, and daring the points of swords and the thunder of artillery, without a fear or a thought of danger.

Words! words! I begin to see I am, indeed, an old man, and garrulous! Let me go back—yes, I see it must be many years!

It was at the close of the last century. I was at that time studying law, the profession my father follow'd. One of his clients was an elderly widow, a foreigner,[6] who kept a little ale-house, on the banks of the North River, at about two miles from what is now the centre of the city. *Then* the spot was quite out of town and surrounded by fields and green trees. The widow often invited me to come and pay her a visit, when I had a leisure afternoon—including also in the invitation my brother and two other students who were in my father's office. Matthew, the brother I mention, was a boy of sixteen; he was troubled with an inward illness— though it had no power over his temper, which ever retain'd the most admirable placidity and gentleness. He was cheerful, but never boisterous, and everybody loved him; his mind seem'd more develop'd than is usual for his age, though his personal appearance was exceedingly plain. Wheaton and Brown, the names of the other students, were spirited, clever young fellows, with most of the traits that those in their position of life generally possess. The first was as generous and brave as any man I ever knew. He was very passionate, too, but the whirlwind soon blew over, and left everything quiet again. Frank Brown was slim, graceful, and handsome. He profess'd to be fond of sentiment, and used to fall regularly in love once a month.

The half of every Wednesday we four youths had to ourselves, and

those who are too coarse to appreciate its delicate ascendency—is a strange and beautiful thing. And in your dream of age, young man, which I have charged you to dream, sad and desolate will that trodden path appear, over which have not been shed the rose tints of this Light of Life.

5. This sentence is preceded by the following: "Love! the mighty passion which, ever since the world began, has been conquering the great, and subduing the humble— bending princes, and mighty warriors, and the famous men of all nations, to the ground before it. Love! the delirious hope of youth, and the fond memory of old age."

6. A widow, an elderly Swiss woman.

were in the habit of taking a sail, a ride, or a walk together. One of these afternoons, of a pleasant day in April, the sun shining, and the air clear, I bethought myself of the widow and her beer—about which latter article I had made inquiries, and heard it spoken of in terms of high commendation. I mention'd the matter to Matthew and to my fellow-students, and we agreed to fill up our holiday by a jaunt to the ale-house. Accordingly, we set forth, and, after a fine walk, arrived in glorious spirits at our destination.

Ah! how shall I describe the quiet beauties of the spot, with its long, low piazza looking out upon the river, and its clean homely tables, and the tankards of real silver in which the ale was given us, and the flavor of that excellent liquor itself. There was the widow; and there was a sober, stately old woman, half companion, half servant, Margery by name; and there was (good God! my fingers quiver yet as I write the word!) young Ninon, the daughter of the widow.

O, through the years that live no more, my memory strays back, and that whole scene comes up before me once again—and the brightest part of the picture is the strange ethereal beauty of that young girl! She was apparently about the age of my brother Matthew, and the most fascinating, artless creature I had ever beheld. She had blue eyes and light hair, and an expression of childish simplicity which was charming indeed. I have no doubt that ere half an hour had elapsed from the time we enter'd the tavern and saw Ninon, every one of the four of us loved the girl to the very depth of passion.

We neither spent so much money, nor drank as much beer, as we had intended before starting from home. The widow was very civil, being pleased to see us, and Margery served our wants with a deal of politeness—but it was to Ninon that the afternoon's pleasure was attributable; for though we were strangers, we became acquainted at once —the manners of the girl, merry as she was, putting entirely out of view the most distant imputation of indecorum—and the presence of the widow and Margery, (for we were all in the common room together, there being no other company,) serving to make us all disembarass'd and at ease.

It was not until quite a while after sunset that we started on our return to the city. We made several attempts to revive the mirth and lively talk that usually signalized our rambles, but they seem'd forced and discordant, like laughter in a sick-room. My brother was the only one who preserved his usual tenor of temper and conduct.

I need hardly say that thenceforward every Wednesday afternoon was spent at the widow's tavern. Strangely, neither Matthew or my two friends, or myself, spoke to each other of the sentiment that filled us in reference to Ninon. Yet we all knew the thoughts and feelings of the others; and each, perhaps, felt confident that his love alone was unsuspected by his companions.

The story of the widow was a touching yet simple one. She was by birth a Swiss. In one of the cantons of her native land, she had grown up, and married, and lived for a time in happy comfort. A son was born to her, and a daughter, the beautiful Ninon. By some reverse of fortune, the father and head of the family had the greater portion of his possessions swept from him. He struggled for a time against the evil influence, but it press'd upon him harder and harder. He had heard of a people in the western world—a new and swarming land—where the stranger was welcom'd, and peace and the protection of the strong arm thrown around him. He had not heart to stay and struggle amid the scenes of his former prosperity, and he determin'd to go and make his home in that distant republic of the west. So with his wife and children, and the proceeds of what little property was left, he took passage for New York. He was never to reach his journey's end. Either the cares that weigh'd upon his mind, or some other cause, consign'd him to a sick hammock, from which he only found relief through the Great Dismisser. He was buried in the sea, and in due time his family arrived at the American emporium. But there, the son too sicken'd—died, ere long, and was buried likewise. They would not bury him in the city, but away—by the solitary banks of the Hudson; on which the widow soon afterwards took up her abode.[7]

Ninon was too young to feel much grief at the sad occurrences; and the mother, whatever she might have suffer'd inwardly, had a good deal of phelgm and patience, and set about making herself and her remaining child as comfortable as might be. They had still a respectable sum in cash, and after due deliberation, the widow purchas'd the little quiet tavern, not far from the grave of her boy; and of Sundays and holidays she took in considerable money—enough to make a decent support for them in their humble way of living. French and Germans visited the house frequently, and quite a number of young Americans too. Probably the greatest attraction to the latter was the sweet face of Ninon.

Spring passed, and summer crept in and wasted away, and autumn had arrived. Every New Yorker knows what delicious weather we have, in these regions, of the early October days; how calm, clear, and divested of sultriness, is the air, and how decently nature seems preparing for her winter sleep.

7. her abode, near by him.

Thus it was the last Wednesday we started on our accustomed excursion. Six months had elapsed since our first visit, and, as then, we were full of the exuberance of young and joyful hearts. Frequent and hearty were our jokes, by no means particular about the theme or the method, and long and loud the peals of laughter that rang over the fields or along the shore.

We took our seats round the same clean, white table, and received our favorite beverage in the same bright tankards. They were set before us by the sober Margery, no one else being visible. As frequently happen'd, we were the only company. Walking and breathing the keen, fine air had made us dry, and we soon drain'd the foaming vessels, and call'd for more. I remember well an animated chat we had about some poems that had just made their appearance from a great British author, and were creating quite a public stir. There was one, a tale of passion and despair, which Wheaton had read, and of which he gave us a transcript. Wild, startling, and dreamy, perhaps it threw over our minds its peculiar cast.[8]

An hour moved off, and we began to think it strange that neither Ninon or the widow came into the room. One of us gave a hint to that effect to Margery; but she made no answer, and went on in her usual way as before.

"The grim old thing," said Wheaton, "if she were in Spain, they'd make her a premier duenna!"

I ask'd the woman about Ninon and the widow. She seemed disturb'd, I thought; but, making no reply to the first part of my question, said that her mistress was in another part of the house, and did not wish to be with company.

"Then be kind enough, Mrs. Vinegar," resumed Wheaton, good-naturedly, "be kind enough to go and ask the widow if we can see Ninon."

Our attendant's face turn'd as pale as ashes, and she precipitately left the apartment. We laugh'd at her agitation, which Frank Brown assigned to our merry ridicule.

Quite a quarter of an hour elaps'd before Margery's return. When she appear'd she told us briefly that the widow had bidden her obey our behest, and now, if we desired, she would conduct us to the daughter's presence. There was a singular expression in the woman's eyes, and the whole affair began to strike us as somewhat odd; but we arose, and taking our caps, follow'd her as she stepp'd through the door. Back of the house were some fields, and a path leading into clumps of trees. At

8. It seemed a wild, startling, dreamy thing, and perhaps it threw over our minds its peculiar cast.

some thirty rods distant from the tavern, nigh one of those clumps, the larger tree whereof was a willow, Margery stopp'd, and pausing a minute, while we came up, spoke in tones calm and low:

"Ninon is there!"

She pointed downward with her finger. Great God! There was a *grave*, new made, and with the sods loosely join'd, and a rough brown stone at each extremity! Some earth yet lay upon the grass near by. If we had look'd, we might have seen the resting-place of the widow's son, Ninon's brother—for it was close at hand. But amid the whole scene our eyes took in nothing except that horrible covering of death—the oven-shaped mound.[9] My sight seemed to waver, my head felt dizzy, and a feeling of deadly sickness came over me. I heard a stifled exclamation, and looking round, saw Frank Brown leaning against the nearest tree, great sweat upon his forehead, and his cheeks bloodless as chalk. Wheaton gave way to his agony more fully than ever I had known a man before; he had fallen—sobbing like a child, and wringing his hands. It is impossible to describe the suddenness and fearfulness of the sickening truth that came upon us like a stroke of thunder.

Of all of us, my brother Matthew neither shed tears, or turned pale, or fainted, or exposed any other evidence of inward depth of pain. His quiet, pleasant voice was indeed a tone lower, but it was that which recall'd us, after the lapse of many long minutes, to ourselves.

So the girl had died and been buried. We were told of an illness that had seized her the very day after our last preceding visit; but we inquired not into the particulars.

And now come I to the conclusion of my story, and to the most singular part of it. The evening of the third day afterward, Wheaton, who had wept scalding tears, and Brown, whose cheeks had recover'd their color, and myself, that for an hour thought my heart would never rebound again from the fearful shock—that evening, I say, we three were seated around a table in another tavern, drinking other beer, and laughing but a little less cheerfully, and as though we had never known the widow or her daughter—neither of whom, I venture to affirm, came into our minds once the whole night, or but to be dismiss'd again, carelessly, like the remembrance of faces seen in a crowd.

Strange are the contradictions of the things of life! The seventh day after that dreadful visit saw my brother Matthew—the delicate one, who, while bold men writhed in torture, had kept the same placid face, and the same untrembling fingers—him that seventh day saw a clay-cold

9. Some earth yet lay upon the grass near by—and amid the whole scene our eyes took in nothing but that horrible covering of death—the oven-shaped mound!

corpse, carried to the repose of the churchyard.[10] The shaft, rankling far down and within, wrought a poison too great for show, and the youth died.

10. a clay-cold corpse, shrouded in white linen, and carried to the repose of the churchyard.

One Wicked Impulse![1]

THAT section of Nassau street which runs into the great mart of New York brokers and stock-jobbers, has for a long time been much occupied by practitioners of the law. Tolerably well-known amid this class some years since, was Adam Covert, a middle-aged man of rather limited means, who, to tell the truth, gained more by trickery than he did in the legitimate and honorable exercise of his profession. He was a tall, bilious-faced widower; the father of two children; and had lately been seeking to better his fortunes by a rich marriage. But somehow or other his wooing did not seem to thrive well, and, with perhaps one exception, the lawyer's prospects in the matrimonial way were hopelessly gloomy.

Among the early clients of Mr. Covert had been a distant relative named Marsh, who, dying somewhat suddenly, left his son and daughter, and some little property, to the care of Covert, under a will drawn out by that gentleman himself. At no time caught without his eyes open, the cunning lawyer, aided by much sad confusion in the emergency which had caused his services to be called for, and disguising his object under a cloud of technicalities, inserted provisions in the will, giving himself an almost arbitrary control over the property and over those for whom it was designed. This control was even made to extend beyond the time when the children would arrive at mature age. The son, Philip, a spirited and high-temper'd fellow, had some time since pass'd that age. Esther, the girl, a plain, and somewhat devotional young woman, was in her nineteenth year.

Having such power over his wards, Covert did not scruple openly to use his advantage, in pressing his claims as a suitor for Esther's hand. Since the death of Marsh, the property he left, which had been in real estate, and was to be divided equally between the brother and sister, had risen to very considerable value; and Esther's share was to a man in Covert's situation a prize very well worth seeking. All this time, while really owning a respectable income, the young orphans

---

1. This story originally appeared in the *Democratic Review* for July–August, 1845, with the title of "Revenge and Requital; A Tale of a Murderer Escaped." The text followed here is that of the revised version which appeared under a new title in *Collect*. In this final revision, Whitman as usual elided the "e" in the past forms of most regular verbs and made changes in punctuation. He eliminated the four formal divisions headed by Roman numerals. Variants from the original, excluding such insignificant differences as those noted above, will be given in the footnotes that follow.

often felt the want of the smallest sum of money—and Esther, on Philip's account, was more than once driven to various contrivances—the pawn-shop, sales of her own little luxuries, and the like, to furnish him with means.

Though she had frequently shown her guardian unequivocal evidence of her aversion, Esther continued to suffer from his persecutions, until one day he proceeded farther and was more pressing than usual. She possess'd some of her brother's mettlesome temper, and gave him an abrupt and most decided refusal. With dignity, she exposed the baseness of his conduct, and forbade him ever again mentioning marriage to her. He retorted bitterly, vaunted his hold on her and Philip, and swore an oath that unless she became his wife, they should both thenceforward become penniless. Losing his habitual self-control in his exasperation, he even added insults such as woman never receives from any one deserving the name of man, and at his own convenience left the house. That day, Philip return'd to New York, after an absence of several weeks on the business of a mercantile house in whose employment he had lately engaged.

Toward the latter part of the same afternoon, Mr. Covert was sitting in his office, in Nassau street, busily at work, when a knock at the door announc'd a visitor, and directly afterward young Marsh enter'd the room. His face exhibited a peculiar pallid appearance that did not strike Covert at all agreeably, and he call'd his clerk from an adjoining room, and gave him something to do at a desk near by.

"I wish to see you alone, Mr. Covert, if convenient," said the new-comer.

"We can talk quite well enough where we are," answer'd the lawyer; "indeed, I don't know that I have any leisure to talk at all, for just now I am very much press'd with business."

"But I *must* speak to you," rejoined Philip sternly, "at least I must say one thing, and that is, Mr. Covert, that you are a villain!"

"Insolent!" exclaimed the lawyer, rising behind the table, and pointing to the door: "Do you see that, sir! Let one minute longer find you the other side, or your feet may reach the landing by quicker method. Begone, sir!"

Such a threat was the more harsh to Philip, for he had rather high-strung feelings of honor. He grew almost livid with suppress'd agitation.

"I will see you again very soon," said he, in a low but distinct manner, his lips trembling as he spoke; and left the office.[2]

2. and he turned at once and left the office.

The incidents of the rest of that pleasant summer day left little impression on the young man's mind. He roam'd to and fro without any object or destination. Along South street and by Whitehall, he watch'd with curious eyes the movements of the shipping, and the loading and unloading of cargoes; and listen'd to the merry heave-yo of the sailors and stevedores. There are some minds upon which great excitement produces the singular effect of uniting two utterly inconsistent faculties—a sort of cold apathy, and a sharp sensitiveness to all that is going on at the same time. Philip's was one of this sort; he noticed the various differences in the apparel of a gang of wharf-laborers—turn'd over in his brain whether they receiv'd wages enough to keep them comfortable, and their families also—and if they had families or not, which he tried to tell by their looks. In such petty reflections the daylight passed away. And all the while the master wish of Philip's thoughts was a desire to see the lawyer Covert. For what purpose he himself was by no means clear.

Nightfall came at last. Still, however, the young man did not direct his steps homeward. He felt more calm, however, and entering an eating house, order'd something for his supper, which, when it was brought to him, he merely tasted, and stroll'd forth again. There was a kind of gnawing sensation of thirst within him yet, and as he pass'd a hotel, he bethought him that one little glass of spirits would perhaps be just the thing. He drank, and hour after hour wore away unconsciously; he drank not one glass, but three or four, and strong glasses they were to him, for he was habitually abstemious.

It had been a hot day and evening, and when Philip, at an advanced period of the night, emerged from the bar-room into the street, he found that a thunderstorm had just commenced. He resolutely walk'd on, however, although at every step it grew more and more blustering.

The rain now pour'd down a cataract; the shops were all shut; few of the street lamps were lighted; and there was little except the frequent flashes of lightning to show him his way. When about half the length of Chatham street, which lay in the direction he had to take, the momentary fury of the tempest forced him to turn aside into a sort of shelter form'd by the corners of the deep entrance to a Jew pawnbroker's shop there. He had hardly drawn himself in as closely as possible, when the lightning reveal'd to him that the opposite corner of the nook was tenanted also.

"A sharp rain, this," said the other occupant, who simultaneously beheld Philip.

The voice sounded to the young man's ears a note which almost made him sober again. It was certainly the voice of Adam Covert. He made some commonplace reply, and waited for another flash of lightning to show him the stranger's face. It came, and he saw that his companion was indeed his guardian.

Philip Marsh had drank deeply—(let us plead all that may be possible to you, stern moralist.) Upon his mind came swarming, and he could not drive them away, thoughts of all those insults his sister had told him of, and the bitter words Covert had spoken to her; he reflected, too, on the injuries Esther as well as himself had receiv'd, and were still likely to receive, at the hands of that bold, bad man; how mean, selfish, and unprincipled was his character—what base and cruel advantages he had taken of many poor people, entangled in his power, and of how much wrong and suffering he had been the author, and might be again through future years. The very turmoil of the elements, the harsh roll of the thunder, the vindictive beating of the rain, and the fierce glare of the wild fluid that seem'd to riot in the ferocity of the storm around him, kindled a strange sympathetic fury in the young man's mind. Heaven itself (so deranged were his imaginations) appear'd to have provided a fitting scene and time for a deed of retribution, which to his disorder'd passion half wore the semblance of a divine justice. He remember'd not the ready solution to be found in Covert's pressure of business, which had no doubt kept him later than usual; but fancied some mysterious intent in the ordaining that he should be there, and that they two should meet at that untimely hour. All this whirl of influence came over Philip with startling quickness at that horrid moment. He stepp'd to the side of his guardian.

"Ho!" said he, "have we met so soon, Mr. Covert? You traitor to my dead father—robber of his children![3] I fear to think on *what* I think now!"

The lawyer's natural effrontery did not desert him.

"Unless you'd like to spend a night in the watch-house, young gentleman," said he, after a short pause, "move on. Your father was a weak man, I remember; as for his son, his own wicked heart is his worst foe. I have never done wrong to either—that I can say, and swear it!"

"Insolent liar!" exclaimed Philip, his eye flashing out sparks of fire in the darkness.

Covert made no reply except a cool, contemptuous laugh, which stung the excited young man to double fury. He sprang upon the lawyer, and clutch'd him by the neckcloth.

"Take it, then!" he cried hoarsely, for his throat was impeded by the fiendish rage which in that black hour possess'd him. "You are not fit to live!"

He dragg'd his guardian to the earth and fell crushingly upon him, choking the shriek the poor victim but just began to utter. Then, with

3. "robber of his children—scoundrel!—wretch!"

monstrous imprecations, he twisted a tight knot around the gasping creature's neck, drew a clasp knife from his pocket, and touching the spring, the long sharp blade, too eager for its bloody work, flew open.

During the lull of the storm, the last strength of the prostrate man burst forth into one short loud cry of agony. At the same instant, the arm of the murderer thrust the blade, once, twice, thrice, deep in his enemy's bosom! Not a minute had passed since that fatal exasperating laugh— but the deed was done, and the instinctive thought which came at once to the guilty one, was a thought of fear and escape.

In the unearthly pause which follow'd, Philip's eyes gave one long searching sweep in every direction, above and around him. *Above!* God of the all-seeing eye! What, and who was that figure there?

"Forbear! In Jehovah's name forbear;" cried a shrill, but clear and melodious voice.

It was as if some accusing spirit had come down to bear witness against the deed of blood. Leaning far out of an open window, appear'd a white draperied shape, its face possess'd of a wonderful youthful beauty. Long vivid glows of lightning gave Philip a full opportunity to see as clearly as though the sun had been shining at noonday. One hand of the figure was raised upward in a deprecating attitude, and his large bright black eyes bent down upon the scene below with an expression of horror and shrinking pain. Such heavenly looks, and the peculiar circumstance of the time, fill'd Philip's heart with awe.

"Oh, if it is not yet too late," spoke the youth again, "spare him. In God's voice, I command, 'Thou shalt do no murder!'"

The words rang like a knell in the ear of the terror-stricken and already remorseful Philip. Springing from the body, he gave a second glance up and down the walk, which was totally lonesome and deserted; then crossing into Reade street, he made his fearful way in a half state of stupor, half-bewilderment, by the nearest avenues to his home.

When the corpse of the murder'd lawyer was found in the morning, and the officers of justice commenced their inquiry, suspicion immediately fell upon Philip, and he was arrested. The most rigorous search, however, brought to light nothing at all implicating the young man, except his visit to Covert's office the evening before, and his angry language there. That was by no means enough to fix so heavy a charge upon him.

The second day afterward, the whole business came before the ordinary judicial tribunal, in order that Philip might be either committed for the crime, or discharged. The testimony of Mr. Covert's clerk stood alone. One of his employers, who, believing in his innocence, had deserted him not in this crisis, had provided him with the ablest criminal counsel in New York. The proof was declared entirely insufficient, and Philip was discharged.

The crowded court-room made way for him as he came out; hundreds of curious looks fixed upon his features, and many a jibe pass'd upon him. But of all that arena of human faces, he saw only *one*—a sad, pale, black-eyed one, cowering in the centre of the rest. He had seen that face twice before—the first time as a warning spectre—the second time in prison, immediately after his arrest—now for the *last* time. This young stranger—the son of a scorn'd race[4]—coming to the court-room to perform an unhappy duty, with the intention of testifying to what he had seen, melted at the sight of Philip's bloodless cheek, and of his sister's convulsive sobs, and forbore witnessing against the murderer. Shall we applaud or condemn him? Let every reader answer the question for himself.

That afternoon Philip left New York. His friendly employer own'd a small farm some miles up the Hudson, and until the excitement of the affair was over, he advised the young man to go thither. Philip thankfully accepted the proposal, made a few preparations, took a hurried leave of Esther, and by nightfall was settled in his new abode.[5]

And how, think you, rested Philip Marsh that night? *Rested* indeed! O, if those who clamor so much for the halter and the scaffold to punish crime, could have seen that sight, they might have learn'd a lesson there! Four days had elapsed since he that lay tossing upon the bed there had slumber'd. Not the slightest intermission had come to his awaken'd and tensely strung sense, during those frightful days.[6]

Disturb'd waking dreams came to him, as he thought what he might do to gain his lost peace. Far, far away would he go! The cold roll of the murder'd man's eye, as it turn'd up its last glance into his face—the shrill exclamation of pain—all the unearthly vividness of the posture, motions, and looks of the dead—the warning voice from above—pursued him like tormenting furies, and were never absent from his mind, asleep or awake, that long weary night. Anything, any place, to escape such horrid companionship! He would travel inland—hire himself to do hard drudgery upon some farm—work incessantly through the wide summer days, and thus force nature to bestow oblivion upon his senses, at least a little while now and then. He would fly on, on, on, until amid different scenes and a new life, the old memories were rubb'd entirely out. He

4. a scorned and persecuted race
5. took a hurried leave of Esther, with a sad foreboding, which indeed proved true, that he should see her no more on earth, and by nightfall was settled in his new abode.
6. An additional sentence closes the paragraph:

would fight bravely in himself for peace of mind. For peace he would labor and struggle—for peace he would pray!

At length after a feverish slumber of some thirty or forty minutes, the unhappy youth, waking with a nervous start, rais'd himself in bed, and saw the blessed daylight beginning to dawn. He felt the sweat trickling down his naked breast; the sheet where he had lain was quite wet with it. Dragging himself wearily, he open'd the window. Ah! that good morning air—how it refresh'd him—how he lean'd out, and drank in the fragrance of the blossoms below, and almost for the first time in his life felt how beautifully indeed God had made the earth, and that there was wonderful sweetness in mere existence. And amidst the thousand mute mouths and eloquent eyes, which appear'd as it were to look up and speak in every direction, he fancied so many invitations to come among them.[7] Not without effort, for he was very weak, he dress'd himself, and issued forth into the open air.

Clouds of pale gold and transparent crimson draperied the eastern sky, but the sun, whose face gladden'd them into all that glory, was not yet above the horizon. It was a time and place of such rare, such Eden-like beauty! Philip paused at the summit of an upward slope, and gazed around him. Some few miles off he could see a gleam of the Hudson river, and above it a spur of those rugged cliffs scatter'd along its western shores. Nearer by were cultivated fields. The clover grew richly there, the young grain bent to the early breeze, and the air was filled with an intoxicating perfume.[8] At his side was the large well-kept garden of his host, in which were many pretty flowers, grass plots, and a wide avenue of noble trees. As Philip gazed, the holy calming power of Nature—the invisible spirit of so much beauty and so much innocence, melted into his soul. The disturb'd passions and the feverish conflict subsided. He even felt something like envied peace of mind—a sort of joy even in the presence of all the unmarr'd goodness. It was as fair to him, guilty though he had been, as to the purest of the pure. No accusing frowns show'd in the face of the flowers, or in the green shrubs, or the branches of the trees. They, more forgiving than mankind, and distinguishing not between the children of darkness and the children of light—they at least treated him with gentleness. Was he, then a being so accurs'd? Involuntarily, he bent over a branch of red roses, and took them softly between his hands—those murderous, bloody hands! But the red roses neither wither'd nor

And now, O, pitying Heaven, if he could only lose his remorse in one little hour of wholesome repose!

7. to come forth, and be among them.

8. with an intoxicating perfume from the neighboring apple-orchards, snowy in their luxuriant bloom.

smell'd less fragrant. And as the young man kiss'd them, and dropp'd a tear upon them, it seem'd to him that he had found pity and sympathy from Heaven itself.[9]

9. In the original version of the tale, this paragraph is the climax rather than the conclusion, and the paragraph which now concludes the tale does not appear. The omitted conclusion, shown below, though overly sentimental and melodramatic, turns the story into propaganda for the anti-hanging cause and, interestingly perhaps for those who like to see adumbrations, shows young Marsh finding salvation through nursing cholera victims. The original conclusion continues in the following fashion:

> After desolating the cities of the eastern world, the dreaded Cholera made its appearance on our American shores. In New York, hardly had the first few cases occurred, when thousands of the inhabitants precipitately left town, and sought safety in the neighboring country districts. For various reasons, however, large numbers still remained. While fear drove away so many—poverty, quite as stern a force, also compelled many to stay where they were. The desire of gain, too, made a large number continue their business as usual, for competition was narrowed down, and profits were large. Besides these, there was, of the number who remained, still another class, every name among whom is brightly kept in the records writ by God's angels. These were the men and women, heedless of their own small comfort, who went out amid the diseased, the destitute, and the dying, like merciful spirits—wiping the drops from hot brows, and soothing the agony of cramped limbs—speaking words of consolation to many a despairing creature, who would else have been vanquished by his soul's weakness alone—and treading softly but quickly from bedside to bedside, with those little offices which are so grateful to the sick, but which can so seldom be obtained from strangers. O, Charity and Love! sister throbbings in the heart of great Humanity! Sweetly, but ever surely, step you forth from the very tempest of those horrors, which whirl away by wholesale man's virtue and his life! Even in carnage and pestilence, sad fruits of the evil that will work from ourselves—when hate, selfishness, and all monstrous vice threaten to beat the good utterly out of mortal hearts—the Genius of Perfection which our Maker gave us, springs up loftily and cheerfully from the ruin, and laughs to scorn the taunts of those malignant fiends, who please themselves in the depression of our better nature! Yes: then, to cancel the weight of wickedness, appear large deeds of devotion and love;—then come forth heroes of charity and brotherly kindness, whose meek courage is greater than the courage of war:—then favorite messengers of heaven enter into the hearts of noble women, who go forth and relieve the scene of its sombre gloom, like lamps at night. And though the number be few, their sum of holiness affords a leaven large enough for the freshness and healthiness of an otherwise unwholesome world! Ye true sons and daughters of Christ! I bow before you with a reverence I never pay either to earthly rank or intellectual majesty!
>
> Such, during the cholera season in New York, was the character of a small and sacred band who, with no union except the union of that sublimest of impulses, good will to man, went wherever they could find themselves needed or useful. *One* among them seemed even more ardent and devoted than the rest. Wherever the worst cases of the contagion were to be found, he also was to be found. In noisome alleys and foul rear-buildings, in damp cellars and hot garrets, thither came he with food, medicine, gentle words, and gentle smiles. By the head of the dying, the sight of his pale calm face and his eyes moist with tears of sympathy, often divested death of its severest terrors. At midnight hovered he over the forms of sick children, hushing their fretful cries, solacing them to rest with a soft voice, and cooling their hot cheeks with his own

Though against all the rules of story-writing, we continue our narrative of these mainly true incidents (for such they are,) no further. Only to say that *the murderer* soon departed for a new field of action—that he is

hands and lips, disdainful of the peril he inhaled at every breath. At night too, when not occupied with other cares, he went prying and peering about, threading that dirtiest and wretchedest section of the city, between Chatham and Centre streets, pausing frequently, and gazing hither and thither. And when his well trained ear caught those familiar sounds, those wailings of anguish and fear, how uneeringly would he direct his feet to the spot whence they proceeded. There, like an unearthly help, vouchsafed from above, he would at once take the measures experience had proved most efficacious, not seldom finding his reward the next day in the recovered safety of his patient.

This messenger of health to many, and peace to all, this unwearied, unterrified angel of mercy and charity, was Philip Marsh. His heart swelled with an engrossing wish to cancel, as far as he could, the great outrage he had committed on society by taking the life of one of its members. A great crime sometimes revolutionizes a character. For that purpose he would cheerfully have endured any pains or privations, however severe; and he rejoiced in all the additional risk he ran, for the preservation or recovery of those unhappy sufferers. It even seemed as if he were thus making interest in the Courts of Heaven. How many new comers to the immortal land must have passed its golden arches, with the thought of *his* devoted sympathy fresh within them. Who should say he was not already interceded for at the throne of God?

Late one evening, Philip was walking slowly home, faint with the labors of the day, to gain that repose which would fit him for farther efforts. His course led him through one of those thoroughfares that intersect the eastern part of Grand street; and in the solemn stillness of the time, his attention was arrested by the low sobbing of a child whose face could be indistinctly seen at an open basement window. Philip stepped closer, paused, and leaning down, saw that it was a young boy.

"Why are you crying, my little son?" said he.

The child ceased his sobs and looked up, but made no answer.

"Are you alone here?" continued Philip. "Is your father or mother sick?"

"My brother is sick," answered the child. "I have no father. He is dead."

"Did he die of the cholera, then?"

"No," replied the boy, "a bad man killed him a year ago."

Philip's heart quivered as if some harsh instrument had cut into it. A dim forboding, not without joy too, came dreamily to him.

"What is your name, my poor boy?" he asked.

"Adam Covert," said the child.

And at the same moment Philip was down the area steps, and had entered the door.

By the death of Covert, his two children were left without any protector, and almost without a shelter. The lawyer's business was conducted on a plan so entirely without method—the knowledge of its details being confined to himself almost exclusively—that it would have been difficult for any one to realize the smallest sum over the demands against him. In this state of things several rapacious creditors came in, and took possession of all that remained.

The elder of the two young Coverts was a lad of about eighteen, an industrious and intelligent youngster, whose earnings now sufficed for the support of himself and his little brother. They rubbed along tolerably well, until the coming of the cholera, which broke up the boarding-house where they had made their home, dispersed the boarders, and drove off the frightened landlady and her family among some distant country relations. The orphans, too poor to

still living—and that this is but one of thousands of cases of unravel'd, un-punish'd crime—left, not to the tribunals of man, but to a wider power and judgment.

go with the rest, obtained permission to occupy the basement of the house, and the elder continued his avocations for a while longer, when unfortunately his business stopped, and of course his wages with it.

The afternoon previous to Philip's accidental encounter with the child at the window, poor living and a disturbed mind had done their work on the un-employed lad, and he began to feel the symptoms of the prevailing illness. There was no aid, no friend, no doctor near. He went forth into the street, but feared that he might perhaps die there upon the public walk, and returned to his dwelling again, comforting his brother as well as he could.

And now, Philip, thanking the indulgence of God, which had vouchsafed him this happiness, was the nurse, the friend, and the physician of the sick youth. Hardly for a moment stirred he from the room. He always carried about him the medicines necessary in such cases, and here all his experience and skill were taxed to their utmost.

Heaven blessed those exertions, and the boy recovered his health again.

But this was Philip's crowning act of recompense. From the very hour when his young patient was beyond danger, the over-wearied man began to droop. His illness however was not long. He wrote a short note to his sister, who was many miles away at the house of a distant relative—bequeathed his property to the boys whom he had made fatherless—(after the death of Covert [Philip, Marsh logically, not Covert], the orphans of course received their in-heritance at once)—and a few hours afterward, calmly passed Philip Marsh from the circuit of that life, which, young as he was, had been to him little else than a scene of crime, suffering and repentance.

Some of my readers may, perhaps, think that he ought to have been hung at the time of his crime. I must be pardoned if I think differently.

Some Fact-Romances[1]

As far as the essential parts of the following little incidents are concerned, the reader has the pledged personal veracity of the writer—must it be said, not only as a writer, but as a man?—that they literally came to pass, as now told. They may not be considered so romantic as if they had merely an imaginary existence—for though fact is indeed stronger than fable, it is hardly ever realized to be so. Even while we are thrilled most deeply by the sight or hearing of a real death under affecting circumstances, we do not look upon it as equally sentimental with a death described in a novel, or seen upon the stage.

Still, truth has a great charm—and I would try it against romance, even on romance's chosen ground of love and death. Therefore have I rummaged over the garners of my observation and memory for the following anecdotes—and therefore I present them, with a determination to go not a bit beyond the limits of fact. Pope's lady friend was charmed with Plutarch, until she found that he was an authentic biographer—so called —and then she threw his works away. I have more confidence in the judgment of intelligent American women, and men too, than to think they can act after such a fashion.

I.[2] On the Huntington south shore of Long Island, there is a creek, near the road called "Gunnetaug,"[3] and the mouth of this creek, emptying into the bay, is reported to be so deep that no lines have ever yet sounded its bottom. It sometimes goes by the name of "Drowning Creek," which

---

1. The text followed here is that of the first and only complete version of the "Romances," which appeared in *The Aristidean* for December 1845. The *Aristidean* text has not until now been reprinted in full; but three of the five sketches (I, II, V) were reprinted in the *Brooklyn Daily Eagle* in 1846 during the early months of Whitman's editorship of that paper (see Appendix). The variants in the *Eagle* versions (except for minor changes in punctuation and word order) are given in the footnotes that follow.

2. This sketch was reprinted in the *Eagle* on December 16, 1846, under the title of "A Fact-Romance of Long Island," where it has no conventional paragraphing. Whitman as editor of the *Eagle* employed a series of periods apparently to indicate, in a rather cavalier fashion at times, breaks in thought or topic as a space-saver in the very limited format of the typical four-page daily of the time. None of the series of periods (which range from twenty-one to six) which indicate possible breaks in thought in the *Eagle's* version of the three "Fact-Romances" correspond consistently with the paragraphing of the *Aristidean* version.

3. Consistently printed as "Gunnetang" in the *Aristidean* version, but corrected to the proper spelling—"Gunnetaug"— in the *Eagle*.

was given to it by a circumstance which I[4] will relate. It is a universal summer custom on Long Island to have what are called "beach-parties;" that
is, collections of people, young and old, each bringing a lot of provisions
and drink, and who sail over early in the morning to the beach, which
breaks off the Atlantic waves from the island's[5] "sea-girt shore," and spend
the day there. Many years ago, such a party went over from Gunnetaug.[6]
The leader of the rest, and owner of the boat, was a young farmer of the
neighborhood, a fellow full of life and fun, who, with many others, had
his sweetheart and his sister on board. The day was fine, and they enjoyed the jaunt gloriously. They bathed in the surf, danced, told stories,
ate and drank, amused themselves with music, plays, games, and so on,
and ranged over the beach in search of the eggs of the sea-gull, who lays
in no nest but the warm sand, exposed to the sun, which makes a
first rate natural eccaliobeon. (I have sometimes gathered a hundred of
these eggs on the sandbanks there in an hour; they are palatable, and
half the size of hen's eggs.)

Towards the latter part of the afternoon, the party[7] set out on their
return, and made the greater haste, as a thunder-shower seemed to be
gathering overhead. They had crossed the bay, and were just entering the
mouth of the creek I[8] have mentioned, when the storm burst, and a sudden flaw of wind capsized the boat. Most Long Islanders are good
swimmers, and as the stream was but a few yards wide, the men supported the women and children to the banks. The young man, the owner
of the boat, grasped his sister with one arm, and struck out for the shore
with the other. When he was within a rod of it, he heard a slight exclamation from the upturned boat, and turning his head, he saw the girl he
loved slip into the water. Yielding to a sudden impulse, he shook off his
sister, swam back, dived, and clutching the sinking one by her hair and
dress, brought her safely to the shore. He then again swam back for his

4. "we": the editorial "we" which Whitman overlooks once in his revision of
this sketch.
    5. our island's
    6. The remainder of this paragraph has a somewhat different arrangement and
some additions in the *Eagle* version:
> They formed a cheerful and healthy set, full of animal spirits. They bathed
> in the surf—danced—told stories—ate and drank—amused themselves with
> music, plays, games, and so on—and ranged upon the beach in search of the
> eggs of the sea-gull, who lays them in no nest except the warm sand, exposed
> to the sun, which makes a first rate natural Eccallobeon. (I have sometimes
> gathered a hundred of these eggs, on similar excursions, in an hour: they are
> palatable and about half the size of hen's eggs.) The owner of the boat which
> carried the party over the bay was a young farmer who had his sister and his
> sweetheart on board.
    7. they   8. we   9. *but beat and dived in vain.*

sister, and for many long and dreadful minutes beat the dark waters, and dived—but beat and dived in vain.[9] The girl drowned, and her body was never more seen.

From that time forth the young man's character was entirely changed. He laughed no more, and no more engaged in the country jollities. He married his sweetheart, but it was a cold and unfriendly union. About a year from this, he began to pine and droop strangely.[10] He had no disease—at least none that is treated of in medical works—but his heart withered away, as it were. In dreams, the chill of his sister's dripping hair was against his cheek, and he would awake with a cry of pain. Moping and sinking thus, he gradually grew weaker and weaker, and at last died. The story is yet told among the people[11] thereabouts; and often, when sailing out of the creek, have I looked on the spot where the poor girl sank, and the shore where the rescued one escaped.

II.[12] Not long since, an aged black widow-woman occupied a basement—perhaps she still lives there—in one of the streets leading down from Broadway to the North river.[13] She had employment from a number of families, who hired her at intervals to cook, nurse, and wash for them; and in this way she gained a very decent living. If I[14] remember right, the old creature had no child, or any near relative; but was quite alone in the world, and lived when at home in the most solitary manner. Always she had her room and humble furniture as clean as a new glove, and was remarkable every where for her agreeable ways,[15] and good humor—and all this at an age closely bordering on seventy. Opposite to the residence of this ancient female, was a row of stables for horses and public vehicles, doctors' gigs, and such like.[16] At any hour of the day and evening, groups of hostlers and stable-boys[17] were working or lounging about there—and the ears of the passer-by could hardly fail often to hear coarse oaths and indecent ribaldry.[18] The old black woman, smoking her

10. "strangely" is deleted.   11. the country people
12. This "Fact-Romance" was reprinted in the *Eagle* on November 12, 1846, under the title of "The Old Black Widow," followed by this remark in parentheses: "A narrative the truth of whose essentials is vouched for by the Editor of this print." The sketch is not paragraphed, even by series of periods, except for the last sentence, which is preceded by ten periods and a dash.
13. Some years ago, (and not many, either) an aged black woman, a widow, occupied a basement in one of the streets leading down to the North river, in New York city.
14. we   15. for her neatness, agreeable ways
16. Opposite to where the ancient female lived, was a row of stables for horses, cabs, private vehicles on livery, and such like.
17. stout stable boys
18. could hardly fail to hear joking and laughter, and often coarse oaths and indecent ribaldry.

pipe of an evening at her door over the way, suffered considerable annoyance from this swearing[19] and obscenity. She was a pious woman, not merely in profession but practice.[20] For several weeks, at intervals, she had noticed a barefooted young girl, or twelve or thirteen years, strolling about, and frequently stopping at the stables. This girl was a deaf mute, the daughter of a wretched intemperate couple in the neighborhood, who were letting her grow up as the weeds grow.—With no care and guidance for her young steps, she had before her the darkest and dreariest of prospects. What, under such circumstances, could be expected of her future years but degradation, misery and crime? The old woman[21] had many anxious thoughts about the little girl,[22] and shuddered at the fate which seemed prepared for her. She at last resolved[23] to make an effort in behalf of the hapless one. She had heard of the noble institutions provided for the deaf and dumb, and how the sealed avenues of the senses are almost opened to them again there. Upon making inquiry, she found that in the case of her young neighbor, the payment of a certain sum of money—two hundred dollars, I[24] think it was—would be necessary, preparatory to her admission into a certain New-York institution.[25] Whether any payment was required after this, I[26] have forgotten, but the sum in advance was indispensable. The old woman had got quite well acquainted with the child, and discovered in her that quickness and acuteness for which her unfortunate kind are remarkable. She *determined* to save her—to turn her path aside from darkness to light. Day after day, then, and night after night, whenever her work would permit, went forth the old woman, with letters and papers, to beg subscriptions from the charitable, for that most holy object. Among the families where she was known, she always succeeded in getting something—sometimes half a dollar, sometimes two, and sometimes five and even ten dollars. But where she was a stranger, she rarely received any answer to her request, except a rude denial, or a contemptuous sneer. Most of them suspected her story to be a fabrication—although she had provided herself with incontestible proofs of its truth, which she always carried with her. For a long time,[27] it seemed a hopeless effort, and yet she persevered—contributing from her own scanty means every cent that she could spare. Need I[28] say that heaven blessed this poor creature's work[29]—that she succeeded in getting the requisite sum, and that the girl was soon afterwards an inmate of the Asylum. Whether the aged widow still lives in her basement, and

19. their swearing
20. The sentence continues: and faithfully tried to worship God, and walk in the paths of duty.
21. The old black widow

what has happened since in the life of the girl, I[30] know not. But surely a purer or more elevated deed of disinterested love and kindness never was performed! In all that I[31] have ever heard or read, I[32] do not know a better refutation of those scowling dogmatists who resolve the cause of all the actions of mankind into a gross motive of pleasing the abstract self.

III. I became acquainted some seasons since with a gentleman who had emigrated from France, and then lived in a pleasant country town, about twenty miles from this metropolis. He was a mild, but somewhat eccentric person; and on the farm which he owned—for he possessed considerable wealth—everything was permitted to go to rack. Cattle strayed away, fences fell, hay was unmowed; and if the owner had not drawn a handsome income from funds in the city, everybody in his house might have starved to death. The people round about thought him deranged, which perhaps was sometimes not far from the truth. But he never offended or harmed anybody, and was therefore permitted to go his own way, without any one's interference. He had three children, all of them grown and away from home. The sons were employed in some mercantile establishment in New-York, in which city the daughter, who was married, also lived. The wife of the emigrant was a gentle-mannered and most lady-like woman, of a delicate appearance, and always looked to me like one in a hopeless consumption. The neighbors said she was never seen to smile. One day the gentleman set out for New-York, with the intention of procuring medical advice for his wife, who accompanied him. After arriving there, and consulting several physicians, he took a sudden notion, the second day afterwards, to return to his farm, and carry his wife with him. The physicians pronounced the lady's removal highly improper; but he made his preparations in half an hour and without the knowledge of his children, started away. The wife, so weak that she could not sit upright, was carried in a kind of covered wagon, on a bed. They crossed the Brooklyn ferry, and when out near Bedford, the gentleman gave the reins of the horses to a hired man who accompanied him, and declared his intention of going forward on foot. He did so. The hired man drove on a couple of miles, and then stopped a while, jumped on the ground, and lifted the covering of the wagon to see how the sick woman was getting on. She was a lifeless corpse! The man stood for a minute motionless with horror. He then drove the wagon aside from the middle of the road, unhitched both the horses, tied one to a tree, jumped on the back of

22. this little girl   23. determined   24. we
25. the New York Institution   26. we
27. "For a long time" is deleted.
28. we   29. sacred work   30. we   31. we   32. we

the other, and rode rapidly forward to overtake the husband. Three hot weary miles ahead he came up to him. He told his story, and the other listened, but made no answer. The hired man impressed upon him the necessity of returning immediately, but he declined, and rushed wildly forward on the turnpike toward the town where he lived. Arrived there, he passed directly by his own door, without stopping, and went down to a swampy wood of considerable extent, that lies a couple of miles beyond the village. In that wood, he wandered about for three days and nights, and when found at the end of that time, all pale, ragged, weak and bloody, was a confirmed maniac. They sent him off to one of the Insane Retreats, where, if alive, he no doubt remains at this moment.

The hired man, when he came back to the corpse, carried it to the nearest house, and then returned to New-York, and gave information to the sons, who, of course, took measures to have the due ceremonies of burial immediately performed.

IV.[33] Saunders, that unhappy boy, now in the State's Prison for his forgeries on his employers, Austin & Wilmerding, once boarded in the same house with me. Soon after his arrest, I visited the Centre-street "Tombs," and went into his cell to see him. He gave me a long account of the commission of the crime, and of his doings down to the time of his capture at Boston. It was all a disgusting story of villany and conceit. He was a flippant boy, whose head, I think, was turned by melodramas and the Jack Sheppard order of novels[34]—all but one little item. When he had received the money, and every moment was worth diamonds to him—he intended to sail in the Great Western, it will be remembered—he spent an hour in going up to a pawnbroker's shop in the Bowery, to get a little piece of jewellery he had in pledge there—*a keepsake from his dead mother.* He told me in his cell that he would have given a thousand dollars for another half hour, yet *he could not go away without that locket.* That half hour cost him the doom he afterwards had meted out to him.

---

33. Mabbott, p. 124, in a note to his reprinting of this "Fact-Romance," says: "The New York Directory for 1842 lists a Frederick Sanders or Saunders, as a clerk living at 145 Barrow Street, who is perhaps the man. Austen, Wilmerding and Co., auctioneers, were located at 30 Exchange Street, corner of William." Joseph Jay Rubin, "Whitman and the Boy-Forger," *American Literature,* X (May 1938) 214–216, identifies Henry Saunders as having passed, in 1843, forged checks to ten New York banks for a total of $30,000.

34. *Jack Sheppard,* a popular novel by the English author William Harrison Ainsworth, is the semi-fictional account of the career of a notorious English criminal. A few months after the publication of the "Fact-Romances" in *The Aristidean,* Whitman favorably reviewed Ainsworth's *The Tower of London* in the *Eagle* (May 19, 1846), finding it full of incident and interest.

35. This "Fact-Romance" was reprinted in the *Eagle* on December 24, 1846, with the title "An Incident On Long Island Forty Years Ago." The sketch, so charm-

V.[35] When my mother was a girl, the house where she and her parents[36] lived was in a gloomy wood, out of the way from any village or thick settlement. One morning in August,[37] my grandfather had some business a number of miles from home, and putting[38] a saddle on his favorite horse Dandy—a creature he loved next to his wife and children— he rode away[39] to attend to it. When nightfall came, and my grandfather did not return, my grandmother began to feel a little uneasy. As the night advanced, she and her daughter sitting up impatient for the return of the absent husband and father, a terrible storm gathered,[40] in the middle of which their ears joyed to hear the well-known clatter of Dandy's hoofs. My grandmother sprung to the door, but upon opening it, she almost fainted in my mother's arms. For there stood Dandy, saddled and bridled,[41] but no signs of my grandfather. My mother stepped out, and found that the bridle was broken, and the saddle soaked with rain and covered with mud. Sick at heart, they returned into the house. It was now after midnight, and the storm had quite passed over. Then in the stillness of their dreary watching, they heard something in the next room —the "spare-room"—which redoubled their terror.[42] They heard the slow heavy footfall of a man walking. Tramp! tramp! tramp! it went—three times solemnly and deliberately, and then all was hushed again. By any,[43] who, in the middle of the night, have had the chill of a vague unknown horror creep into their very souls, it can well be imagined how they passed the time now. My mother sprang to the door and turned the key, and spoke what words of cheer she could force through her lips to the ears of her terrified parent.

The dark hours crept slowly on, and at last a little tinge of daylight was seen through the eastern windows. Almost simultaneously with it, a bluff voice was heard some distance off, and the plash[44] of a horse galloping along the soft wet road. That bluff halloo came to the pallid and exhausted females, like a cheer from a passing ship to starving mariners on a wreck

ing and so personal in contrast with the conventional morbidity of the rest of the "Romances," is very probably an actual reminiscence of Whitman's mother, and the house "in a gloomy wood" is very probably the Van Velsor homestead at Cold Spring, Long Island. Whitman describes the homestead's appearance in 1881 ("Only a big hole from the cellar, with some little heaps of broken stone, green with grass and weeds, identified the place.") in "The Maternal Homestead," *Specimen Days*.

36. her parents and their family   37. One August Morning
38. he put   39. and rode away
40. came   41. bridled and saddled
42. They returned sick at heart into the house...........It was just after midnight, and the storm was passing off, when in the dreary stillness of their sleepless watch, they heard something in the room adjoining (the 'spare room,') which redoubled their terror.
43. By any one   44. and then the quick dull beat

at sea. My grandmother opened the door this time to behold the red laughing face of her husband, and to hear him tell how, after[45] the storm was over, and he went to look for Dandy, whom he had fastened under a shed, he discovered that the skittish creature had broken his bridle,[46] and run away home—and how he could not get another horse for love or money at that hour of the night[47]—and how he was fain forced to stop until nearly daylight. Then told my grandmother her story—her terror and her fears, and[48] how she had heard heavy footfalls in the parlor—whereat my grandfather laughed, and walked to the door between the rooms, and unlocked it, and saw nothing but darkness, for the shutters were closed.[49] My mother and grandmother followed timidly, though they now began to fear the discovery of some comical reason for their alarm.[50] My grandfather threw open the shutters; and then they all swept their sight round the room[51]—after which such a guffaw of laughter came from the husband's capacious mouth, that Dandy, away up in the barn-yard, sent back an answering neigh, in recognition.

Three or four days previously, my mother had broken off from a peach tree in the garden, a branch uncommonly full of fruit, of a remarkable size and beauty.[52] She brought it in, and placed it[53] amid the flowers and other simple ornaments, on the high shelf over the parlor fire-place. The night before, while the mother and daughter were watching, three of the peaches, over-ripe,[54] had dropped, one after another,[55] on the floor, and my mother's and grandmother's terrified imaginations had converted the harmless fruit into human heels![56] There, then, was the mystery,[57] and there lay the beautiful peaches—which my grandfather laughed at so convulsively, that my provoked grandame,[58] after laughing a while too, picked them up, and half jokingly, half seriously, thrust them so far into the open jaws of her husband, that he was nigh to have been choked in good earnest.[59]

---

45. how, when, after   46. his fastening
47. "of the night" is deleted.
48. "her terror and her fears, and" is deleted.
49. Sentence continues: "and it was yet quite a while to sunrise."
50. though they now began to feel a little ashamed.
51. My grandfather threw open the shutters of one window, and his wife those of the other. Then with one sweep of their eyes round the room, they paused a moment
52. of a remarkable beauty and ripeness.
53. stuck it   54. over-full in their ripeness
55. after the other   56. cowhide heels!
57. Here was the mystery   58. grandmother
59. and half jokingly and half seriously thrust them so far into the open jaws of her husband, that he was nigh to have been choked indeed.

The Shadow and the Light of a Young Man's Soul[1]

WHEN the young Archibald Dean went from the city—(living out of which he had so often said was no living at all)—went down into the country to take charge of a little district school, he felt as though the last float-plank which buoyed him up on hope and happiness, was sinking, and he with it. But poverty is as stern, if not as sure, as death and taxes, which Franklin called the surest things of the modern age. And poverty compelled Archie Dean; for when the destructive New-York fire of '35 happened, ruining so many property owners and erewhile rich merchants, it ruined the insurance offices, which of course ruined those whose little wealth had been invested in their stock. Among hundreds and thousands of other hapless people, the aged, the husbandless, the orphan, and the invalid, the widow Dean lost every dollar on which she depended for subsistence in her waning life. It was not a very great deal; still it had yielded, and was supposed likely to yield, an income large enough for her support, and the bringing up of her two boys. But, when the first shock passed over, the cheerful-souled woman dashed aside, as much as she could, all gloomy thoughts, and determined to stem the waters of roaring fortune yet. What troubled her much, perhaps most, was the way of her son Archibald. "Unstable as water," even his youth was not a sufficient excuse for his want of energy and resolution; and she experienced many sad moments, in her maternal reflections, ending with the fear that he would "not excel." The young man had too much of that inferior sort of pride which fears to go forth in public with anything short of fashionable garments, and hat and boots fit for fashionable criticism. His cheeks would tingle with shame at being seen in any working capacity: his heart sunk within him, if his young friends met him when he showed signs of the necessity of labor, or of the absence of funds. Moreover, Archie looked on the dark side of his life entirely too often; he pined over his deficiencies, as he called them, by which he meant mental as well as pecuniary wants .... But to do the youth justice, his good qualities must be told, too. He was unflinchingly honest; he would have laid out a fortune, had he possessed one, for his mother's comfort; he was not indisposed to work, and work faithfully, could he do so in a sphere equal to his ambition; he had a benevolent, candid soul, and none of the darker vices which are so common among the young fellows of our great cities.

1. This tale appeared in the *Union Magazine*, June 1848.

A good friend, in whose house she could be useful, furnished the widow with a gladly accepted shelter; and thither she also took her younger boy, the sickly, pale child, the light-haired little David, who looked thin enough to be blown all away by a good breeze. And happening accidentally to hear of a country district, where for poor pay and coarse fare, a school teacher was required, and finding on inquiry that Archie, who though little more than a boy himself, had a fine education, would fill the needs of the office, thither the young man was fain to betake him, sick at soul, and hardly restraining unmanly tears as his mother kissed his cheek, while he hugged his brother tightly, the next hour being to find him some miles on his journey. But it *must* be. Had he not ransacked every part of the city for employment as a clerk? And was he not quite ashamed to be any longer a burthen on other people for his support?

Toward the close of the first week of his employment, the entering upon which, with the feelings and circumstances of the beginning, it is not worth while to narrate, Archie wrote a long letter to his mother, (strange as it may seem to most men, she was also his confidential friend,) of which the following is part:

"—You may be tired of such outpourings of spleen, but my experience tells me that I shall feel better after writing them; and I am in that mood when sweet music would confer on me no pleasure. Pent up and cribbed here among a set of beings to whom grace and refinement are unknown, with no sunshine ahead, have I not reason to feel the gloom over me? Ah, poverty, what a devil thou art! How many high desires, how many high desires, how many aspirations after goodness and truth thou hast crushed under thy iron heel! What swelling hearts thou hast sent down to the silent house, after a long season of strife and bitterness! What talent, noble as that of great poets and philosophers, thou dost doom to pine in obscurity, or die in despair! * * * Mother, my throat chokes, and my blood almost stops, when I see around me so many people who appear to be born into the world merely to eat and sleep, and run the same dull monotonous round—and think that I too must fall in this current, and live and die in vain!"

Poor youth, how many, like you, have looked on man and life in the same ungracious light! Has God's all-wise providence ordered things wrongly, then? Is there discord in the machinery which moves systems of worlds, and keeps them in their harmonious orbits? O, no: there is discord in your own heart; in that lies the darkness and the tangle. To the young man, with health and a vigilant spirit, there is shame in despondency. Here we have a world, a thousand avenues to usefulness and to profit stretching in far distances around us. Is *this* the place for a failing soul? Is *youth* the time to yield, when the race is just begun?

But a changed spirit, the happy result of one particular incident, and of several trains of clearer thought, began to sway the soul of Archie Dean in the course of the summer: for it was at the beginning of spring that he commenced his labors and felt his severest deprivations. There is surely, too, a refreshing influence in open-air nature, and in natural scenery, with occasional leisure to enjoy it, which begets in a man's mind truer and heartier reflections, analyzes and balances his decisions, and clarifies them if they are wrong, so that he sees his mistakes— an influence that takes the edge off many a vapory pang, and neutralizes many a loss, which is most a loss in imagination. Whether this suggestion be warranted or not, there was no doubt that the discontented young teacher's spirits were eventually raised and sweetened by his country life, by his long walks over the hills, by his rides on horseback every Saturday, his morning rambles and his evening saunters; by his coarse living, even, and the untainted air and water, which seemed to make better blood in his veins. Gradually, too, he found something to admire in the character and customs of the unpolished country-folk; their sterling sense on most practical subjects, their hospitality, and their industry.

One day Archie happened to be made acquainted with the history of one of the peculiar characters of the neighborhood—an ancient, bony, yellow-faced maiden, whom he had frequently met, and who seemed to be on good terms with everybody; her form and face receiving a welcome, with all their contiguity and fadedness, wherever and whenever they appeared. In the girlhood of this long-born spinster, her father's large farm had been entirely lost and sold from him, to pay the debts incurred by his extravagance and dissipation. The consequent ruin to the family peace which followed, made a singularly deep impression on the girl's mind, and she resolved to get the whole farm back again. This determination came to form her life—the greater part of it—as much as her bodily limbs and veins. She was a shrewd creature; she worked hard; she received the small payment which is given to female labor; she persisted; night and day found her still at her tasks, which were of every imaginable description; long—long—long years passed; youth fled, (and it was said she had been quite handsome); many changes of ownership occurred in the farm itself; she confided her resolve all that time to no human being; she hoarded her gains; all other passions—love even, gave way to her one great resolve; she watched her opportunity, and eventually conquered her object! She not only cleared the farm, but was happy in furnishing her old father with a home there for years before his death. And when one comes to reflect on the disadvantages under which a woman labors, in the strife for gain, this will appear a remarkable, almost an incredible case. And then, again, when one thinks how surely, though ever so slowly and step by step, perseverance has overcome apparently insuperable difficulties, the fact—*for the foregoing incident is a fact*—may not appear so strange.

Archie felt the narrative of this old maid's doings as a rebuke—a sharp-pointed moral to himself and his infirmity of purpose. Moreover, the custom of his then way of life forced him into habits of more thorough activity; he had to help himself or go unhelped; he found a novel satisfaction in that highest kind of independence which consists in being able to do the offices of one's own comfort, and achieve resources and capacities "at home," whereof to place happiness beyond the reach of variable circumstances, or of the services of the hireling, or even of the uses of fortune. The change was not a sudden one: few great changes are. But his heart was awakened to his weakness; the seed was sown; Archie Dean felt that he *could* expand his nature by means of that very nature itself. Many times he flagged; but at each fretful falling back, he thought of the yellow-faced dame, and roused himself again . . . . . Meantime, changes occurred in the mother's condition. Archie was called home to weep at the death-bed of little David. Even that helped work out the revolution in his whole make; he felt that on him rested the responsibility of making the widow's last years comfortable. "I shall give up my teacher's place," said he to his mother, "and come to live with you; we will have the same home, for it is best so." And so he did. And the weakness of the good youth's heart never got entirely the better of him afterward, but in the course of a season, was put to flight utterly. This second time he *made* employment. With an iron will he substituted action and cheerfulness for despondency and a fretful tongue. He met his fortunes as they came, face to face, and shirked no conflict. Indeed, he felt it glorious to vanquish obstacles. For his mother he furnished a peaceful, plentiful home; and from the hour of David's death, never did his tongue utter words other than kindness, or his lips, whatever annoyances or disappointments came, cease to offer their cheerfullest smile in her presence.

Ah, for how many the morose habit which Archie rooted *out* from his nature, becomes by long usage and indulgence rooted *in*, and spreads its bitterness over their existence, and darkens the peace of their families, and carries them through the spring and early summer of life with no inhalement of sweets, and no plucking of flowers!

Lingave's Temptation[1]

"ANOTHER day," utter'd the poet Lingave, as he awoke in the morning, and turn'd him drowsily on his hard pallet, "Another day comes out, burthen'd with its weight of woes. Of what use is existence to me? Crush'd down beneath the merciless heel of poverty, and no promise of hope to cheer me on, what have I in prospect but a life neglected, and a death of misery?"

The youth paused; but receiving no answer to his questions, thought proper to continue the peevish soliloquy.[2] "I am a genius, they say," and the speaker smiled bitterly, "But genius is not apparel and food. Why should I exist in the world, unknown, unloved, press'd with cares, while so many around me have all their souls can desire? I behold the splendid equipages roll by—I see the respectful bow at the presence of pride—and I curse the contrast between my own lot, and the fortune of the rich. The lofty air—the show of dress—the aristocratic demeanor—the glitter of jewels—dazzle my eyes; and sharp-tooth'd envy works within me. I hate these haughty and favor'd ones. Why should my path be so much rougher than theirs? Pitiable, unfortunate man that I am! to be placed beneath those whom in my heart I despise—and to be constantly tantalized with the presence of that wealth I cannot enjoy!" And the poet cover'd his eyes with his hands, and wept from very passion and fretfulness.

O, Lingave! be more of a man! Have you not the treasures of health and untainted propensities, which many of those you envy never enjoy? Are you not their superior in mental power, in liberal views of mankind, and in comprehensive intellect? And even allowing you the choice, how would you shudder at changing, in total, conditions with them! Besides, were you willing to devote all your time and energies, you could gain property too: squeeze, and toil, and worry, and twist everything into a matter of profit, and you can become a great man, as far as money goes to make greatness.

Retreat, then, man of the polish'd soul, from those irritable com-

1. The text followed here is that of *Collect*. The place and date of the original publication of the story is not known, but a clipping of an earlier version, with Whitman's corrections for *Collect*, is in the Feinberg Collection. As usual, Whitman's revisions for *Collect* consist of the deletion of the "e" in the past forms of most regular verbs, the elimination of excessive capitalization, some very slight changes in punctuation, the combining of some paragraphs, and the expunging or alteration of a few passages. The more important variants in the earlier text of the story are given in the footnotes that follow.

2. Sentence continues: without waiting any further.

plaints against your lot—those longings for wealth and puerile distinction, not worthy your class. Do justice, philosopher, to your own powers. While the world runs after its shadows and its bubbles, (thus commune in your own mind,) we will fold ourselves in our circle of understanding, and look with an eye of apathy on those things it considers so mighty and so enviable. Let the proud man pass with his pompous glance —let the gay flutter in finery—let the foolish enjoy his folly, and the beautiful move on in his perishing glory; we will gaze without desire on all their possessions, and all their pleasures. Our destiny is different from theirs. Not for such as we, the lowly flights of their crippled wings. We acknowledge no fellowship with them in ambition. We composedly look down on the paths where they walk, and pursue our own, without uttering a wish to descend, and be as they. What is it to us that the mass pay us not that deference which wealth commands? We desire no applause, save the applause of the good and discriminating—the choice spirits among men. Our intellect would be sullied, were the vulgar to approximate to it, by professing to readily enter in, and praising it. Our pride is a towering, and thrice refined pride.

When Lingave had given way to his temper some half hour, or thereabout, he grew more calm, and bethought himself that he was acting a very silly part. He listen'd a moment to the clatter of the carts, and the tramp of early passengers on the pave below, as they wended along to commence their daily toil. It was just sunrise, and the season was summer. A little canary bird, the only pet poor Lingave could afford to keep, chirp'd merrily in its cage on the wall. How slight a circumstance will sometimes change the whole current of our thoughts! The music of that bird abstracting the mind of the poet but a moment from his sorrows, gave a chance for his natural buoyancy to act again.

Lingave sprang lightly from his bed, and perform'd his ablutions and his simple toilet[3]—then hanging the cage on a nail outside the window, and speaking an endearment to the songster, which brought a perfect flood of melody in return—he slowly passed through his door, descended the long narrow turnings of the stairs, and stood in the open street. Undetermin'd as to any particular destination, he folded his hands behind him, cast his glance upon the ground, and moved listlessly onward.

Hour after hour the poet walk'd along—up this street and down that— he reck'd not how or where. And as crowded thoroughfares are hardly the most fit places for a man to let his fancy soar in the clouds—many a push and shove and curse did the dreamer get bestow'd upon him.

3. his simple toilet in short order   4. to whom the voice attached

The booming of the city clock sounded forth the hour twelve—high noon.

"Ho! Lingave!" cried a voice from an open basement window as the poet pass'd.

He stopp'd, and then unwittingly would have walked on still, not fully awaken'd from his reverie.

"Lingave, I say!" cried the voice again, and the person to whom the voice belong'd[4] stretch'd his head quite out into the area in front, "Stop man. Have you forgotten your appointment?"

"Oh! ah!" said the poet, and he smiled unmeaningly, and descending the steps, went into the office of Ridman, whose call it was that had startled him in his walk.

Who was Ridman? While the poet is waiting the convenience of that personage, it may be as well to describe him.[5]

Ridman was a *money-maker*. He had much penetration, considerable knowledge of the world, and a disposition to be constantly in the midst of enterprise, excitement, and stir. His schemes for gaining wealth were various; he had dipp'd into almost every branch and channel of business. A slight acquaintance of several years' standing subsisted between him and the poet. The day previous a boy had call'd with a note from Ridman to Lingave, desiring the presence of the latter at the money-maker's room. The poet return'd for answer that he would be there. This was the engagement which he came near breaking.

Ridman had a smooth tongue. All his ingenuity was needed in the explanation to his companion of why and wherefore the latter had been sent for.

It is not requisite to state specifically the offer[6] made by the man of wealth to the poet. Ridman, in one of his enterprises, found it necessary to procure the aid of such a person as Lingave—a writer of power, a master of elegant diction, of fine taste, in style passionate yet pure, and of the delicate imagery that belongs to the children of song. The youth was absolutely startled at the magnificent and permanent remuneration which was held out to him for a moderate exercise of his talents.

But the *nature* of the service required! All the sophistry and art of Ridman could not veil its repulsiveness. The poet was to labor for the advancement of what he felt to be unholy—he was to inculcate what would lower the perfection of man. He promised to give an answer to the proposal the succeeding day, and left the place.

Now during the many hours there was a war going on in the heart of the poor poet. He was indeed *poor;* often, he had no certainty whether he

5. as well to explain.   6. specifically the nature of the offer

should be able to procure the next day's meals. And the poet knew the beauty of truth, and adored, not in the abstract merely, but in practice, the excellence of upright principles.

Night came. Lingave, wearied, lay upon his pallet again and slept. The misty veil thrown over him, the spirit of poesy came to his visions, and stood beside him, and look'd down pleasantly with her large eyes, which were bright and liquid like the reflection of stars in a lake.

Virtue, (such imagining, then, seem'd conscious to the soul of the dreamer,) is ever the sinew of true genius. Together, the two in one, they are endow'd with immortal strength, and approach loftily to Him from whom both spring. Yet there are those that having great powers, bend them to the slavery of wrong. God forgive them! for they surely do it ignorantly or heedlessly. Oh, could he who lightly tosses around him the seeds of evil in his writings, or his enduring thoughts, or his chance words—could he see how, haply, they are to spring up in distant time and poison the air, and putrefy, and cause to sicken—would he not shrink back in horror? A bad principle, jestingly spoken—a falsehood, but of a word —may taint a whole nation! Let the man to whom the great Master has given the might of mind, beware how he uses that might. If for the furtherance of bad ends, what can be expected but that, as the hour of the closing scene draws nigh, thoughts of harm done, and capacities distorted from their proper aim, and strength so laid out that men must be worse instead of better, through the exertion of that strength—will come and swarm like spectres around him?

"Be and continue poor, young man," so taught one whose counsels should be graven on the heart of every youth, "while others around you grow rich by fraud and disloyalty. Be without place and power, while others beg their way upward. Bear the pain of disappointed hopes, while others gain the accomplishment of their flattery. Forego the gracious pressure of a hand, for which others cringe and crawl. Wrap yourself in your own virtue, and seek a friend and your daily bread. If you have, in such a course, grown gray with unblench'd honor, bless God and die."

When Lingave awoke the next morning, he despatch'd his answer to his wealthy friend, and then plodded on as in the days before.[7]

---

7. When Lingave awoke the next morning, there was no vacillating in his mind about the answer he should make to Ridman. He despatched that answer, and then plodded on as in the days before.

Appendix A

PUBLICATION HISTORY OF WHITMAN'S
FICTION

"Death in the School-Room (a Fact)" was first published in the *Democratic Review*, IX (August 1841) 177–181. It was reprinted without alteration in the *Long Island Farmer*, August 10, 1841; *Ladies Garland*, V (September 1841) 73–75; *Brooklyn Daily Eagle*, while Whitman was still its editor, on December 24, 1847—the last two sentences, however, being omitted in the *Eagle*. With unimportant changes, the original version was reprinted by Whitman in *Specimen Days and Collect*, pp. 340–344, and the *Complete Prose Works*, pp. 340–344. Whitman's literary executors reprinted this final version of the story in the ten-volume 1902 edition of *The Complete Writings*, VI, 5–15.

"Wild Frank's Return" first appeared in the *Democratic Review*, IX (November 1841) 476–482, and was reprinted without alteration in the *Long Island Farmer*, January 11, 1842. In a slightly revised form, the story was reprinted in *Specimen Days and Collect*, pp. 353–357; *Complete Prose Works*, 353–357; *Complete Writings*, VI, 39–49.

"The Child and the Profligate" was first published as "The Child's Champion" in the *New World*, November 20, 1841. Radically revised, the story appeared under its present title in the *Columbian Magazine*, II (October 1844) 149–153. The *Columbian* version, with a few minor changes, was reprinted, during Whitman's editorship, in the *Brooklyn Daily Eagle*, January 27–29, 1847. With further revisions, the tale was reprinted in *Specimen Days and Collect*, pp. 361–366; *Complete Prose Works*, pp. 361–366; *Complete Writings*, VI, 60–73.

"Bervance: or, Father and Son" was first published in the *Democratic Review*, IX (December 1841) 560–568, and has been reprinted only once: UPP, I, 52–60.

"The Tomb Blossoms" first appeared in the *Democratic Review*, X (January 1842) 62–68. It was reprinted, with changes, in *Voices from the Press; A Collection of Sketches, Essays, and Poems*, by practical printers, ed. by James J. Brenton (New York, Charles B. Norton, 1850), pp. 27–38; *Philadelphia Press*, October 23, 1892; UPP, I, 60–67. Both *Press* and UPP reprinted the text from *Democratic Review*.

"The Last of the Sacred Army" was first published in the *Demo-

cratic Review, X (March 1842) 259–264, and was reprinted again, without revision, in the *Democratic Review*, XXIX (November 1851) 463–466; *UPP*, I, 72–78.

"The Last Loyalist" was first printed under the title of "The Child-Ghost; a Story of the Last Loyalist" in the *Democratic Review*, X (May 1842) 451–459. Revised, it was reprinted as "The Last Loyalist" in *Specimen Days and Collect*, pp. 349–353; *Complete Prose Works*, pp. 349–353; *Complete Writings*, VI, 28–38.

"Reuben's Last Wish" was published in the New York *Washingtonian* (changed by January 1843 to the *Washingtonian and Organ*), May 21, 1842. So far as is known, the story has not been reprinted until now.

"A Legend of Life and Love" first appeared in the *Democratic Review*, XI (July 1842) 83–86, and was at once reprinted in the New York *Tribune*, July 6, 1842, and in *Brother Jonathan*, July 9, 1842. It was slightly revised for publication in Whitman's paper, the *Brooklyn Daily Eagle*, June 11, 1846. The *Eagle* version was reprinted, with some evident errors, in *GF*, II, 377–386. The original version was reprinted in *UPP*, I, 78–83.

"The Angel of Tears" was first published in the *Democratic Review*, XI (September 1842) 282–284. Very slightly revised, it was reprinted in the *Brooklyn Evening Star*, February 28, 1846. The *Democratic* version was reprinted in *UPP*, I, 83–86.

Franklin Evans; or The Inebriate. A Tale of the Times was originally published in the *New World*, II (No. 10, Extra Series, November 1842) 1–31. Reprinted as an off-print from the *New World*, probably in 1843, the novel was given an altered title: *Franklin Evans: Knowledge is Power. The Merchant's Clerk, in New York; or Career as a Young Man from the Country* (New York, J. Winchester, n.d.). After considerable revision and deletion, the novel was reprinted a third time—this time in the *Brooklyn Daily Eagle*, November 16–30, 1846—as "A Tale of Long Island" with the new title of *Fortunes of a Country-Boy; Incidents in Town—and his Adventures at the South*, by "J. R. S . . . . . ." Why Whitman disguised his authorship of the tale in the *Eagle* is not known. Omitted in the *Eagle* version were the introduction, the conclusion, the imbedded tales, several incidents, and the chapter mottoes. In addition, the latter portion of the novel was radically revised. The original *New World* version was reprinted in *UPP*, II, 103–221, and as a book, with an introduction by Emory Holloway (New York: Random House, 1929). The imbedded tales—"The Death of Wind-Foot" and "Little Jane"— were reprinted separately. "The Death of Wind-Foot," with a number of verbal variants, was reprinted in the *American Review*, June 1845, and again, without change from the *American* text, as "The Death of Wind-Foot. An Indian Story," in the *Crystal Fount and Rechabite Recorder* (New York), V (October 18, 1845) 81–84. "Little Jane" was reprinted, with few changes, in the *Brooklyn Daily Eagle*, December 7, 1846, and again, with a few more changes, in *Collect*.

The Madman began with its first installment in the New York *Washingtonian and Organ*, January 28, 1843. No issues of the *Washingtonian* containing further installments have been found. So far as is known, no portion of the story has been reprinted until now.

"The Love of Eris: A Spirit Record" was first published as "Eris: A Spirit Record" in the *Columbian Magazine*, I (March 1844) 138–139. Slightly revised, and under its present title, it was reprinted in the *Brooklyn Daily Eagle*, August, 18, 1846. The *Columbian* version was reprinted *UPP*, I, 86–89; the *Eagle* version in *GF*, II, 369–376.

"My Boys and Girls" was published in *The Rover*, III (April 20, 1844) 75, and was reprinted in Mabbott, pp. 107–113.

"Dumb Kate" originally appeared as "Dumb Kate.—An Early Death," in *Columbian Magazine*, I (May 1844) 230–231. This first version of the tale—except for the omission of two sentences—was reprinted in the *Brooklyn Daily Eagle*, July 13, 1846. Somewhat revised, and with its present short title, it was reprinted in *Specimen Days and Collect*, pp. 370–371; *Complete Prose Works*, pp. 370–371; *Complete Writings*, VI, 85–88.

"The Little Sleighers. A Sketch of a Winter Morning on the Battery" was published in the *Columbian Magazine*, II (September 1844) 113–114, and was reprinted in *UPP*, I, 90–92.

"The Half-Breed: A Tale of the Western Frontier" originally appeared as "Arrow-Tip" in *The Aristidean*, I (March 1845) 36–64. The novelette, with a number of minor revisions, was reprinted under its present title in the *Brooklyn Daily Eagle*, June 1–6, 8, 9, 1846. The *Eagle* version was reprinted in Mabbott, pp. 23–76.

"Shirval: A Tale of Jerusalem" was published in *The Aristidean*, I (March 1845) 12–15, and was reprinted in Mabbott, pp. 81–85. Whitman revised and paged the tale for inclusion in *Collect* but did not use it. The Feinberg Collection has a unique clipping of the *Aristidean's* "Shirval" with Whitman's annotations for revision in the margins.

"Richard Parker's Widow" first appeared in *The Aristidean*, I (April 1845) 111–114. It was reprinted in Mabbott, pp. 87–97.

"The Boy Lover" originally appeared in the *American Review*, I (May 1845) 479–482, and was reprinted, without revision, in the *Brooklyn*

Daily Eagle, January 4–5, 1848. With some revision, it was reprinted in *Specimen Days and Collect*, pp. 357–361; *Complete Prose Works*, pp. 357–361; *Complete Writings*, VI, 49–60.

"One Wicked Impulse!" originally appeared in the *Democratic Review*, XVII (July-August 1845) 105–111, as "Revenge and Requital; A Tale of a Murderer Escaped." The story was reprinted, without revision and under the same title, in the New York *Weekly News* (edited by John L. O'Sullivan, who also edited the *Democratic Review*) on August 16, 1845. Professor G. Thomas Tanselle reported his discovery of this reprint in "Whitman's Short Stories: Another Reprint," *Papers of the Bibliographical Society of America*, LVI (First Quarter, 1962) 115. It was again reprinted, except for two minor word changes and the omission of the last two sentences, in the *Brooklyn Daily Eagle*, September, 7–9, 1846, as "One Wicked Impulse! (a tale of a Murderer escaped.)." After a radical revision, which included the deletion of the final fourth of the tale, the story was reprinted under its present title in *Specimen Days and Collect*, pp. 344–349; *Complete Prose Works*, pp. 344–349; *Complete Writings*, VI, 15–28.

"Some Fact-Romances" was published in *The Aristidean*, I (December 1845) 444–449, and consisted of an introduction and five short untitled narratives. Though all five of the "Romances" have been reprinted separately, the complete original version has not been reprinted until now. "Fact-Romance" I was reprinted, with some revision, as "A Fact-Romance of Long Island" in the *Brooklyn Daily Eagle*, December 16, 1846; the *Eagle* version was reprinted in *UPP*, I, 146–147. "Fact-Romance" II was reprinted, with a few revisions, as "The Old Black Widow" in the *Brooklyn Daily Eagle*, November 12, 1846; the *Eagle* version was reprinted in *UPP*, I, 138–139. "Fact-Romance" III was reprinted in Mabbott, pp. 102–103. "Fact-Romances" IV was reprinted in Thomas Ollive Mabbott, "Walt Whitman and *The Aristidean*," *American Mercury*, II (June 1924) 206–207, and in Mabbott, p. 104. "Fact-Romance" V was reprinted, with some revisions, as "An Incident On Long Island Forty Years Ago" in the *Brooklyn Daily Eagle*, December 24, 1846; the *Eagle* version was reprinted in *UPP*, I, 149–151. The two introductory paragraphs to "Some Fact-Romances" were reprinted in Mabbott, p. 101.

"The Shadow and the Light of a Young Man's Soul" was published in the *Union Magazine of Literature and Art*, II (June 1848) 280–281; it was reprinted in *UPP*, I, 229–234.

The place and date of the first publication of "Lingave's Temptation" is not known. A unique clipping of the tale, apparently taken from the periodical in which it originally appeared, is in the Feinberg Collection, with Whitman's revisions for *Collect*. The story, with the revisions, was reprinted in *Specimen Days and Collect*, pp. 366–368; *Complete Prose Works*, pp. 366–368; *Complete Writings*, VI, 73–80.

Addendum

"Death in the School-Room (a Fact)" was also reprinted without change in *The Mauch Chunk Courier* (Mauch Chunk, Penna.) October 25, 1841. This reprint was reported by Professor William White in "Whitman as Short Story Writer: Two Unpublished Manuscripts," *Notes and Queries*, CVII (n.s. IX) (March 1962) 87–89.

Appendix B

CHRONOLOGY
OF WALT WHITMAN'S LIFE AND WORK

1819   Born May 31 at West Hills, near Huntington, Long Island.

1823   May 27, Whitman family moves to Brooklyn.

1825 – 30   Attends public school in Brooklyn.

1830   Office boy for doctor, lawyer.

1830 – 34   Learns printing trade.

1835   Printer in New York City until great fire August 12.

1836 – 38   Summer of 1836, begins teaching at East Norwich, Long Island; by winter 1837 – 38 has taught at Hempstead, Babylon, Long Swamp, and Smithtown.

1838 – 39   Edits weekly newspaper, the *Long Islander*, at Huntington.

1840 – 41   Autumn 1840, campaigns for Van Buren; then teaches school at Trimming Square, Woodbury, Dix Hills, and Whitestone.

1841   May, goes to New York City to work as printer in *New World* office; begins writing for the *Democratic Review*.

1842   Spring, edits a daily newspaper in New York City, the *Aurora;* edits *Evening Tattler* for short time.

1845 – 46   August, returns to Brooklyn, writes for Brooklyn *Evening Star* (daily) and *Long Island Star* (weekly) until March, 1846.

1846 – 48   From March, 1846, until January, 1848, edits Brooklyn *Daily Eagle;* February, 1848, goes to New Orleans to work on the *Crescent;* leaves May 27 and returns via Mississippi and Great Lakes.

1848 – 49   September 9, 1848, to September 11, 1849, edits a "free soil" newspaper, the Brooklyn *Freeman*.

1850 – 54   Operates printing office and stationery store; does free-lance journalism; builds and speculates in houses.

1855   Early July, *Leaves of Grass* is printed by Rome Brothers in Brooklyn; father dies July 11.

1856   Writes for *Life Illustrated;* publishes second edition of *Leaves of Grass* in summer and writes "The Eighteenth Presidency!"

1857 – 59   From spring of 1857 until about summer of 1859 edits the Brooklyn *Times;* unemployed, winter of 1859–60, frequents Pfaff's bohemian restaurant.

1860   March, goes to Boston to see third edition of *Leaves of Grass* through the press.

1861   April 12, Civil War begins; George Whitman enlists.

1862   December, goes to Fredericksburg, Virginia, scene of recent battle in which George was wounded, stays in camp two weeks.

1863   Remains in Washington, D.C., working part time in Army Paymaster's Office, visits soldiers in hospitals.

1864   Mid-June, returns to Brooklyn because of illness.

1865   January 24, appointed clerk in Department of Interior, returns to Washington; meets Peter Doyle; witnesses Lincoln's second inauguration; Lincoln assassinated, April 14; May, *Drum-Taps* is printed; June 30, is discharged from position by Secretary James Harlan but reemployed next day in Attorney General's Office; autumn, prints *Drum-Taps and Sequel*, containing "When Lilacs Last in the Dooryard Bloom'd."

1866   William D. O'Connor publishes *The Good Gray Poet.*

1867   John Burroughs publishes *Notes on Walt Whitman as Poet and Person;* July 6, William Rossetti publishes article on Whitman's poetry in London *Chronicle;* "Democracy" (part of *Democratic Vistas*) published in December *Galaxy.*

1868   William Rossetti's *Poems of Walt Whitman* (selected and expurgated) published in England; "Personalism" (second part of *Democratic Vistas*) in May *Galaxy;* second issue of fourth edition of *Leaves of Grass*, with *Drum-Taps and Sequel* added.

1869   Mrs. Anne Gilchrist reads Rossetti edition and falls in love with the poet.

1870   July, is very depressed for unknown reasons; prints fifth edition of *Leaves of Grass*, and *Democratic Vistas* and *Passage to India*, all dated 1871.

1871   September 3, Mrs. Gilchrist's first love letter; September 7, reads "After All Not to Create Only" at opening of American Institute Exhibit in New York.

1872   June 26, reads "As a Strong Bird on Pinions Free" at Dartmouth College commencement.

1873   January 23, suffers paralytic stroke; mother dies May 23; unable to work, stays with brother George in Camden, New Jersey.

1874   "Song of the Redwood-Tree" and "Prayer of Columbus."

1875   Prepares Centennial Edition of *Leaves of Grass* and *Two Rivulets* (dated 1876).

1876   Controversy in British and American press over America's neglect of Whitman; spring, begins recuperation at Stafford Farm, at Timber Creek; September, Mrs. Gilchrist arrives and rents house in Philadelphia.

1877   January 28, gives lecture on Tom Paine in Philadelphia; during summer gains strength by sun-bathing at Timber Creek.

1878   Spring, too weak to give projected Lincoln lecture, but in June visits J. H. Johnson and John Burroughs in New York.

1879   April 14, first lecture on Lincoln in New York; September, makes trip to Colorado, long visit with brother Jeff in St. Louis.

1880   January, returns to Camden; summer, visits Dr. R. M. Bucke in London, Ontario.

1881	April 15, gives Lincoln lecture in Boston; returns to Boston in late summer to read proof of *Leaves of Grass*, being published by James R. Osgood; poems receive final arrangement in this edition.
1882	Osgood ceases to distribute *Leaves of Grass* because District Attorney threatens prosecution unless the book is expurgated; publication is resumed by Rees Welsh in Philadelphia, who also publishes *Specimen Days and Collect;* both books transferred to David McKay, Philadelphia.
1883	Dr. Bucke publishes *Walt Whitman*, biography written with poet's cooperation.
1884	Buys house on Mickle Street, Camden, New Jersey.
1885	In poor health; friends buy a horse and phaeton so that the poet will not be "house-tied"; November 29, Mrs. Gilchrist dies.
1886	Gives Lincoln lecture in Philadelphia.
1887	Gives Lincoln lecture in New York; is sculptured by Sidney Morse, painted by Herbert Gilchrist, J. W. Alexander, Thomas Eakins.
1888	Horace Traubel raises funds for doctors and nurses; *November Boughs* printed; money sent from England.
1889	Last birthday dinner, proceedings published in *Camden's Compliments*.
1890	Writes angry letter to J. A. Symonds, dated August 19, denouncing Symonds' interpretation of "Calamus" poems, claims six illegitimate children.
1891	*Good-Bye My Fancy* is printed, and the "death-bed edition" of *Leaves of Grass* (dated 1892).
1892	Dies March 26, buried in Harleigh Cemetery, Camden, New Jersey.

Index

Index

Page numbers for fictional characters indicate the first mention of the character.